Other Books by the Same Author

BOOKS DEALING WITH THE GENERAL PRIN-
CIPLES OF GEOGRAPHY

Asia: A Geography Reader. Chicago, 1912.

The Red Man's Continent. New Haven, 1919.

Principles of Human Geography (with S. W. Cushing).
New York, 1920.

Business Geography (with F. E. Williams). New York,
1922.

Modern Business Geography (with S. W. Cushing).
Yonkers, 1924.

The Character of Races. New York, 1924.

West of the Pacific. New York, 1925.

BOOKS DEALING WITH THE EFFECT OF CLIMATE

The Pulse of Asia. Boston, 1907.

Palestine and Its Transformation. Boston, 1911.

Civilization and Climate. New Haven, 1915.

World Power and Evolution. New Haven, 1919.

BOOKS DEALING WITH THE NATURE AND
CAUSES OF CLIMATIC CHANGES

Explorations in Turkestan. Expedition of 1903 (with
others). Washington, 1914.

The Climatic Factor, as Illustrated in Arid America. Washington, 1914.

Earth and Sun: An Hypothesis of Weather and Sunspots.
New Haven, 1923.

Climatic Changes (with S. S. Visher). New Haven, 1922.

Quaternary Climatics (with T. C. Jones and E. Asters).
Washington, 1925.

THE PULSE OF PROGRESS

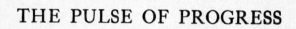

THE
PULSE OF PROGRESS

INCLUDING A SKETCH OF JEWISH HISTORY

BY

ELLSWORTH HUNTINGTON

Research Associate in Geography in Yale University

WITH A CHAPTER ON CLIMATIC CHANGES

BY

G. C. SIMPSON

Director of the British Meteorological Service

CHARLES SCRIBNER'S SONS
NEW YORK · LONDON
1926

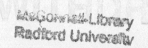

PREFACE

THREE primary considerations have led to the writing of this book. The first is the modern movement for setting forth the results of scientific research, not only in technical publications, but in clear, interesting, and non-technical form without the encumbrance of references, footnotes, and details of proof. The second is the frequently expressed opinion of a number of friends that the ideas as to man and his environment which I have set forth in a dozen books ought to be summarized in a single volume. In the third place, some one ought soon to write a history of human progress which will take full account of recent advances in our knowledge of human geography, ethnography, economics, sociology, and biology. As a preparation for this, it seems highly desirable that persons who have original ideas along these lines should set them forth in such a way that they can be subjected to criticism.

At first the plan was to limit the book strictly to the three purposes named above. As usually happens, however, the progress of the work soon led to the addition of new material in order to round out the subject. Chapters II, III, and IV present the results of new investigations made especially for this book. Other new material is scattered in smaller bits elsewhere. Chapters V to X are mainly a restatement, rearrangement, and revision of material published during the last twenty years in the books and articles mentioned in the list preceding the index. It has not seemed necessary or advisable to use quotation-marks, although sections of as much as two or three pages have, in some cases, been taken, almost unchanged, from some of the books. The source, however, is indicated in all such cases.

Another section of the book, Chapters XI to XVI, forms a comprehensive, though brief, history of the Jewish people. It is designed as an illustration of the way in which the principles of the preceding chapters throw light on history. Originally I intended to use a number of examples instead of devoting so much space to one. In the spring of 1925, however, I agreed to give a course of lectures to Sunday-school teachers on the Geography of Palestine. That caused me to read the Bible again, with the express purpose of divesting myself of all preconceptions. I attempted to read the book as though it were absolutely unknown, and to find out what it teaches as to the geographical, sociological, and biological as well as the political, religious, and economic interpretation of history. The results were so illuminating and surprising that it seemed worth while to use the Jews as the main illustration of this volume.

The last two chapters attempt to show the application of some of the previous sections to certain problems upon which men's minds are actively centred to-day.

This book was not planned or written as a text-book. Nevertheless, it sets forth certain fundamental facts, principles, and relationships in such a way that it seems well fitted for use, at least as a supplementary text, in classes in human geography, sociology, oriental and Biblical history, and the philosophy of history.

In a book of this nature the author naturally relies almost entirely upon himself. I am indebted, however, to my colleague, Professor G. F. Dahl, for reading the chapters on Jewish history, and for many most valuable suggestions. My good friend Professor S. S. Visher has read the entire proof and has pointed out many places where improvement could be made. I am also indebted to *Scribner's Magazine, The Forum,* and *Economic Geography* for the use of material which appeared in the form of articles in those journals.

Yale University,
  New Haven, Conn.
    June, 1926.

CONTENTS

ILLUSTRATIONS

THE PULSE OF PROGRESS

CHAPTER I

THE RHYTHM OF PROGRESS AND DECAY

ALL history is a record of pulsations. No country, no race, no type of civilization moves steadily forward or steadily backward. All alike make progress at some periods, stagnate at others, and at certain times move backward. This is true also of individuals on the one hand and of species of plants and animals on the other. In fact, it is one of the most universal laws of nature. No matter whether the general tendency is upward or downward, the line of movement is not straight, but sinuous. One of the main tasks of history—perhaps the greatest—is to explain why nations or smaller communities constantly undergo such pulsations.

Almost innumerable factors co-operate to this end, but all can be summed up under the three headings of physical environment, heredity, and social or cultural environment. Among animals and plants the physical environment is responsible for the great majority of the minor pulsations and for many of the long ones, while heredity accounts for at least a part of the longer fluctuations. Social environment plays relatively little part, for changes in social habits usually do not take place at all, or occur only with extreme slowness even among animals where the social system is so highly organized as among ants, bees, and wasps. Among men, on the other hand, although changes in physical environment and heredity produce profound effects, social and cultural changes are so rapid and obvious that they constantly force themselves upon our attention. Nevertheless, the pulsations due to the other causes must be clearly understood if the cultural changes are to be rightly interpreted.

For these reasons the purposes of this book are first to explain the workings of some of the chief factors of physical environment and biological inheritance; second, to show how the workings of these factors are connected with one another and with cultural changes; and third, to discuss a few examples which show how physical environment, biological inheritance, and cultural progress have worked together to produce the fluctuations of history.

Although man has powers far beyond those of animals, he is not essentially different from his fellow creatures in his primal relationships to heat, cold, and moisture; to food, drink, and shelter; to mountains, rivers, plains, and seas; and to vegetation, animals, insects, and bacterial parasites. Since all these factors vary from place to place, and since most of them vary from year to year, or era to era, it is obvious that we can never know exactly how much effect to ascribe to cultural conditions until we have first isolated the effects of the environmental factors. But even that is not enough, for when we have isolated the environmental effects we are still in danger of confusing the effects of changes in biological inheritance with those of new cultural conditions. Hence the biological factors must also be considered. Only when that is done can we really measure the importance of such great cultural conditions as religion, education, government, art, science, commerce, industry, and the complex rules of social intercourse.

Let us, therefore, begin with the most obvious facts of physical environment. In order to simplify our problem as much as possible, let us start with the periodic vicissitudes to which animals are subject, and then proceed to the more complex human relationships. A concrete example is often much better than an abstract discussion. Accordingly let us examine the stormy life-history of a single animal, the little rodent known as the lemming. This short-tailed, yellowish-brown cousin of the mouse, about five inches long, is best known in Norway, where it normally inhabits the cold highlands above the limits of evergreen trees. There it grubs about for lichens, moss, grass, and roots, or gnaws the tender shoots of the dwarf birches which form the largest vegetation of these almost unpeopled highlands. The lemming is a restless, courageous little creature: when brought to bay it sits upright with its back against a stone, hissing and biting. Each year the mother lemming brings forth two broods, numbering three to eight, so that the lemming population increases with great rapidity unless somehow held in check.

Perhaps the strangest fact about this little rodent is that occasionally it invades the lowlands of Norway and Sweden in hosts that may well be called armies. Something, no one knows what, impels them all to travel in the same direction. Slowly and steadily they advance across the country. Up hill, down dale they go, across brooks and hills, rivers and mountains, travelling by night, feeding by day, and often remaining for some time to enjoy the rich vegetation of some pleasant valley. Then they go on, always in the same direction, and even swimming across lakes several miles in width. Devastation marks their progress, for they nibble the young shoots of trees, and eat the crops in the fields. Bears, wolves, foxes, dogs, wildcats, stoats, weasels, eagles, hawks, and owls accompany the lemmings and gorge upon the helpless little creatures. Man, the fiercest and most deadly of all beasts of prey, strives also to kill them. Even domestic cattle, goats, and reindeer join in decimating the army of lemmings, stamping them to the ground with their feet, and sometimes eating their bodies, so it is said. Vast numbers also die from disease, but still the rest press on.

Nothing stops the lemmings until the sea is reached. They plunge into the salty water as boldly as into a little brook, and bravely swim until they perish from exhaustion. None turns back. Thousands, hundreds of thousands, perhaps millions may be drowned when a major lemming migration reaches the Atlantic Ocean on the coast of Norway. But for every thousand drowned spectacularly in the ocean perhaps ten thousand are eaten by the beasts of prey which hang like an army on their rear and flanks. And for every ten thousand thus destroyed a hundred thousand may perish from plague. What kind of plague it is does not yet appear, but it wipes out all except a hardy remnant.

So strange are these repeated wanderings of the lemmings that the ancient Norwegian peasants believed that the little creatures fell from the sky. How could they be so abundant otherwise? Later generations, seeking the scientific causes of the phenomena of nature, suspected that the animals were acting in obedience to an instinct inherited from the Miocene period, millions of years ago. Therefore, to our day, so it was supposed, the lemmings plunge into the Atlantic Ocean seeking the submerged continent of Atlantis to which their ancestors were wont to resort when driven from their usual homes by overpopulation or scarcity of food.

The modern explanation is that in favorable years the lemmings find plenty of food and have few enemies. They multiply exceedingly, and replenish the earth, as the ancient Hebrews were urged to do. But as they multiply, the food supply becomes relatively scarce, partly because the lemmings themselves eat it up faster than it can replace itself, and partly because the weather is not always favorable to vegetation. As the lemmings increase in number their enemies also increase, for an abundance of rodents means an abundance of food for bears, weasels, owls, and many other animals; it also means abundant food for the far more dangerous creatures known as bacteria. At length there comes a time when the stress of overpopulation becomes too much for the lemmings, and they begin to migrate. That is the signal for increased destruction, for the migrants are not so well protected from beasts of prey as was the case when they were in their own familiar territory, and bacterial diseases run riot because the animals are crowded thickly together. When a migration comes to an end, all but a scanty and hardy remnant have been exterminated.

Then the process of building up a new population begins once more. At such times the number of young born in each litter appears to be unusually high; food is abundant because there are few rodents to eat it; enemies are scarce because they tend to die out when their supply of food is cut off by the destruction of the lemmings. Thus the population of lemmings may increase manyfold in a single year, and in two or three years the little beasts are again numerous.

It has remained for Doctor C. S. Elton, of Oxford, to show that these lemming migrations are by no means an uncommon or irregular occurrence. On the contrary, they are typical of what happens throughout nature. In all the far northern parts of the world, including North America and Asia as well as Europe, Doctor Elton finds indications that lemming migrations take place with a fairly regular periodicity averaging a little over three years. This may be because it takes about that length of time for the lemmings to increase to the point where they are too numerous for the food supply. The fact that lemming migrations take place simultaneously in North America, Europe, and Asia, however, seems to Doctor Elton to join with other facts in indicating that climatic conditions are the primary cause of the fluctuations in numbers.

Practically every other species of animal is subject to similar rhythmic pulsations in number and health. Almost every householder outside the cities knows not only that mice and rats tend to invade the house in the autumn, but that some years the invasion is far worse than others, either because the number of animals that have lived to maturity in the fields that year is unusually large, or because the weather and the food supply are unusually bad. Doctor Elton describes a region in Canada where the hunters say that sometimes one can shoot half a dozen muskrats in a couple of hours any day, while two or three years later, in the very same place, the same man can scarcely find a dozen in two or three months. Birds show similar variations. One year the flickers with their showy black crescents and yellow breasts appear in great numbers, as do the bluebirds, perhaps, and the humming-birds. Another year, in the same places, scarcely a bird of these species is seen. And so it goes. The mosquitoes are almost unendurable all summer, one year, and appear only for a few days the next; the locusts swarm by the million and bring ruin and famine this summer, and then for years one sees only a few solitary individuals. The same is ob-

viously true of plants. One year the grass is tall and thick, and
the haymakers rejoice. If we used the same terms for plants as
for animals, we should say that in those years the grass population is very large and healthy. The next year it is scarce and
sickly.

Rhythms, pulsations, or cycles seem to be the law of organic
life. Among animals the cycles regularly have essentially the
same form; a few hardy individuals to begin with—survivors of
the preceding cycle; then abundant food, large families, few
enemies, good health, and rapid increase in numbers; next pressure upon the food supply, poorer health, more enemies because
the enemies, whether visible or invisible, have flourished by
reason of abundant food; then pestilence, migration, the wiping
out of vast numbers, and a low birth-rate because the creatures
are not strong.

This same law applies to human beings. We often fail to
realize this because human ingenuity is able to bridge many of
the smaller cycles so that their effect is almost neutralized. We
also fail in part because progress has recently been so rapid that
we are generally on the up grade even in the worst part of a
cycle. Nevertheless, almost every one is familiar with the cycles
of business which reach their zenith in times of great prosperity,
high prices, abundant work, and great expansion, and then fall
to a nadir of depression, deflation, scanty work, low prices, general discouragement, and even financial panic. The causes and
mechanism of periods of depression and of panic have been discussed most voluminously, and there is still a wide diversity of
opinion. Nevertheless, it is almost universally agreed that poor
crops are at least an important contributing element. Poor
crops of course are usually the result of deficient rainfall. The
exact conditions in this respect in the United States are illustrated in Figure 1. The depth of the shading indicates the degree to which the inhabited parts of the country suffered from
deficient rainfall. The asterisks indicate financial panics. Each
period of poor rainfall is closely accompanied by a panic. In
countries like Russia, India, and China the connection between

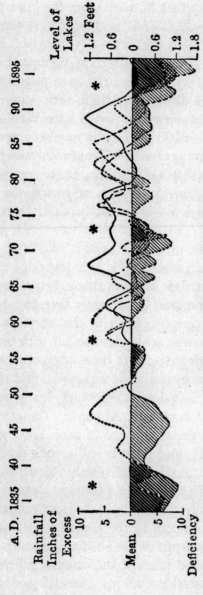

* Financial Panic in the United States.
—— Rainfall of New England.   —— Rainfall of Mississippi Valley.
··· Rainfall of Ohio Valley.   ··· Rainfall of level of Great Lakes.
Depth of shading is proportional to the part of the inhabited area of the United States
suffering from deficiency of rainfall.

Note.—See Appendix of level of the Great Lakes.

The Relation of Rainfall to Commercial Crisis.
Drawn from Clayton's figures.

FIG. 1. PANICS AND RAINFALL IN THE UNITED STATES.
From *The Pulse of Asia.* Courtesy of Houghton Mifflin Company.

rainfall, crops, and human prosperity is closer than in America. Even the World War and the succeeding period of revolution and unrest in Russia did not produce any such severity of suffering—any such distress and disease—as did the droughts and crop failures which brought the dire famine of 1921.

Climatic fluctuations also have a great effect upon health and the death-rate even in our own day. In spite of the gratifying decline in the death-rate of the majority of civilized countries during the last few decades, great variations of health still occur. Even if we omit such spectacular events as the influenza epidemic of 1918, there remain a large number of fluctuations which are obviously climatic, and which have a most potent effect upon human progress. For example, in June, 1925, a sudden hot spell covering a large part of the United States caused the number of deaths to be between fifteen and sixteen thousand larger than the normal at that season. If each life thus snuffed out possessed an average value of $7,000, which is less than the usual estimate, the loss to the United States was $100,000,000.

In 1926 a rather open and fairly warm winter up to about the middle of February was followed by an unusually cold and inclement period during March and early April. This at once led to an unusually large number of colds, much pneumonia, and some influenza, as well as other illnesses. As a result the number of deaths was approximately 75,000 greater than normal from the middle of February to the middle of April. Those lives were worth about $500,000,000. In other words, two short periods of unfavorable weather took from the pockets of the people of the United States a cool $600,000,000, more than $5 for every man, woman, and child. Unless the deaths happened to touch us individually we did not notice how greatly they disturbed our financial situation. That is merely because we are still extraordinarily stupid. If 100,000 cows should be killed by bad weather within a few days, or if 100,000 people should be killed in an earthquake, almost everybody would be talking about it; the farmers would probably ask for special legislation to help them over the calamity; and relief funds would be raised and taxes remitted for the benefit of the stricken regions. But because the weather takes its extra toll of deaths quietly, we do not notice them. Nevertheless, we are just that much poorer than we would have been if the weather had been normal. In reality, our activities are interrupted as badly as if half a billion dollars or more were suddenly, ruthlessly, and indiscriminately seized by the government for taxes.

In a book called *The King of the Thundering Herd*, Mr. C. Hawkes describes the wholesale slaughter by which the millions, or tens of millions, of bison in the western plains of America were practically exterminated in the space of about a dozen years when railroads first penetrated the plains and crossed to the Pacific coast. Never in all biological history, so far as we have exact knowledge, has there been a more rapid diminution of any species. But before the bison were exterminated old hunters noted a strange fact. According to them two new species had come into existence. Down in the southern plains of Texas they found a rangy beast with uncommonly long legs, a variety, or a ~ the hunters said, which was so fleet that it could find safet, ...ight instead of merely waiting for the enemy and trying to ward him off by sheer strength in the old, stupid, blundering way of most buffaloes. In the mountains of Wyoming quite a different kind of bison had evolved. This was a relatively short-legged beast, which was very agile on the hillsides and could quickly scramble out of the way and thus escape the hunter. The two types were so different from each other and from the standard type, that if they had not been exterminated they might actually have given rise to new species.

The extermination of the buffaloes had been so ruthless that only two particular types of variants had been able to survive. So long as such variants remained in the original herd, they interbred with the ordinary animals, and their peculiarities quickly disappeared. Being isolated, like bred with like, and the new types began to become fixed. The same thing happens with human beings. In Iceland, as I have shown in *The Character of Races*, a highly selected and hence highly specialized type of people has remained almost unchanged for a thousand years. The reason is that the Icelanders have been almost completely isolated. In New England an equally selected and specialized type, the old Puritans, has almost disappeared in three hundred years because it has mingled with all sorts of other types that have followed it to America. In such ways, time and again, the fundamental character of groups of people seems to suffer alteration, first one way and then another.

Other kinds of fluctuations are a well-known feature of history. The World War represents one type, the introduction of machinery and the growth of modern transportation another, the Reformation and the Renaissance a third, and the Dark Ages still a fourth. From beginning to end, both in organic evolution and in history, we find the same unconquerable tendency toward constant pulsations. Where the pulsations reach their most extreme form old species are extinguished and new ones arise to take their place, as in the glacial period. In the realm of history a similar condition appears when the progress of a cycle brings about the collapse of civilization and the introduction of periods of relative barbarism, followed by a new civilization of a different type. So common is this phenomenon that Doctor Flinders Petrie once wrote a most suggestive little book on *Revolutions in Civilization*, based on changes in art, but also dealing with similar revolutions in other phases of life. Every historian finds himself face to face with the problem of why the country or period in which he is especially interested shows such varying rates of progress or decline.

The illustrations which have just been given are typical of the kinds of phenomena and the principles that we shall deal with in this book. In the future, as in the past, great wars, religious revivals, inventions, political upheavals, the careers of men of genius, and the rise and decay of social institutions will doubtless occupy a large share of the interest of historians. But it is to be hoped that there will also be a growing tendency to inquire how these cultural conditions are related to two other sets of facts, one geographical, the other biological. Thus a new philosophy of history may gradually become prevalent. This new philosophy fully accepts the idea that the rise and fall of nations depend largely upon the mode of organization of society, and the status of government, education, commerce, industry, science, art, philosophy, religion, the home, and a host of other cultural conditions. These social mainsprings of human action are the most interesting aspects of history. But the new philosophy asks how these social phenomena are related to the geographical and biological foundations which seem to underlie the whole structure of organic and historic evolution. In succeeding chapters we shall try to show how some of these foundations exert their influence.

CHAPTER II

THE HANDICAP OF POOR LAND

HISTORY abounds in indications of persistent differences between good land and poor. Do these differences follow definite laws, or do they occur haphazard? The ideal way to obtain a reliable answer would be to procure exact data as to the conditions on good land and poor among people in all stages of culture from primitive savages upward. That is impossible at present. Nevertheless, we can make a careful analysis of the differences between good land and poor in a few places, and can then form some estimate of how far the facts in these areas agree with the less exactly known facts elsewhere. The statistics of the United States are excellent for this purpose. There we have the world's largest and most varied area where good and uniform methods of gathering statistics are in use everywhere.

The main thing that man wants from the land is a good crop. Any combination of soil and relief that yields large or valuable crops with a small amount of labor is highly desirable, and any that yields small crops is undesirable. The best measure of the value of a piece of land is the crop which it yields *for a given amount of human effort*, but no one has yet measured human effort on farms of different kinds. Accordingly, for the present the best available measure of whether the farm land in a given region is good or poor appears to be its selling price. Other things may be cheap in countries like Japan and China, but much rice land sells at prices of $500 or $1,000 per acre. The value depends upon soil, relief, climate, stage of culture, accessibility of markets, and various minor factors which need not be considered. For the present we want to eliminate all the others except soil and relief. Climate and stage of culture can be eliminated by using small areas which, nevertheless, have pronounced dif-

ferences of soil and relief. Almost all of the States east of the
Mississippi form such areas, so that the effects of climate and
stage of culture are largely eliminated when the counties with
good and poor land are compared *in an individual State.*

Accessibility to markets has far less effect upon the price of
land than is usually supposed. The best markets, of course, are
found in the largest cities, but such cities are by no means the
chief centres of areas where the farm land is most costly. On a
map of the average value of farm land (Figure 2), Boston, New
York, Los Angeles, and Seattle, for example, are surrounded by
small patches of heavy shading indicating high value per acre.
This is doubtless due in part to the fact that farm land close to
cities has a value as residence property as well as for farming.
But the land around each of these cities is relatively good for
crops, so that it would command a comparatively high price
even if there were no great cities near at hand. Other great cities
are by no means the centres of the darkest shading in their respective areas. Look at Philadelphia in its pale patch; Chicago
in a dark area, but with a still darker patch 100 or 200 miles to
the southwest; Cincinnati in a relatively light patch with dark
patches on each side; and St. Louis, Baltimore, Detroit, San
Francisco, Milwaukee, St. Paul, Minneapolis, and many other
large cities which are not located in the centres of the darkest
parts of the map. The largest of all the black patches is in western
Iowa, not far from Omaha, but evidently it owes only a small
fraction of the value of its land to that relatively small city.
The second largest patch lies in northern Illinois, but the value
of the land actually declines toward Chicago. And look at the
irrigated patches scattered over the dry Western States. Very
few are situated near large markets, but the majority have land
of high value. Nearness to markets and to facilities for transportation is evidently a minor factor in determining the value of
farm land. Such land is valuable for what it produces. The
large black patches in Illinois and Iowa are areas where the yield
of corn per acre runs steadily high, year after year, and where
other crops grow correspondingly well. The soil and, to a lesser

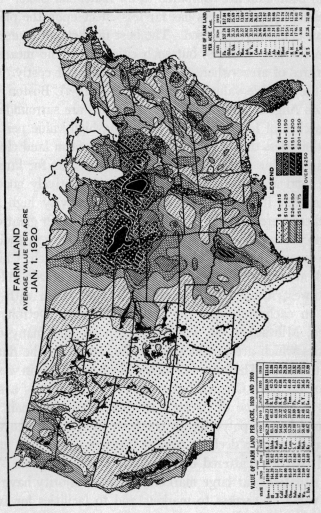

FIG. 2. VALUE OF FARM LAND PER ACRE IN THE UNITED STATES.
From *Economic Geography.* Courtesy of Dr. W. E. Ekblaw.

degree, the relief are the main reasons for both of these patches, as well as for the local differences of shading in almost every other part of the map.

Abundant other evidence, such as the value of good land in practically all parts of China and Japan, regardless of where the cities are located, seems to prove that nearness to markets is a minor factor in determining the value of farm land. Such land is valuable for what it produces; if it is capable of high productivity it will be provided with all the railroads, or other means of communication that it needs, so far as the stage of human culture permits, or at least it will attract enough people so that it will provide its own market. Hence if we omit the large cities and compare the counties containing the least valuable land with those containing the most valuable land in almost any of the States in the eastern half of the United States, we may feel fairly certain that the differences which we find are due largely to the effect of soil and relief upon productivity.

We will confine our study to the eastern half of the United States, not only because the differences of climate, altitude, and relief within any given State are relatively slight compared with farther west, but because that section has been settled so long that people have generally shaken down, as it were, into a fairly permanent condition. Let us use the ten States of Ohio, Indiana, Illinois, Iowa, and Minnesota in the north, Kentucky and Tennessee in the centre, and Georgia, Mississippi, and Arkansas distinctly southern. In each State let us choose the fifteen counties where the value of the farm land is highest per acre, and the fifteen where the value is lowest. But we will omit all counties containing towns of over 10,000 population, for we want to study the rural people, those who are close to the land.*

In most respects the contrast between good land and poor is

---

* Because of an error made by an assistant, Monroe County, Ind., is included among the poor counties of that State, although it contains Bloomington, a town of over 11,000 population. The effect of this is merely to make the poor counties appear better than would otherwise be the case. The mistake was discovered so late that it did not seem worth while to make all the new calculations that its correction would involve. Additional details and maps pertaining to this chapter appear in *Economic Geography*, vol. 3, 1926, pp. 335-357.

of the same sort in each of our ten States. In a number of cases,
however, the Southern States with their Negro population differ
from the Northern, and there are other suggestive departures
from uniformity. One of the most uniform features, as might
be expected, is the greater income per farm on the good land
than on the poor, as appears in the following table:

INCOME PER FARM, 1919

	Good Land	Poor Land	Ratio of Good to Poor
Iowa	$5,945	$3,480	1.7
Illinois	5,710	1,760	3.2
Minnesota	3,860	1,740	2.2
Ohio	3,830	2,180	1.8
Indiana	3,460	1,625	2.1
Georgia	2,200	805	2.7
Kentucky	1,910	785	2.4
Arkansas	1,810	1,090	1.7
Tennessee	1,745	1,155	1.5
Mississippi	1,370	1,010	1.4

The farm income is found by taking the value of all crops,
wool, dairy products, and poultry products in 1919, the year
covered by the last census, adding one-tenth of the value of the
live stock to represent roughly the value of the new animals
raised each year in excess of the value of their food, and sub-
tracting the amounts spent for labor, fertilizer, and feed. Even
in Mississippi, where the contrast is least marked, the average
farmer in the counties with good land gets about $140 of income
for every $100 received by the farmer on the poor land, while in
Illinois the corresponding figures are $320 against $100.

Similar conditions prevail almost everywhere. Even the
seeming exceptions like Florida generally turn out to be merely
cases where other factors enter into the matter. The most valuable farm land in Florida is located in the sandy peninsula along
the central parts of the coast, especially in the west. In northern
Florida, the soil is chemically much richer than in the peninsula, but the autumn rain makes it difficult to raise cotton;
killing frosts damage the orange-trees; and the heavier, although
richer, soils are not good for winter vegetables and oranges.

Half a century ago there was no market for the oranges and winter vegetables that might have been grown in the sandy soils of southern Florida, and the value of such land was negligible. To-day a new stage of culture with its marvellous transportation facilities makes the sandy soil the most valuable. Thus in Florida, as elsewhere, the farm land that yields the highest financial return for a given amount of labor brings the highest price; and the social, economic, and racial contrasts between good land and poor are the same as in the other States. Other seeming exceptions disappear in the same way. Hence our first tentative generalization is that, other things being equal, the farmers who live on poor land have smaller incomes than their neighbors on good land. If the farmers have small incomes, it is practically certain that the merchants, artisans, professional men and laborers in the same region also have small incomes, and the standards of living are low.

All this seems so obvious that the reader may wonder why I have wasted a page or so in discovering it. The main reason is that we want to be sure of our ground. We want to know not only the kind of handicaps that hamper a man on poor soil, but their magnitude.

Here is another handicap, a minor one to be sure, but not unimportant. In all of our ten States except Georgia, the farmers on the poor land pay a higher rate of interest on their mortgages than do those in the good counties. In Georgia the rates are practically identical. Where other causes, such as climate and race, combine with poor soil and rugged relief to depress the value of the land, the rate of interest rises especially high. Thus in our ten States the average rates are as follows: Northern rich land, 5.5 per cent; Northern poor land, 6.0; Southern rich land, 6.8; Southern poor land, 7.2.

The main cause of these differences appears to be the salability of the land. Other things being equal, the greater the value of the land per acre, the more easily it can be sold. It is on run-down farms, not New York skyscrapers, that the "For Sale" signs grow mossy. Accordingly the following figures as to the average value of farm land per acre in the selected counties of our ten States give some idea of the ease with which the farms can be sold: Northern rich land, $202; Northern poor land, $60; Southern rich land, $73; Southern poor land, $12. These figures, however, by no means wholly explain the interest rates, for the Southern good land is worth more than the Northern poor land, but pays higher interest. The relative abundance of capital in the North, and the general activity of all kinds of business help to keep the Northern rates low, while the fact that colored people carry part of the Southern mortgages helps to keep the rates high there.

The speed with which the population is growing is often supposed to have much to do with the rate of interest, but our ten States give no support to this idea. From 1910 to 1920 the Northern rich counties, where the interest rate is only 5.5, suffered a loss in rural population, while the northern poor counties, where the interest rate is 6.0, experienced a gain. In the South the opposite conditions prevailed, for the counties with good land gained in population while the poor counties lost. For our present purpose, however, the essential point is that in practically every State, if the farmer on poor soil tries to carry a mortgage, he is subject to the handicap of being obliged to pay a relatively high rate of interest compared with his neighbor on good land.

Another handicap is that this same man on poor soil has to pay relatively high for almost everything. His house and barns are much poorer than those of his fellow farmer in the same State on good soil, but they cost him much more in proportion to his income. The same is true of implements, even though they are not half so good as those of his more fortunate competitor. Here are the figures for the combined value of buildings, machinery, and implements expressed as percentages of the values of the farm land: Northern rich land, 17.2; Northern poor land, 33.4; Southern rich land, 26.8; Southern poor land, 43.8. It is very costly to be poor.

Still another disadvantage which suggests itself in this connection is the sparsity of the population and the scarcity of towns on the poor land. Does this make it difficult to find markets, conduct good schools, obtain medical care, and gain the benefit of contact with the rest of the world? In Minnesota where there are only 7 people per square mile on the poor land compared with 24 on the good, this seems to be the case. So, too, in Georgia, where the corresponding numbers are 16 and 60, and in the other Southern States, where smaller contrasts of the same kind prevail. In the North, however, the differences in the density of population on the two kinds of land are very slight, and in Illinois there are more people per square mile on the poor land than on the good. In fact, for the four Northern States, aside from Minnesota, the density of population is practically the same on both kinds of land, being 42 per square mile on the poor, and 43 on the good. The density on the poor land is probably unfavorable.

So far as towns are concerned, the good land undoubtedly has an advantage in the South, but this becomes insignificant in the North. Of course, we have excluded counties containing towns of over 10,000 people, but, even so, in the South the towns of 2,500 to 10,000 people contain only 2 per cent of the inhabitants of the poor counties against 14 per cent for the good, but in the five Northern States these figures become 16 and 18. Because of their greater prosperity the counties with good land can support more stores, lodges, movies, ministers, physicians, carpenters, teachers, and other people of the kinds who live in small towns. In the North, however, in the purely rural communities, this by no means increases the urban population so much as might be expected.

Let us next inquire into the causes of the poverty and other disadvantages of the counties with poor land. Is the land alone responsible, or must the people themselves bear part of the blame? Let us see, for example, whether the racial character of the inhabitants has anything to do with the matter. Do native whites, foreign-born immigrants, or Negroes show any special predilection for one type of land or the other? Taking all the Northern States together, the percentages of native whites on the two kinds of land are almost identical, averaging between 91 and 92 in both cases. Such a high figure is normal, for purely rural communities generally contain a large percentage of native-born in practically all parts of the United States. The foreign-born farmers amount to about 7½ per cent on both the good and the poor land of the North. The Negroes are negligible there, amounting at most to 2 per cent in the poorer part of Ohio. Evidently there is no systematic tendency for either natives or foreigners to predominate on either kind of land in the North, and the differences in the prosperity and progressiveness of our two sets of counties can scarcely be due to race.

In the five Southern States the native whites form 64 per cent of the population on the good land, and 79 on the poor, the remainder of the population being practically all Negroes. The fact that 35 per cent of the population on the good land is colored, and only 20 per cent on the poor, must tend to diminish rather than increase the economic contrast between the two kinds of land. Since the colored people regularly have low incomes, their presence in large numbers must work to the disadvantage of the counties with good land in the South. Hence it seems clear that the racial composition of the population is in no sense a cause of the contrasted prosperity of the farmers on the good land and the poor. The good land, however, does cause a concentration of Negroes, and that in itself is a highly important fact.

Let us next inquire whether the farmers in poor regions put forth any special effort in order to raise their standards to those of their fellow citizens on the good land. In other words, does the poverty of the land stimulate thrift, industry, and other good qualities, as is often supposed? Indications along this line might appear in at least four ways which we can test statistically; the farmers on poor land might (1) enlarge their farms, (2) work harder than their neighbors on better land, (3) employ greater intelligence, and (4) restrict their families. It seems as though persons of high intelligence, or even of moderate intelligence, ought to adopt all four methods.

Do the farmers on poor land enlarge their farms in order to

produce as much as do their rivals on the good land? By no means. In the five Northern States of our comparison the farms on the poor land systematically average smaller than the others, no matter whether we consider the entire farms or the improved part that is under cultivation. In Illinois, Iowa, and Minnesota, where most of the land was originally parcelled out in quarter-sections of 160 acres apiece, the average size of the farms in the good areas in 1920 was 164, 174, and 184 acres, respectively, against 112, 151, and 154 in the poor areas. This means that the farmers on the good land tend to increase their holdings, while those on the poorer land have sold part of what they originally acquired. This tendency becomes still more significant when one considers that on an average about 89 per cent of the good soil is improved, and only 68 per cent of the poor. One must also remember that the farmers on the good land produce more per acre than do those on the poor land, the average values of crops per acre in 1919 being $33.90 on the good land of our five Northern States and $21.30 on the poor. If the farmers on the poor land were to enlarge their farms so as to get the same return per farm as do the farmers on the good, the average size of their farms in our five Northern States would have to be 297 acres in comparison with 143 for the farms on good land. Actually the average size of the farms on poor land is only 120 acres.

In the South the average farm on poor land is larger than on good, but this is merely because a large part of the best land is rented to colored farmers who are content with small farms because their standards of living—and working—are low. In the North the owner of a big farm frequently runs it himself by means of hired help. A similar owner in the South rarely does much farming. He rents his land to tenants, mainly colored, and devotes his attention to keeping them going. Although exact data are not available, it is certain that so far as *ownership* is concerned the contrast between the good and poor lands is of the same kind in the South as in the North. A small white aristocracy still owns most of the land in the best farming regions of the South. Thus neither in the North nor South is there any evidence that the farmers on the poor land make up for the lack of productivity of their land by cultivating or owning a larger area than do the farmers on the good land. The opposite is emphatically the case. On the poor land the farms tend to decrease in size: on the good land they increase.

Do the farmers on the poor land make up for the handicap of their soil by more intensive cultivation? A rough answer is found in the amount of labor per acre performed by men and horses. In the absence of exact data let us assume that a man or a horse works equally hard on both kinds of land. The average value of the horses on the good land of our ten States, to be sure, is $98, against $92 on the poor, while for mules the corresponding figures are $156 and $131. Incidentally it may be added that so far as the figures have been tabulated the cattle and swine on the rich farms are also worth more per head than on the poor farms. Presumably the more valuable draft animals do better work than the less valuable ones, but that is merely a guess. It is certain, however, that the number of horses and mules per acre of improved land is almost everywhere greater on the good land than on the poor, the only exceptions being Iowa and Minnesota, where the amount of farm machinery is at a maximum. The average number of horses and mules per 100 acres of improved land in all our ten States is 5.3 on the good land, and 4.7 on the poor.

Do the people on the poor land make up for their deficiency in work animals by working harder themselves? Let us assume that on both kinds of land the farmer's own family, including himself, provides work amounting to a man and a half for the eight months during which there is much work to be done. As a matter of fact, the number of children per family is greater on the poor land than on the good. Moreover, the older boys are perhaps less likely to go away to school or to become clerks in the grocery at the "Corner," simply because their opportunities in these lines are limited. Thus the families on the poor land probably provide more days of labor per year than do their more fortunate neighbors. Let us add to the work done by the family the amount of labor hired from outside as calculated from the amount spent for this purpose according to the census. We will assume that the rate paid per month is the same in all parts of each State, although it is actually lower in the poor parts. Reckoned in this way, each acre of improved land on the farm of the good counties gets 5.5 days of work during the year, while each acre on the poor farms gets 6.5. Inasmuch as we have consistently given the poorer counties the benefit of the doubt, and inasmuch as the work done by animals is greater on the good land than on the poor, the actual amount of labor per acre of cultivated land is probably about the same in both cases. There certainly is no evidence that the total amount of work per person on the poor farms is any greater than on the good. Even if each acre of improved poor land gets 6.5 days of work per year, as compared with 5.5 on the good land, the average number of improved acres per farm where the soil is poor is only 60.2, in contrast with 86.3 where the soil is good. It almost looks as though the farmers did not work so hard on the poor land as on the good.

How about the intelligence with which the farms on the two kinds of land are run? Some indication along this line may possibly be furnished by the amount spent for fertilizer. Here at first sight we seem to find a case where the farmers on the poor land go ahead of the others. In 1919 they spent 38 cents per acre on artificial fertilizers, whereas the farmers on the good land spent only 36 cents. But this difference is trivial and would be wiped out if we omitted Georgia, where the expenditure for fertilizer, mainly on cotton land, is far greater than in any other State. Moreover, the value of the live stock per improved acre amounts to $16.23 on the good land compared with $12.73 on the poor. The amount of manure varies almost as much, for this difference is considerably greater than the corresponding difference in the value of animals per head. Moreover, on good land the animals are generally stall-fed more frequently than on poor, where the proportion of pasture-land is large. Both of these conditions indicate a greater supply of manure per acre on good land than on poor. Thus, so far as fertilizers are concerned, the two kinds of farms are almost on a par.

Another test of the intelligence of the farmers is found, perhaps, in the extent to which implements and machinery are employed. In this respect the farmers on the good land everywhere stand notably ahead. Even if we reckon on the basis of the value of machinery per acre of improved land, the averages are $8.32 against $5.55. There seems to be no way—at least no statistical way—of determining whether the difference in the use of machinery is due to the intelligence of the farmers or to their financial status as determined by the soil. But at any rate the use of machinery agrees with the size of the farms, the amount of labor, and the use of fertilizers in failing to afford any evidence that the farmers on the poor land employ special methods to increase their production and thus diminish the gap between themselves and their neighbors.

Even if the farmers on the poor land do not use methods which raise their production toward the level of their neighbors on the good land, do they not, at least, have the wisdom to limit the size of their families, and thus maintain high standards of living? On which type of land would you expect the families to be larger? On the poor land, almost every one answers. That is correct. But why do we assume that the people on poor land will have larger families than those on good land? Does not this assumption carry with it the implication that the people on the poor land are relatively lacking in foresight, thrift, or self-control? If they were wise, would they not restrict their families after the French fashion, so that each family could pass on a good "dot" to its one girl, and a farm to the boy? In extenuation of their course it may be said that many children are a help to the farmer, but that is true only so long as plenty of land is available so that as the families increase in size the amount of hired labor can be diminished, or the size of the farms increased. But there is practically no hired help on the poorer farms, and the stage when new land can be profitably and easily put under cultivation is long past in practically all parts of our ten States.

The only exceptions are northern Minnesota, where the poor land of that State is located, and possibly north-central Arkansas, which is also a region of poor land.

If the average income per farmer, and the average size of the family are used as a means of locating a point for each of our twenty groups of counties on what is known as a dot chart, one sees at once that practically all the dots indicating an income of less than $2,200 lie not far from a straight line. This means that except in unusual cases the number of children per family decreases systematically as the income of the farmers rises. Contrary to what is usually supposed, there is no indication of larger families among the Negroes than among the whites. The Kentucky mountains have the largest families (7.1) and lowest incomes ($785) among the whole of our twenty groups of counties, but there the people are almost purely native whites with only 1 per cent of Negroes. In the good counties of Mississippi, on the contrary, where the percentage of Negroes rises to 62, the size of the families (4.3) is less than would be expected from the general trend of the other dots. Possibly this may be due in part to a high death-rate and in part to the migration of colored people to the North during the war.

When the income gets above $2,500, according to the exaggerated scale of 1919, a distinct change occurs. The size of the families diminishes much more slowly than before in proportion to the increase in income. By the time the income reaches $5,000 on the 1919 scale the decrease has given place to an increase, and as $6,000 is approached the farmers in the best parts of Illinois and Iowa have families as large as those where the income is about $1,800. In other words, there seems to be a hint that as the income becomes larger the number of children actually begins to increase. This would be a most hopeful sign if it were true. Unfortunately the word "family," as used by the census, includes servants, boarders, and anybody else who happens to live in a house and take his meals there. It takes no account of the children who have gone away from home. Thus while we know, with great exactness, how many pigs are born to a litter in any given section of the United States, the census gives us no exact idea as to the size of real families. It seems as if we ought to know as much about parents and their children as about sows and their pigs. Fortunately, the Census Bureau is now collecting data which partially supply the necessary facts.

To return to our main theme, among farmers with an income too small to allow servants to be kept, the census family and the real family are practically identical except as the young people go away from home. When the income reaches a certain size hired "help" is kept, and that makes the census families appear to be less restricted than is actually the case. Thus what our data really show is that among farmers, as among other people, the number of children varies almost inversely as the income. And the income depends directly upon the quality of the land. The poorer the land the greater the number of children. This suggests a very distinct inferiority on the part of the poorer farmers. They apparently permit themselves to have large families when they know that the children are going to be a burden, and cannot be well educated or well provided for. Perhaps this will change when birth-control is well understood.

Further indications along this same line are afforded by the degree to which the farmers own their farms. Here our data show great uniformity. With the single exception of the Negroes of Tennessee, the percentage of farmers who run their own farms is smaller—often much smaller—where the land is good than where it is poor. This is true no matter whether we deal with white people, colored people, or foreign immigrants. On good land some of the farmers save enough so that they can afford to rent their farms and retire to the villages; or they prosper so much that they buy farms in addition to their own. As old age approaches they perhaps rent one of the farms. They can do this easily, for their good land is in demand. Where the land is poor, few farmers are able to lay up enough to purchase new land, and it is relatively hard to find tenants for poor farms. Moreover, there appears to be a stronger tendency for the young people to move to the towns from the good land than from the poor. The fact that many such young people inherit farms which are rented to tenants helps them greatly in establishing themselves in business, or in going into professions. But regardless of just how it happens, one of the most basic facts about farming all over the world is that on good land the percentage of tenancy tends to be high.

Certain kinds of tenancy are advantageous. A son may be his father's tenant; an immigrant, or the ambitious native son of poor parents may rent a farm which he ultimately buys. As a matter of fact, however, such tenants are a small minority. The majority, and in some places an overwhelming majority, as in the better farming regions of the South, are tenants who never get beyond the stage of tenancy. Thus a high percentage of tenancy is generally a bad sign. It indicates a large proportion of relatively incompetent people who are not capable of getting the land into their own possession, and who tend to be careless in their methods of cultivation.

Tenancy also indicates something of the opposite sort. In spite of individual exceptions, the people who own farms and rent them to others are generally above the average in ability. Such ability in themselves or in their families is one of the main reasons why they own land. In many cases they are able to lease farms to others because they have succeeded so well that they own more land than they care to cultivate, or else are able to make a living in less arduous, more interesting, or more profitable ways than farming. The lawyer in the small town, the merchant who runs the post-office, the local judge, the congressman, and the college professor who grew up on the farm are often among the owners who rent their farms to tenants. Thus tenancy may mean a division of the population into a relatively prosperous land-owning group, and a much less prosperous group of tenants. In the Northern States, and especially in those that are newer, this division has not progressed far, and the two groups are not socially separated. In the South the division has gone so far that we may speak of a white aristocracy in contrast with a peasantry. This peasantry consists mainly of Negroes, but also contains an appreciable number of poor whites who have not made the grade, so to speak, and hence have dropped to an almost permanent position of inferiority.

Among foreign-born white immigrants the percentage of tenants is less than among either native whites or Negroes. Moreover, the farms owned by the foreign-born average of higher value than those belonging to either of the other groups. Perhaps this is because it requires unusual initiative and vigor for a foreign immigrant to leave the city and settle on an American farm. In each of our ten States where the numbers are large enough to be significant, the percentage of tenants is least among the foreign-born, and greatest among the Negroes. The average percentages of tenant-farmers for all ten States are as follows:

	Negroes	Native Whites	Foreign-born
Good land............	73.3	47.7	32.2
Poor land............	55.1	26.5	8.9

But even if there are more tenants on good land than on poor, what of it? Does that fact have any effect in attracting or repelling special kinds of people? It probably tends to make the farmers on the poor land intermediate between the land-owning group and the tenants on the good land. A man who is not able to buy a farm where the soil is very rich, but who is independent enough to want to be his own master, is likely to move to a place where he can afford to buy a farm. That, of course, is more likely to be in a county with poor land than in one where the land is unusually good. How great an effect such conditions have upon the character of the population it is impossible to say, but the amount of movement from county to county, or State to State, is much larger than is often realized. This is especially true while a region is being settled. The United States Census shows how many people move away from the State where they were born. Surprising as it may seem, the percentage of the native-born inhabitants who have moved away is greatest in the States west of the Mississippi. The States where this percentage rises above 35 are Nevada, 53; Wyoming, 40; Kansas, 37; Iowa, 36; and Vermont, 38. No data are available as to how many people have moved to other counties in their own States. If we had data for such movements, we should probably find that in a State like Iowa perhaps two-thirds of all the people move away from their birthplace. This means that a tremendous process of sifting is going on whereby people are shuffled around, and finally settle in regions which, in one way or another, are adapted to their temperaments or capacities. The importance of this shuffling can scarcely be overrated.

Fortunately, the facts as to foreign-born illiteracy and as to the persons in *Who's Who* enable us to determine whether this shuffling takes place according to the laws of chance, or according to a definite selective principle. Here are the figures for illiteracy in our groups of counties with good land or poor:

PERCENTAGE OF ILLITERACY AMONG

	NATIVE WHITES		NEGROES		FOREIGN-BORN WHITE	
	A Good Land	B Poor Land	C Good Land	D Poor Land	E Good Land	F Poor Land
North..............	1.0	1.8	9.5	10.4	5.0	8.2
South..............	5.5	7.7	28.2	27.8	8.3	8.0

The figures for native whites and for northern Negroes are just as we should expect—low on the good land, higher on the poor—but they throw little or no light on the problem of whether the people on poor land are inherently less competent than those on good land. Illiteracy, so most people would say, is more common on the poor land than on the good, because the poverty of the soil restricts people's opportunities. Among the southern Negroes, however, those living on the poor soil are a trifle better educated than those on the good. If sauce for the goose is sauce for the gander, the reverse ought seemingly to be the case. If poverty, poor roads, poor schools, sparse population, and stifled ambition are really the main reasons why the whites are more illiterate on the poor land than on the good, as is commonly supposed, should not similar conditions in intensified form also make the colored people more illiterate on the poor land? Yet the opposite is the case.

It is sometimes said that where the colored people are a small minority, as in the poor counties, they come into contact with the whites so much that they become like the dominant race in many respects. Undoubtedly there is much truth in this. Where aliens are few and scattered, they tend to become like the people around them; where many aliens live together, they preserve their old characteristics. Nevertheless, another factor may be equally important. The poor lands of the South have often been a place of refuge for Negroes. In the days of slavery the ambitious freedman could rarely afford to buy land in the rich parts of the South, even if he were permitted to do so. In the poor regions, however, land was cheap and abundant, and the population sparse until after the Civil War. Of course, the poor whites hated the thought of competition with the Negroes. Nevertheless, some freedmen settled among them in regions where the land was poor and cheap, and the white population sparse and ignorant. Those freedmen were, on the whole, an especially fine type. Rarely could any others win freedom. Moreover, when once they were free, it required courage and initiative to settle in new regions where the sparse inhabitants were none too friendly.

Somewhat similar conditions still prevail. Negroes rarely buy farms where the soil is especially good. Those who till such soil are mainly tenants of the white man. But a Negro with thrift and initiative wants a farm of his own. Therefore the enterprising tenant is likely to move to some place where the land is cheap enough for him to buy it. Naturally he goes from the richer soil to the poorer, thus bringing to the poorer soil a selected type of Negro. Such people are better educated than their less ambitious neighbors who stay on the rich soil, and their children tend to follow in their steps. The relative superiority of the colored people on the poor soil may be due to this cause quite as much as to contact with the whites.

Among the foreign-born whites the conditions are the same as among the Negroes. In the North, where most of the foreign-born are found, the relative illiteracy of the foreign-born whites on the poor soil has little or nothing to do with the local opportunities for education. Only a handful of immigrants settle on the farms as children. The vast majority come as adults, whose degree of literacy depends on their childhood environment. Some process evidently sorts out a relatively illiterate type to settle on the farms where the land is poor. Of course, the sorting is very haphazard and incomplete, but that does not alter the general fact. Here is the way it seems to work. The competent immigrant tends not only to be better educated than the incompetent, but to save more money. When he gets ready to buy a farm he chooses a better one than does his less competent and more ignorant fellow countryman. Needless to say, the more expensive farms are located where the land is fertile. Even if a competent and industrious immigrant happens to settle on a poor farm, he is almost certain to prosper more than does his incompetent and illiterate neighbor. If he moves to a new farm, as often happens, the chances are that it will be better than his old one. The incompetent immigrant, on the contrary, who is also likely to be illiterate, can rarely afford a good farm. If he attempts to swing one, he frequently gets into debt, fails to pay on his mortgage, and ultimately may have to move to a farm that is cheaper.

In the little table given above it will be noticed that in the South the difference between the illiteracy of immigrants on good soil and poor is negligible. In the real South, in distinction from Kentucky and Tennessee, the 4,000 foreign-born persons of our chosen counties on the good land in Georgia, Mississippi, and Arkansas are more illiterate than the 1,400 on the poor land. This is presumably because social conditions put the foreign-born immigrant in a position analogous to that of the Negroes. The intelligent immigrant does not like to settle where he must compete with Negroes. The more intelligent he is, the more likely he is to avoid the regions of good soil and abundant Negroes,

unless he can at once afford to become an employer or landlord.
Thus, among the foreign-born farmers of both the North and the
South, there seems to be evidence of a process of selection which
brings one kind of farmer to land that is good and another to
land that is poor. Which kind will go to each place depends
upon social conditions such as slavery, tenancy, and the relative
position of the white and colored races, but the distribution of
the social conditions in turn is due largely to the geographic
environment.

This same process of migration and se.ection is well illustrated
by the people in *Who's Who in America*. That biographical
volume tells where some 25,000 of the more competent people of
the United States now live, and where they were born. Here is a
little table showing how 172 of these persons, who happen to live
in our twenty groups of counties, are distributed per 100,000 of
the population.

PERSONS IN "WHO'S WHO" PER HUNDRED THOUSAND INHABITANTS

	Good Land	Poor Land		Good Land	Poor Land
Ohio..................	3.6	2.2	Kentucky.............	11.6	1.1
Indiana*..............	5.1	3.7	Tennessee............	4.7	1.8
Illinois...............	3.4	2.0	Georgia..............	4.2	0.0
Iowa.................	11.0	2.9	Mississippi...........	1.3	0.8
Minnesota............	0.4	2.2	Arkansas.............	1.0	0.5
Total North...........	4.6	2.5	Total South..........	4.2	1.9

* In the present tabulation Monroe County, Ind., is omitted, thus conforming exactly to our rule of omit-
ting counties containing towns of over 10,000 population. See note on page 13.

In nine States out of ten the figures for good land are larger
than for poor. In Minnesota alone is the preponderance the other
way. But the good counties there have only one person in *Who's
Who* and the poor only five, so that the exceptional character of
that State is presumably a mere accident. Perhaps there is some
special reason why competent people leave the counties having
good land but no cities in Minnesota. At any rate ten persons
who were born in the good counties of that State live in other
counties of the same State, while only one person born in the

poor counties lives in some other part of the State. Thus, other
things being equal, the proportion of eminent residents appears
to be regularly larger on good land than on poor.

But we want to know whether this condition arises because
of the greater opportunities of the good land, or because these
same opportunities attract a gifted type of people who give the
good land an hereditary advantage, so to speak. The answer lies
in the following classification of the birthplaces of the persons in
Who's Who:

PERSONS IN "WHO'S WHO" PER MILLION INHABITANTS IN
COUNTIES WITH GOOD VERSUS POOR SOIL

Birthplace	NORTHERN STATES		SOUTHERN STATES	
	Good Land	Poor Land	Good Land	Poor Land
Home county............................	9	5	6	2
Other counties of home State............	15	9	13	3
Other States............................	22	11	19	3

The first line shows that the good land, in proportion to its
population, excels the poor land two or three fold in giving birth
to eminent persons who later reside in the counties of their
birth. That may be either because the people in the good counties are inherently superior to those in the others or because they
have better opportunities. The other two lines tell a different
tale. They show that the good land has from two to six times as
much power to attract people from other counties and other
States as has the neighboring poor land. This would be still
more evident if we were to use counties containing towns of over
10,000 population, for gifted people gravitate toward the towns,
and the towns are larger and more numerous on the good land
than on the poor. But it is better to understate the case than to
overstate it.

This discussion of *Who's Who* is very significant. Although
it is based on only a few people, it is confirmed by thousands
more who are used in other tabulations. Its importance lies in
its indication that when people migrate to new homes the most

competent are much more likely to go to places where the land is good than to those where it is poor. Of course they are still more likely to go to cities, but that is another question. The people who happen to get into *Who's Who* are not essentially different from the rest of us. If they tend to go anywhere in large proportions, we may be quite sure that people of slightly less ability do likewise. And so on down the line until we come to the immigrant farmers. As to them we have positive evidence that they do exactly as do the people in *Who's Who*. Some of the more competent undoubtedly settle on poor land, but a larger percentage go to good land.

Thus the average caliber of the newcomers tends to be higher on good land than on poor, at least in the earlier stages of development. Only when tenancy becomes so well established that the tenants form an inferior class like the Negroes, is there much likelihood that this general tendency will be checked through its conflict with still stronger tendencies. Moreover, in any region where there is a concentration of relatively competent people, the ability of the parents tends to be handed down from generation to generation, both by physical inheritance and by training. Thus the contrast between the scanty incomes on the poor land and the good incomes on the good land appears to be due not only to the direct economic and social effect of the land, but to the types of people who unconsciously sort themselves out as settlers in one place or the other. This appears to be true not only in diverse parts of the United States, but also in other parts of the world. The conditions in China, India, Turkey, Germany, France, England, Mexico, and many other countries parallel those in the United States so closely in this respect that there seems good reason to believe that we are dealing with an almost universal principle.

CHAPTER III

MIGRATIONS IN THE UNITED STATES

IF we would rightly interpret the past and thereby learn how to direct the future, we must understand the great problem of migration. What kinds of people migrate, and in what kinds of places do they settle? What motives lead to migration, especially to the steady drifting from place to place which is constantly occurring? What kinds of people stay at home? And why? One way to get light on this problem is by analyzing a great many migrants and finding out what proportion of them belong to different types. Now it happens that *Who's Who* affords one of the best available records of individual migrations. Most of the people in that book have migrated away from their old homes. Is there any difference in this respect between doctors and professors, for example, or between business men and lawyers? The movements of the people in *Who's Who* are more important than those of the rank and file of the population, but there is no sharp distinction between the two. The principles which guide the migrations of the leaders also guide those of the rest of the people.

Let us divide the people in *Who's Who* into groups according to their occupations. We will limit ourselves to Ohio, Indiana, Illinois, Iowa, and Minnesota. Some of these States, like Ohio, are old enough to be thoroughly established, while others, like Minnesota, still have many elements of newness. In the following table all the people who live in these five States and are included in *Who's Who* are classified according to their occupations and according to whether they were born in one of the following places: (1) the county where they now live, (2) other counties of the State where they now live, (3) other States of the United States, (4) other countries. The first column sums up the facts as to the degree to which persons born within the United States migrate from one part of the country to another. A low number means that people do not migrate much; a high number means that a large proportion were born in counties or States other than those where they now live. Obviously, the people who still live in their natal counties have not been appreciably influenced by the spirit of migration. Those who live in other counties of the same State have been influenced only a little. We have given such people an index number of one, and have assumed that those who move from one State to another feel the migratory influence twice as much as do those who move only from one county to another within their own State. On that basis our table is arranged according to the tendency toward migration in fifteen groups of occupations. If we add the persons who come from foreign countries and assume that they feel the impulse to migrate twice as much as do those who move from one State to another, the occupations arrange themselves in nearly the same order as in the table, except that musicians have the highest index, while philanthropists have a low one. This does not fairly represent the case, for the foreign musician is not hampered at all by the language of a new country, while a lawyer is terribly hampered.

Occupations	A	B	C	D	E	F
	Index of Migration	PERCENTAGE BORN IN				No. of Persons
		Home County	Other Counties of home State	Other States	Other Countries	
Farmers..................	.72	45	25	20	10	20
Government officials.......	1.09	27	33	35	5	382
Lawyers..................	1.27	20	26	45	9	321
Editors, journalists........	1.31	20	22	49	9	159
Doctors, surgeons, etc......	1.34	17	25	48	9	309
Authors, lecturers, etc......	1.35	20	20	50	10	240
Business men.............	1.36	21	17	54	8	545
Artists, architects.........	1.43	17	15	53	15	120
Musicians................	1.44	12	10	38	40	95
Philanthropists, publicists..	1.59	9	22	66	3	77
Labor leaders.............	1.65	8	8	72	12	25
Engineers................	1.67	8	14	71	7	175
Scientists................	1.69	6	15	68	11	428
Educators................	1.69	4	20	64	12	810
Religious leaders..........	1.77	3	13	67	17	407

This little table is full of significance. Unfortunately the farmers and labor leaders are so few that their percentages in columns B to E have little value, but their positions in column A are probably nearly correct. The number of farmers is astonishingly small—only 20 out of the 3,993 persons included in our table, or about half of one per cent. Yet in the five States under consideration farmers constitute 20 per cent of all the gainfully employed persons. Evidently a farmer, as such, has little chance to distinguish himself. As a matter of fact, however, the number of farmers in *Who's Who* is greater than the figures suggest. Many people who start life as farmers distinguish themselves as politicians, editors, or business men. That is one of the great troubles with farming. The competent farmers leave the soil, and the rest of the farmers have a hard time because they have few leaders. But for our present purpose the important fact about farmers is that the few who do distinguish themselves do not migrate much. Nearly half of the twenty in our table were born in the counties where they now live, and another quarter were born within the States of their present residence.

Of course it is true that a large part of the people who settled the United States and other new countries were farmers, but that is not inconsistent with our statement that the farmer type of mind does not tend to migrate. Even in our own day most of the men in the world are farmers, and in the past this was true even in regions like Massachusetts, where now the great majority are engaged in manufacturing. Moreover, during the last four centuries the incentives to migration on the part of the farmers have been extraordinarily strong because such vast areas of good new land have been available. Accordingly the actual number of farmers who migrate to other States and other countries is huge. Nevertheless, in proportion to their numbers the men who have the farmer type of mind show less tendency to move away from home than do those of almost any other large group, unless it be laborers.

Among the farmers who are candidates for *Who's Who* the man who is to attain conspicuous success needs a large farm, where he can develop new methods and try experiments. A wide acquaintance also helps greatly if he attempts to lead in such reforms as co-operative methods, and the like. A man who inherits broad acres and a good name has a great advantage in this respect, and such a man naturally does not care to migrate. Such conditions have much to do with the relative immobility of the better farmers all over the world. But in addition to this, the kind of temperament which makes a man a great success on a farm does not seem to be the kind which fills him with the desire to migrate. The good farm boy and the good sailor boy are quite different. But note an interesting fact. The farmers in new countries like the United States, Canada, Australia, and Argentina do not have nearly such a strong tendency toward the patient, industrious, but relatively unenterprising type as do those of older countries all over the world. Yet the great advances in farming have been made in the Old World. The rotation of crops, the use of fertilizers, the best methods of cultivation are largely the product of Europe. Our contributions have been mainly along the lines of the use of machinery, they have been the work of engineers and inventors rather than of farmers. Does this mean that Europe has kept at home the best and the worst of her farmers—the leaders and the peasants? Has she sent out to the rest of the world an intermediate type? Or does it merely indicate that because the soil is poor and the population dense in Europe the demand for improved and intensive methods of agriculture was great, while in the United States abundant land and extensive agriculture created a demand for machinery?

The only other group in our table whose index of migration is anywhere nearly so low as that of the farmers is the government officials. They too are stay-at-homes. The reason is clear. The temperament that succeeds in politics is generally the kind that makes friends easily. The successful politician must have the power to ingratiate himself with his neighbors, he must keep in close touch with the people around him, he must conciliate them, and make himself liked. It is a great advantage to him to be able to swap funny stories in the corner grocery; but if he is too inquisitive, too progressive, too much of a reformer, he gets into trouble. A man with the political temperament usually finds it easy to pick up a job in his youth, even when jobs are scarce. He's such a good fellow, you know. This in itself relieves him somewhat of the compulsion which many young men feel to get away from home in order to carve out a career. Moreover, in almost no other occupation does mere acquaintance count for so much. A politician is enormously helped by being able to meet a host of boyhood friends and clap them on the back. "Hello, Bill; how's the kids? Remember that time you and Johnny and me went over to Small's Creek after pickerel, and you got a three-pounder and a ducking?" One such slap may be worth many votes. But when an engineer is planning a new type of bridge it does not help him much to slap an old friend on the back and catalogue the ages of his children. Thus the political type of mind finds its opportunities at home rather than far away. It may be a real advantage politically if a man is not pricked into restlessness by curiosity, altruism, or ambition, as happens so often to people of other temperaments.

It is often, and perhaps justly, said that America does not know how to play politics, and can be beaten by Europe in diplomacy every time. Our local government is certainly inferior to that of the countries whence the bulk of our older population is derived, and even our national government has a vast amount to learn from countries like England. Can this arise in part from the fact that the migrants from Europe to America have included relatively few of the classes of society endowed by nature with the higher type of political capacity? Curiously enough, the United States seems to possess a greater power of inventing political ideas than of making them work. Moreover, our efficiency in this respect seems to be declining. But certainty in this matter is impossible. We can merely raise the query whether the greater progress of both agriculture and statesmanship in Europe than in America is connected with the relative lack of migratory impulse among the more competent people whose minds run in those directions.

What has just been said about government officials applies

more or less to lawyers. Curiosity, altruism, and the spirit of adventure are rarely the moving impulses in the legal mind. As a
rule the lawyer does not prosper in a new environment. Like the
politician, he needs a knowledge of all the local ins and outs. If
he knows the private history of his clients and their opponents,
their business ventures, matrimonial troubles, and unsatisfied
ambitions, so much the easier does he find it to succeed. He needs
also a long schooling in the technic of the law as applied in his
own local community. With that should go the widest possible
acquaintance with the judges, attorneys, and others connected
with the courts in which he practises. A teacher or preacher may
be as successful his first year as his tenth or twentieth; but unless
a lawyer's reputation precedes him, or he is called to a new place
for a special purpose, he can almost never hope for immediate
success after migrating to a new home. If we were to study *Who's
Who* more fully, we should probably find that the differences in
the migratory tendency of the various groups would be much
more pronounced if we were to take account only of changes of
residence after the period of maturity had been reached. Look
around among the lawyers of your acquaintance and see how
many have moved into town since they were thirty years of age.
Then look at the engineers, ministers, and professors, and see how
different they are.

Among lawyers the tendency to migrate, or rather not to
migrate, is about the same as among journalists, medical men,
literary men, and business men. These five groups rank with the
farmers and officials as stay-at-homes. Of course all kinds of
people who are sufficiently gifted to be included in *Who's Who*
migrate a good deal, but relatively speaking the seven groups in
the upper part of our table do not change their places of residence very much. About half of each group was born in a State
or country other than that where they now live. If we had figures
for the rank and file, we should undoubtedly find that the proportion born beyond the limits of the States where they now
live is much smaller than this. If we could also eliminate those
whose last change of residence occurred before they had made

an appreciable start in their careers, we should presumably find that only an insignificant fraction move far from the places where they begin their careers.

The reasons for this are easy to understand. In journalism, medicine, and many kinds of business a local clientele or a fund of local knowledge is highly important. An editor or reporter in a new city is like a fish out of water so far as local news is concerned. A doctor's success depends largely on his ability to build up a local practice and a local reputation. The very great doctor may be called from Boston to Chicago in consultation, and may even have such a reputation that he can afford to give up his old clientele and move to another city with the assurance of an immediate practice. But that is the exception. Doctors, like journalists and business men, may migrate in their youth before they become established in their profession, but thereafter they tend strongly to stay in one place. The more successful a business man is, the more likely he is to own a large plant of some kind. His factory, his store, his printing-house, or his equipment as a contractor cannot easily be disposed of. He is held to his old home, even though he knows that he could succeed much better elsewhere. Even if a business man has not advanced to the point of being an owner or manager, his value in a place where he has lived many years is often much greater than his value anywhere else, because he knows the local conditions of trade, traffic, and people. The engineer who designs a great bridge, or an electric-light plant, on the contrary, has little or no need of such local knowledge. He can make his plan in one place almost as well as in another, but a salesman needs to know his customers.

Literary men fall into this group of stay-at-homes because they are not called away to definite centres as are scientists and teachers. It makes little difference where an author or lecturer has his home, for the audience to which he appeals usually lives all over the country. The politician's audience is always primarily local until he gets the presidential bee in his bonnet. So, too, is that of the reporter. The audience of the novelist and essayist, on the contrary, has almost no connection with any special locality.

It is interesting to see how allied occupations fall close together in our little table. Thus artists and musicians have practically the same migratory index. They stand together in an intermediate position between the stay-at-homes and the gadabouts. They likewise combine the characteristics of these two types. One distinct type of artist stays at home and paints the local scenery and the local people, or becomes the local architect. The other type is attracted to the great cities and the great institutions, and is likely to wander far afield. In the same way musicians are quite sharply divided into those whose reputation is purely local and those who acquire a national or international reputation which carries them all over the country and abroad. Of course, both types are found in every occupation, and there are all gradations between them, but in art and music the separation between the two types seems to be unusually clear.

The remaining groups of our table form the gadabouts— philanthropists, labor leaders, engineers in the more technical sense, scientists, educators, and religious leaders. At first sight it seems odd that philanthropists and labor leaders should fall together, but they are really very similar. Both represent the type of mind which is filled with zeal to help its fellow men in ways which are not primarily religious. The member of the philanthropic group, even if he happens to be a Y. M. C. A. man or a social-settlement worker, is capitalistic in his affiliations, while the labor leader fraternizes with the common workman. But, after all, it would be easy to turn a labor leader into a philanthropist by giving him plenty of money and a large vested interest in things as they are; and many a good potential philanthropist has become a labor leader because of some little accident which threw him into antagonism to capital.

The philanthropist obviously is not so likely to change his home as is the labor leader. Of course, people like Y. M. C. A. workers are very mobile because the institutions in which they find their occupation are located only in a relatively few of the larger centres of population, and men are called from one centre to another very freely. On the other hand, the thorough-going philanthropist and many of the publicists who compose the major part of this group are persons quite comfortably equipped with this world's goods. They are likely to enjoy retaining their citizenship in the old home—unless the taxes are too high—even though they may own a bit of sand in Florida or some rocks in California. At least there is no special urge upon them to change their places of residence. The labor leader, on the contrary, is just the type that moves freely about. But his movements are limited by the fact that as a rule he is attached to a special industry, such as coal-mining, or cotton-weaving, and cannot well go beyond the geographical limits thus set.

The last part of our table consists of four groups which are highly migratory—engineers of all the more highly trained sorts, scientists who are mostly teachers or workers in research institutions, educators whose work is primarily education rather than science or religion, and finally religious leaders, most of whom are ministers. Why are these people so mobile? Why should no more than 8 per cent remain in the counties in which they were born? Is it because of their restless temperament? Are they led forth by a spirit of adventure, curiosity, altruism, or faith? Or does the nature of their work compel them to migrate?

Except in the case of the religious leaders, work of the types done by these groups with high indexes of migration is not to be found anywhere and everywhere, as is the work of the lawyer, physician, and business man. Theirs are highly specialized occupations. In many a town of fifty or even a hundred thousand population there is no chance for a mining engineer, or even for a high-grade chemist, while a professor of European history would starve. Such people may be born in all sorts of environments, but they have to migrate in order to find opportunities to practise their professions. Moreover, the temperaments which lead people into these professions also tend to make them eager to travel, eager to find new truth, see new ways of life, and have new experiences. The engineering type of mind grows restive when cooped up in a small place where the lawyer and politician are happy. The scientist is so filled with curiosity that he must fare forth to some place where he can find answers to his questions. Thus temperament as well as occupation is a powerful factor.

Lastly we come to religion, the migratory occupation *par excellence*. This is not merely because ministers in our day are obliged to move from church to church every few years. The matter goes deeper than this, for among religious leaders no less than 17 per cent of those included in *Who's Who* were born abroad. The fact seems to be that all through the ages the religious enthusiasts have been extremely migratory. The ideal religious leader is filled with the spirit of missions. Think of the wandering friars in the days of old, the pilgrims to holy Jerusalem and Mecca, the pious fakirs of India, the Puritans journeying to new homes that they might worship God in peace, the Huguenots, Friends, and Mormons, faring forth to untried lands for love of God and of some abstract truth or falsehood. Think of the Parsees who suffered the loss of all things and migrated from place to place in Persia and India rather than give up their Zoroastrian faith and accept that of Mohammed. How about the ancient hermits such as St. Augustine in North Africa? Think, too, of the missionaries, that incredibly adventurous crew who in all ages have courted adventure, danger, and death in the hope of saving souls in the uttermost corners of the earth. Not even among explorers and soldiers can one find such an inveterate tendency to wander far afield under the impulse of a great emotion and a great conviction. As I write I think of a charming family where the father gave up his occupation as a life-insurance agent because, forsooth, he became convinced that the taking out of an insurance policy argued lack of faith in God's protecting fatherhood. That family left a pleasant home in a pleasant suburb in order to live on a farm near people who believed as they believed. Does any other power on earth, unless it be stark hunger or the edge of the sword, impel people to wander so widely?

Look back now at the table on page 34. On the whole it

shows a steady progress from the unimaginative practical types of people to the imaginative idealists. When read from the bottom upward it almost seems, in a rough way, to epitomize the history of new lands like America. In the United States the first noteworthy group of colonists was actuated primarily by religious motives. The majority, to be sure, were farmers by profession, but religion was what interested them. The type of mind which makes a man an educator was also strongly represented, as appears from the speed with which universal education became prevalent. So, too, was the type which is filled with curiosity. That slant of mind makes explorers in an age when vast new lands are being discovered; while in our day it makes scientists. The ingenious type of handy man who is clever at adapting himself to all sorts of new conditions also figured largely among the early settlers, and that type is now represented by the engineer and inventor. Only in later and safer days did the wave of migration to America contain a predominant proportion of persons among whom the main motive was economic. That type of mind finds its expression in *Who's Who* in the business men.

The parallel between our table of migratory indexes and the order in which people come to a new country is indeed very rough, so rough that perhaps it has no real significance. But at least it is interesting to note that the lines along which the United States, Canada, New Zealand, and Australia differ most from the countries whence came their people are those in which the migratory index is highest. Even though America seems to-day to be irreligious, it is even now more deeply moved by religious considerations than is any great country of Europe or Asia. Where else does a question like fundamentalism so grip the thoughts of the people? Where else have religious sects multiplied in any such prolific fashion? But deeper than these signs in its significance is the fact that the new Anglo-Saxon lands are far and away the leaders in all sorts of missionary and philanthropic efforts. England, Scotland, and Bavaria indeed stand high, but in proportion to their population they cannot compare with the United States in the number and activity of their missionaries all over the world. Religious activity is one of the few lines along which the supremacy of the United States is practically unquestioned. Is this because religious leaders are a highly migratory type, and hence not only have come to America in large numbers but still go out from among us?

The fields of education, science, and invention present conditions closely similar to those of religion. The facts as to education are as clear as with respect to religion. Our educational system may have much to learn from older countries. Nevertheless, no other parts of the world were so prompt to adopt the policy of universal education and to provide all sorts of schools from the kindergarten to the university at the public expense. To-day it is doubtful whether any old country is searching so eagerly and earnestly to find the best new methods as is America. Even more conclusive is the position of America, seconded by Canada, Australia, and New Zealand in the field of foreign education. Go to China. The great warehouses may be British, but the schools and colleges scattered all over the land are mainly American, or based on American models. Visit Turkey, Persia, Africa, or even India, and one finds that, in proportion to their numbers, the Americans are doing vastly more for education than are any other people, unless it be New Zealanders or Canadians. The educational spirit is one of our most distinctive characteristics, and our educators are one of our most mobile and migratory groups of people. Are these two facts connected with any general law which causes persons with the educational temperament to be migratory?

As a last example take the realm of science. It is true that in the past pure science has made more progress in Europe than in America. Yet in proportion to our numbers this may not have been the case for some generations in the past, and it is quite surely not so to-day. In applied science the supremacy of the United States is almost universally recognized. Where else can one catalogue so many inventions such as the telephone, telegraph, sewing-machine, airplane, and a host of clever automatic machines? Where else are inventions which germinate in some other country so quickly adopted and so rapidly made practical, as in the case of the steam-engine, locomotive, automobile, wireless, and many others? No other country issues anything like so many patents in proportion to the number of its inhabitants.

In the field of business we are apt to pride ourselves on our supremacy, and it is true that companies like the Standard Oil, United States Steel, and American Telephone and Telegraph are among the world's great marvels. But a sober analysis of our achievements in proportion to our natural resources makes it very doubtful whether we can claim any superiority in business over countries like Britain, Germany, and the Netherlands. If the Swiss had as much oil as we, would they not have a Standard Oil Company? If Sweden were as large and rich as the United States, would not its telephone and telegraph company rival ours? Even as things now are, the great British, German, and French iron and steel combinations, their great textile-mills, and their superb chemical plants rival anything that we can show. But when it comes to inventions those countries frankly admit that we surpass them. Is this, too, due to the fact that people with the types of mind represented by the scientists and engineers in our table are more migratory, and hence more likely to come to America than is the business type? Whatever may be the answer to questions such as this, it is clear that the tendency to migrate varies greatly according to people's occupations and temperaments. Moreover, this variation is systematic, as appears from the similarity of the data for individual States, and for the South when compared with the North. This means that if migration takes place for generation after generation from one region to another, the composition of the population in the two regions will ultimately become different. If the American rule holds elsewhere, as seems probable, the region from which migration takes place will ultimately be relatively strong in the fields of agriculture, government, law, and journalism; the region toward which migration is directed will contain an especially large proportion of competent engineers, scientists, educators, and religious leaders. If such a condition once becomes established, it tends to persist. It is perpetuated not only by biological inheritance, but by the equally strong social inheritance whereby an accepted custom has almost the force of law in moulding education and social usages. If all this is true, a careful investigation of migrations may explain many of the important tendencies of history.

Let us look at the matter in still another way. What kind of eminent persons come from the chief foreign countries? What we want to know is not the absolute number of such persons, but their number in proportion to the foreign-born immigrants. That is what appears in the table on page 47. Except in the left-hand column and the lower line, all the figures show the number of *Who's Who* persons in proportion to the men over twenty-one years of age. In the column for Old Russia, for example, the figure 16 opposite "literature" means that among the 263,000 men born in Russia and living in Ohio, Indiana, Illinois, Iowa, or Minnesota, literary men of prominence are 16 per cent as numerous as among a similar number of average native whites in the same States. But those same Russians include musicians at the rate of 185 for every 100 included among a similar number of native white Americans.

In the next to the bottom line of the table it appears that our immigrants from Old Russia provide leaders of all kinds at the rate of only 8 where native whites would provide 100. Of course the new language and the new customs are a great handicap. Suppose, for the sake of argument, that a rank of 33 for a foreigner from a country that does not use English is as creditable as 100 for Americans. I doubt whether the handicap is really so great, but it is well to err on the side of leniency. On that basis the Old Russians equal the Americans in engineering, and are almost six times as good in music, but only one-fourth as good when all occupations are considered. Italians are a trifle better. Their rank of 50 in medicine is well above 33, while in music they are eight times as prolific as we should expect on the basis of our own achievements and their handicaps. Otherwise, however, they fail to provide leaders. Old Austria rises above

NUMBER OF FOREIGN-BORN PERSONS IN "WHO'S WHO," 1924–1925, IN
OHIO, INDIANA, ILLINOIS, IOWA, AND MINNESOTA PER EACH 100
THAT WOULD BE EXPECTED IF THE FOREIGN-BORN POPULATION
PRODUCED EMINENT PEOPLE AT SAME RATE AS NATIVE-BORN IN
PROPORTION TO THE MEN OVER TWENTY-ONE YEARS OF AGE

Occupation	A Actual No of Persons	B Old Russia	C Italy	D Old Austria-Hungary	E Scandinavia	F Germany	G France, Switzerland, Belgium, Netherlands	H Ireland	I Great Britain	J Canada	K All
Government.........	19	0	0	16	43	5	0	0	68	49	18
Law................	13	0	0	20	0	12	0	51	33	121	15
Journalism.........	13	0	0	0	55	0	59	0	138	247	31
Medicine...........	31	0	50	14	14	32	30	0	81	477	38
Literature..........	24	16	0	9	18	25	0	36	210	247	38
Business...........	48	4	0	0	20	14	68	45	168	231	33
Art................	15	17	0	20	38	35	250	75	97	262	50
Music..............	38	185	268	104	34	384	150	0	785	468	229
Engineering.........	14	32	0	0	36	11	0	0	122	163	39
Science............	28	5	0	5	10	52	45	20	65	117	25
Education..........	78	2	13	11	22	33	108	21	70	353	38
Religion...........	67	5	0	18	70	54	25	134	310	344	69
All *..............		8	10	13	27	33	54	35	130	245	38
Total number of persons*.............	395	17	8	22	49	65	23	17	94	99	..

* Including two farmers, two social workers, and three labor leaders.

33 only in music, but contributes to a much wider range of professions than does Italy, and hence has a better average. The
high figures for musicians are the natural result of the wealth
of the United States and of the fact that a musician is practically
independent of language and customs. People enjoy Italian
songs even when they do not understand them, and no one
knows when a violin talks German.

The Scandinavians, unlike the other groups speaking foreign languages, do not send us many musicians, but they rise
above our arbitrary standard of 33 in journalism, art, engineering, and especially religion. Nevertheless, their average is only
27. An average of 33 puts the Germans on a par with the native
Americans, unless our standard of 33 eminent men on their part
for 100 on ours is too lenient. France, Switzerland, Belgium, and

Holland, when grouped together, rise far above this standard. In education and art, as well as in music, they actually reach the American level without any allowance for the difficulties of a new country. Even in religion and medicine they only fall a trifle below the standard set on the basis of such an allowance. This group evidently contains good stuff.

Now look at the three English-speaking groups. For them, too, we ought to make some allowance, because they have to learn new customs, even though they speak the language. Perhaps we ought to set a standard of 60 for the Irish, 70 for the British, and 90 for the Canadians, but that is not necessary. The obvious fact is that only in art and religion do the Irish approach equality with the native Americans. Their average is scarcely better than that of the Germans, even though they have no appreciable handicap of language. The British, on the other hand, rank nearly four times as high as the Irish. Only as lawyers do they fail to reach approximately the American level. The Canadians rise still higher. In every line except government they distinctly surpass the rest of us; in religion, education, music and medicine they produce three or four times as many leaders as do the native white Americans.

Would our results be different if we took the whole United States? Not appreciably. Here are the figures for all countries

Portugal	0	Denmark	24
Greece	1	Sweden	25
Finland	2	Ireland	29
Yugoslavia	4	Germany	35
Mexico	4*	Belgium	39
Poland	5	Holland	40
Italy	7	Switzerland	48
Czechoslovakia	10	Wales	87
Russia	11	France	98
Spain	12	United States	100
Austria	14	Scotland	100
Lithuania	16	Canada	104
Hungary	16	England	112
Roumania	20	English Canada	140†
Norway	23	Australia	242†

* These may be the children of missionaries.   † Partly estimated.

which furnished 30,000 or more of the males over twenty-one years of age in the United States in 1920, and also for Australia.

The figures show the number of *Who's Who* people per 95,100 men over twenty-one years of age, and should be interpreted like those in the preceding table.

Compare Ireland's index of 29 with that of Wales, 87; Scotland, 100; Canada, 104, or 140 if we omit French Canada; England, 112; and Australia, 242. Obviously, if we want immigrants who will raise our standards, it is worth while to cultivate Scotland, England, Canada, and Australia.

A foreign country whose people speak some language other than English, and which, nevertheless, supplies us with leaders in as large proportions as we supply them ourselves, or even in half or a third as large proportions, is likewise worth cultivating. Probably some of the seventy-six Frenchmen by birth listed in *Who's Who* are really Americans who were born abroad, but, even so, France almost certainly stands in the forefront as a source of American leaders. But Germany, Belgium, Holland, and Switzerland also make an excellent showing. Scandinavia, on the contrary, seems to be sending us something less than her best. The other countries on our list fall so low that there can be little doubt that their immigrants seriously lower the average of our people.

But all this is not the point that I am here making. What I want to emphasize is that immigrants from different parts of the world differ greatly in average ability. If we were to segregate in one place all the immigrants from countries having an index of ten or less in the last table, and in another all whose index is thirty-five or more, and were to keep the two groups isolated for several generations, how much alike would they be in two hundred years? No one can answer this question precisely, but it seems clear that there would be a great contrast. Just such contrasts, I believe, have arisen time and again through migration, through the isolation of small groups geographically or socially, and through the mixture of one type with another. Are not such contrasts one of the great but neglected clews to the interpretation of history?

CHAPTER IV

THE SIFTING POWER OF CITIES

CITIES are a sign of energy, ability, wealth, and civilization. They are a result of these conditions, and likewise a cause of them. The first essential for the growth of a big city, or even of a small town, is people of special talents. In primitive societies such people may be petty chiefs who gather some of the abler people from the surrounding population and thus start little towns. They may be traders, artisans, artists, medicine-men, priests, and the like, who settle at the crossroads where people can easily find them. In modern cities similar conditions prevail. One of the most essential features of a city is the special abilities and training of its people, and their special adaptation to a great variety of occupations. The competent people gather around themselves a great number of others of less ability who work at their behest.

But does not the growth of cities depend primarily on the excellence of their harbors and transportation systems, and on the density of the population which they serve? This idea is common, but wrong. The harbors and lines of transportation determine the exact spot where cities shall be located, they also determine which of the cities in a given region shall grow fastest. But if a country is inhabited only by savages, or stupid peasants who neither buy nor sell, and who have no desire for improvement, the very best of harbors and the easiest lines of communication will never make a great city.

As to density of population, look at Java. On that tropical island 35,000,000 people—almost as many as in France—are packed into an area no bigger than Iowa, and less than a quarter as large as France. The average square mile contains about 700 people, chiefly agricultural; and many sections contain far more.

Yet Java's largest city, Batavia, has only 300,000 people, and the next, Soerabaya, barely 200,000. Now look at Australia. That continent has only 2 people per square mile; it contains only a sixth as many people as Java. Yet Sydney and Melbourne are places of nearly 1,000,000 people, while Brisbane and Adelaide rival the two greatest cities of Java. But Australia is wealthy and progressive, Java poor and backward.

In the same way, South Carolina, with 55 people per square mile, has no city larger than Charleston, with about 70,000 people; only 18 per cent of its people live in towns of over 2,500. California, on the contrary, with only 22 people per square mile at the last census, contains two of the world's great cities, and almost 70 per cent of its people live in towns of at least 2,500 people. In Russia only about 16 per cent of the population is found in urban communities; in England 80 per cent; Turkey is far less urban than Germany; and China than Japan. Scores of similar comparisons might be made. In practically every case, if large units are used, the regions with small or few cities contain a large percentage of backward, inefficient people like the inert peasants of Russia, Turkey, and China, and the Negroes who form about half the population of South Carolina. The places with a large proportion of city dwellers contain an unusually large proportion of bright, energetic, progressive people.

The contrast between regions with few and many cities is as noticeable in different periods as in different regions. For example, European Russia contains only five cities of over 300,000 population. Five similar cities, with an almost identical population, are found in Pennsylvania, New Jersey, and Maryland, although those States are only an eighth as populous as Russia. Ten years ago the Russian cities averaged much larger than the American. Russia's recent decline in wealth and culture and the extermination or banishment of a large proportion of the leaders have caused the great Russian cities to decline by about 35 per cent, which far exceeds the corresponding rural decline. That seems to be what usually happens when civilization decays. At first, to be sure, the cities may be flooded with country people, but soon they decline, as in Greece, Rome, Mesopotamia, and almost every other place where civilization has notably gone backward.

Does not this indicate that cities are a primary cause of civilization? Not at all. If such were the case, why should the greatest decline in civilization usually follow the greatest concentration in cities? Civilization is the result of human activity and intelligence, and cities are another result of the same cause. But let there be no misunderstanding. As soon as cities are established they become secondary causes whereby civilization is urged forward with still greater rapidity. They are like tools. In fact, that is just what they are—the greatest tools of civilization. With them in his hand, man can accomplish all sorts of things that would otherwise be impossible. But the tool is merely the means, not the cause, of the accomplishment.

If cities are such important tools it is worth while to understand how they are formed and sharpened, and how they wear out. In a nutshell, the general process, as almost every one knows, is this: Cities attract three main types of people: first, the bright, energetic type which possesses special talents; second, a multitude of the duller sort of laborers—the kind who feed automatic machines; and third, the vicious and criminal elements. Fortunately, the attraction of bright minds appears to outweigh that of the dull. Unfortunately, however, the cities lower the birthrate and raise the death-rate. This might be highly advantageous if the changes in both rates affected the intelligent people only a little, and the unintelligent and vicious a great deal. But the fine types are the ones whose birth-rate is especially lowered, while their death-rate is probably raised almost as much as that of the lower classes. And why not? Do they not keep late hours, live indoors, get little sun and fresh air, and spend a great deal of nervous energy on obviously useless things as well as on lowering the death-rate of the most worthless people around them? The net result is that the better classes in the cities tend to die out from generation to generation. The poorer classes either continue to increase, or more probably die out at a slower rate than do those of greater social value. Even in our own day, cities are self-destructive, and in the past they have doubtless been far more so.

Let us look more closely at the process by which the brighter type of people are attracted to the cities. Let us also see what effect this has on the rural districts. *Who's Who in America*, as we have seen, contains the best available record of the migrations of competent persons in the United States. The percentage of such persons is commonly supposed to increase according to the size of the towns in which they live. This is only half true. In the great States of Ohio, Indiana, Illinois, Iowa, and Minnesota, the number of persons in *Who's Who* for 1924–1925 per 100,000 people in communities of various sizes is as follows:

Rural population.. 3
Villages of 2,500 to 5,000.................................. 29
Towns of 5,000 to 10,000................................... 28
Small cities of 10,000 to 25,000........................... 25
Cities of 25,000 to 100,000................................ 28
Cities of 100,000 to 300,000............................... 30
Cities above 300,000....................................... 40

Similar figures prevail in other parts of the country. They indicate that the increase in competent people according to the size of the communities is not regular, but by steps, as it were. First there is a sudden jump from the rural population to the urban population, and second from the small or medium-size cities to the larger ones.

Let us see what the first jump means. It suggests that even when the urban quality is merely such as prevails in little towns of only 3,000 or 4,000 people, it gives those towns a pronounced advantage. All over the United States, the truly rural population contains only a handful of eminent leaders, while in the larger villages the proportion is essentially as great as in all except the largest cities. This sharp distinction between rural and urban appears to hold good almost everywhere and at all periods. Even the rigid caste system of India appears unable wholly to prevent it. In China it seems to be especially strong, because famines promote active migration. Our easy transportation and communication and our many efforts to make farm life more attractive seem only to accelerate the drift from the country to the city.

This wide-spread cityward tendency throws light on many great problems of history. For example, it helps to explain why farmers are so often treated with contempt, why rural populations often play practically no part in history, why the farmers of the United States are chronically in a state of unrest, and why democracy succeeds in some countries and not in others.

The words peasant, boor, rustic, and even farmer convey a certain implication of inferiority. Many farmers are of a very high type; but the average farmer in most parts of the world is crude and rude compared with the average person in a centre of population. He possesses these qualities partly because he lives apart and has little opportunity to become polished, and partly because he and his ancestors have usually had relatively little of the versatility, energy, restlessness, or special talents which cause people to move away from the farms.

The constant sifting of the farm population by the cities seems to be one of the main reasons why old rural communities tend to be especially conservative, and hence play only a negative part in history. They show this in politics, in religion, in their ways of working, in education, and in all sorts of social practices. It is the country people of the United States among whom the literal, fundamentalist interpretation of the Bible is strongest. They are the backbone of the movement against the teaching of evolution, and against the entry of the United States into the League of Nations. It is these same rural people, especially the farmers who have been established for many generations, who are slowest to adopt the methods of modern industry and business.

The persistent loss of leaders and the resultant slowness and conservatism of the rural population go far toward explaining why the farmers are continually sacrificed on the altar of commerce and manufacturing. Our American farmers of the Middle

West vie with the laborers in their insistent cry for special legislation. The manufacturers, merchants, professional people, and
others who compose the bulk of the townspeople aside from the
laboring classes, make no such constant clamor about legislation
in their behalf and about the discriminations against them.
They do, indeed, want many privileges, but when the desire
arises, they set to work and get them. But the farmers, like the
laborers, are generally in difficulty and rarely seem to get what
they want.

One of the most important features of the loss of leaders by
the rural districts is its bearing on democracy. We of the United
States have supposed that we believe in democracy. But can
true democracy flourish where large numbers of farmers, laborers, or any other group fail to think for themselves, and to produce outstanding leaders? Such depletion has probably taken
place on a large scale in almost every old country where the people have long been on the soil. That is, presumably, one reason
why social classes have become so strongly intrenched in such
countries, and why democracy is a farce in countries like Turkey
and Russia. Even if the peasants are still capable of producing
leaders in as large numbers as are the townspeople, those leaders
do not stay on the farms even in Asia; they insist on becoming
wanderers, caravan-men, traders, artisans, pilgrims, scholars, and
the like. Most of them become affiliated with the people in the
towns and die out in a few generations. But democracy can permanently succeed only where there is relative equality among
all the great groups of society.

What has just been said as to the effect of cityward migration
does not apply to the farmers in all regions. Three distinct stages
are recognizable, depending largely upon how long a region has
been settled. Except under special circumstances, the migrant
who settles in a new home tends to be vigorous and progressive
in comparison with the people among whom he has lived hitherto.
It requires more initiative to settle on a pioneer farm than to go
to the city. Thus in its first stages an agricultural population is
relatively active, aggressive, and competent. Such farmers stand

up against other occupations, they ask no special favors, and they get what they want. That stage is represented in the United States by California. There the farming population contains a large number of unusually competent people. It has organized itself into strong fruit-growers' co-operative societies, and other well-managed organizations which meet the great commercial and industrial corporations on equal terms. This is possible, as I see it, because the California farms have not yet been drained of their best men. Even if the leaders live in the towns, as most of them do, they are still identified with farming. That is partly because farming in the irrigated lands of California is especially pleasant and profitable. But the main point is that the California farmers are a picked lot and have not yet suffered degeneration through the weeding out of their able people by the cities.

The second type of farmers consist of those who have been on the land several generations. The cityward migration of their abler elements has not yet taken away practically all the leaders, but enough have gone so that the average ability has been much lessened. Those who remain still struggle valiantly and make a strong bid for public aid. They are still vocal through a few vigorous and able leaders who have not been seduced by the city, or by some other class of society. This seems to be the condition among the great farming States of the Mississippi valley. Something of the pioneer condition still survives, there is much energy and real ability. Nevertheless, genuine farm leaders, with a clear-cut programme and with the capacity to bring the farmers together, are scarce. The men who might have been rural leaders are factory managers, engineers, scientists, lawyers, and the like. They live in villages, towns, and cities; their interests are urban. Whenever a leader of any kind arises among the rural population the chances are nine out of ten—and perhaps ninety-nine out of a hundred—that he will be weaned away from purely rural interests and become identified with something urban. That is the great tragedy of farming.

The third type of farmer is represented in New England. There the process of draining away the stronger elements has gone so far that only in rare cases does one find many strong, forceful farmers like John Coolidge, father of the President. The sons go forth to be merchants in the villages, manufacturers and lawyers in the cities, and presidents of colleges and countries. Thus rural New England is voiceless and discouraged. Its native sons who remain on the farms cannot compete with the energetic, foreign-born immigrants who are pushing in among them. Those native sons inherit farms from their fathers, they know the language and customs of the country, they have every advantage of an early start, but they do not hold their own. Their farms, according to the census of 1920, have an average value of only about $6,000; while their British-born neighbors own farms worth $10,700 on an average; their Irish-born neighbors, $10,000; the French, Dutch, and Swiss, $7,800. Even the immigrant farmers who were born in Scandinavia, Germany, Russia, and Italy excel the native-born Americans in the value of their farms. The only reasonable explanation seems to be that the abler native-born farmers have left the farms in such numbers for several generations that in some places those who remain have been reduced almost to the condition of negligible and inarticulate peasants. The cities have sifted out the men who would have made the farms valuable, and likewise those who might have spoken for the rural districts and the rural occupations.

One or another of these three stages is found in almost every part of the world. In New Zealand, for example, the farmers are a picked lot. They are in the vigorous pioneer stage where they know what they want and get it. New Zealand is almost a farmers' paradise. In China, a similar pioneer stage appears among the vigorous, aggressive farmers who have had sufficient initiative to get away from their old homes and migrate to Manchuria. There they not only prosper, but are "European" in their activity. Not infrequently they employ Europeans, mainly Russians. But back in China itself people of the same stock, who have been living on the land for many generations, provide most pitiful examples of the abject type of peasants. By the constant elimination of the stronger elements, as I have explained in *The*

Character of Races, they seem to have been reduced to a stage where they are little more than animals, mere morons in many cases, who expect to be half-starved practically all the time. Hope is dead within them; they starve and die, unheard, unmourned.

The Russian peasants represent the same sort of thing, but the process of weeding out the aggressive, intelligent elements has not gone quite so far. Yet their patient submissiveness and their dearth of leaders have been their undoing. Could the farmers of New Zealand, Saskatchewan, or California be *trained* to submit to the heartless exploitation of Czardom and the Soviet Committees as the Russian peasants are now submitting? It seems scarcely possible that any system of training, no matter how rigorous, could permanently reduce a vast body of energetic, ambitious men like the California farmers to a state of abject submission such as has long prevailed in Russia. If the material for leadership were there, would it not manifest itself? May not part of the secret of Russia's misfortunes lie in a long, steady process, whereby the abler peasants have been drawn away to the towns? They have gone as retainers of the aristocrats, as servants of the government, as students, carpenters, merchants, and in a hundred other positions.

Thus far we have considered only the number of gifted people in cities compared with country districts. Let us next see what difference there is in the kind of leaders. In the States of Ohio, Indiana, Illinois, Iowa, Minnesota, Kentucky, Tennessee, Georgia, Mississippi, and Arkansas the rural population, that is the population outside of places having at least 2,500 people, amounts to practically thirteen and a half million, or about half of the total. But instead of containing half of the persons in *Who's Who* from those States the rural population contains only the following percentages:

Medicine	3	Art	8
Law	3	Religion	8
Engineering	4	Philanthropy	9
Music	5	Literature	9
Business	5	Education	11
Journalism	6	Government	15
Science	6	Agriculture	20

In other words, at least nine-tenths of all the doctors, lawyers, engineers, musicians, and business men who are needed by the rural districts, if those districts are to hold their own, are found in the cities instead of in the country. At least four-fifths of the rural districts' fair share of the journalists, scientists, artists, religious leaders, philanthropists, and literary people are also in the cities. The only occupations where the rural districts retain even as much as a fifth of the leaders that their population would seem to demand are education, government service, and agriculture. Even among government officials the rural districts have only three leaders where their proportion would be ten. Moreover, it is doubtful whether those three average as high in ability as do the other types of people in *Who's Who*. Many are included merely because of their official positions, not because they have done anything that would otherwise distinguish them.

Among the agriculturists, at least, it would seem as if the rural districts ought to have more than their share in proportion to the population. But actually they have no more than do the great cities of over 100,000 people—only two where they ought to have five on the basis of population, and not a fourth as many, proportionally, as have the towns and cities with from 2,500 to 100,000 people. The majority of the agricultural leaders are not farmers at all, but agronomists, animal husbandmen, dairy experts, and the like. Most of these men were ostensibly trained for the purpose of building up the profession of farming, but they have become scientists. They live in towns where there are agricultural experiment stations and colleges of agriculture. Most of them are interested in farming as a biological science rather than as a business. The meetings that they love to attend are those of the Society of Plant Pathologists or the Ecological Society. The bacterial cause of foot-and-mouth disease interests them at least as much as does the price of corn. A few of them are indeed real farmers, but most of those few are specialists who, perhaps, own large greenhouses or fancy dairies close to the great cities. And, anyhow, in the States under discussion the farmers form only two-thirds of one per cent of all the persons in *Who's Who*.

They are only a tenth as numerous as the doctors and a thirtieth as numerous as the educators. Probably a good many more ought to be included, but it is very doubtful whether all the farmers together can furnish as many real leaders as can the journalists, although the farmers are 200 times as numerous. But it is our habit to leave out the farmers. Is it any wonder that the rural districts are backward, that boys want to get away from the farms, and that the farmers always get the little end of the horn? Leaders are the first essential of success, but the greedy cities remorselessly snatch the leaders from the half of our people who live in the country districts.

Is the drawing power of the cities wholly responsible for the poverty of the rural districts in leaders? We cannot tell what is happening now, for no one knows what the children of to-day will amount to. Nor can we know to what extent an unfavorable environment prevents the development of talent among persons born in the rural districts. But it is easy to find what kinds of people, and how many, were born in places of various sizes. This time we will take persons born in New York, New Jersey, Pennsylvania, Ohio, Indiana, Illinois, and Michigan. As a matter of fact, only the first 2,000 names of such persons in *Who's Who* have been used, but the whole 10,000 would give essentially the same result. We will divide our 2,000 people into three groups. The first consists of all those born in cities having less than 10,000 people in 1920. This means that when the people in the 1924–25 edition of *Who's Who* were born, practically all of these towns contained less than 3,000 people and were distinctly rural. The next group consists of cities which in 1920 had from 10,000 to 300,000 people. When the people in *Who's Who* were born these cities had from 1,000 to 50,000 people as a rule. The third group consists of the twelve cities having a population of approximately 300,000 or more in 1920. These cities ranged from about 30,000 upward when the *Who's Who* people were born.

Two out of three of the people in *Who's Who* for 1924–25 were born between 1855 and 1875. The median year of birth, that is the year having an equal number of births before it and after it,

is 1868. Accordingly, if we take the population in 1860 and 1870
but give double weight to 1870, we get a fairly close estimate of
the average population when our eminent persons were born.
On this basis the rural communities of our first group produced
48 eminent persons per 100,000 people; the small cities, 107; and
the large cities 90.

It is not enough to know that the rural communities produced
far fewer leaders than the cities. We need also to know whether
they produced the same kind. In other words, do the competent
children born of parents who remain in the rural districts turn
to the same occupations as do the children of those who are sifted
out to inhabit the cities? The answer is found in the following
table, showing the percentage of persons of each occupation born
in the rural districts, the large villages and small cities, and the
large cities respectively. Among the 19 farmers or agriculturists,
for example, 14, or 74 per cent, were born in the rural districts
and none in the large cities. Among 357 educators 66 per cent
were born in the rural districts and 13 per cent in the large cities,
leaving 21 per cent for the towns of intermediate size.

	A Born in Rural Districts	B Born in Large Villages and Small Cities	C Born in Larger Cities	D Number of Persons
Agriculture...........	74%	26%	0%	19
Education............	66	21	13	357
Religion..............	62	22	16	157
Science...............	59½	18½	22	197
Philanthropy.........	59	23	18	39
Government..........	56	20	24	208
Medicine.............	48	19	33	151
Journalism...........	47½	20½	32	97
Law.................	46½	23½	30	161
Literature............	44	20	36	185
Music................	41	20	39	39
Engineering..........	40	23½	36½	106
Business.............	36	24	40	194
Art..................	31	16	53	98

This little table is extremely significant. It epitomizes the
rise and fall of civilization. The percentages in the rural column,
on the left, decline steadily because they are arranged in that
way. The percentages for large cities (column C) rise fairly

steadily, while those for large villages and small cities are of about the same size for all occupations. The most obvious fact about the table is that the rural districts produce people who achieve eminence in one set of occupations, and the large cities in quite another, while the intermediate places produce a well-balanced set of men who enter all sorts of occupations. This suggests that the sifting power of the cities is bad for rural districts and large cities, but good for the small cities.

Why are the types of leaders in the country and city so different? It is easy to see why three-fourths of the agricultural leaders are born in the rural districts. But why should 66 per cent of the educators be born there, while only 21 per cent are born in the medium-sized cities, and 13 per cent in the great cities? Is it because the people who dwelt in the American rural districts from 1855 to 1885 inherited a type of mind which made them turn naturally to education? Is it because a country boy can become an educator more easily than he can become a business man or engineer? Or is it because the rural training emphasizes the importance of education, while the urban training emphasizes the importance of money? Would the men of rural birth who are now educators have become literary men, engineers, and business men if they had happened to be born in the great cities? To all of these questions the answer is: "Nobody knows." But somebody ought to know, and it is the world's business to find out as soon as possible. Similar questions and the same answer apply to religious leaders, scientists, philanthropists, and even government officials. Scientists are mainly engaged in education, while many philanthropists are social workers, Y. M. C. A. secretaries, and the like, so that they are closely affiliated with religion.

Music, engineering, business, and art, on the other hand, are primarily city occupations. But why? Do people who are born in cities become artists simply because they have a chance to get special training? Or is artistic genius naturally more prevalent in cities than in rural districts because highly artistic people have for many generations been attracted cityward. Is there any real difference between the type of mind which becomes an engineer and the type which becomes a teacher of science or a scientific investigator?

Doubtless both environment and heredity play a large part in determining a young person's choice of an occupation. Sometimes one and sometimes the other may be dominant. Moreover, each, as it were, creates the other. A musical city, for example, discovers among its children many able musicians who might have become social workers, teachers, or farmers in the rural districts. But that same city attracts musicians because it is a pleasant place for them and the opportunities to practise their profession are lucrative. The children of the musicians are sure to possess much more than the average amount of musical aptitude. Thus environment and heredity co-operate in making the city musical. Similar reasoning applies to every other profession.

Perhaps the most significant of all the features of the preceding table is that the occupations are arranged in essentially the order in which they have come to the front again and again during the rise and fall of nations. In fact, the three columns of the table seem to represent three great stages in the evolution of civilization. The first stage has already been discussed in respect to the farmers. It begins with the pioneer period when a country has been newly settled. It may last many generations as perhaps in England, or come to an end speedily as seems to be happening in Australia. During this stage most of the people live in the rural districts. The largest towns are not much more than over-grown villages, and the drift toward the urban centres is slight. In such a region the farmers are not only numerous, but influential. The successful farmer may be a squire as in England, a plantation-owner as in our South, or simply a prosperous farmer as in early New England. Almost unconsciously, but quite effectively, he sees to it that the farmers have their share of influence in the public councils and that legislation is favorable to their interests. In such a community education is highly honored and many of the brightest young men become teachers. The same is true of religion, science, and philanthropy. Government officials are respected and esteemed, and their occupation attracts persons of a relatively high type. Medicine, journalism, law, and literature receive some attention but are secondary. Music, engineering, business, and art are not well developed. In fact, they are often treated with scorn as being trivial or mercenary. Such conditions appear to have prevailed in early China and early Rome, in England almost down to the manufacturing period, in the United States until the great cityward migration was stimulated by the advent of steam-power, in New Zealand until to-day. They are typical of a sturdy, rigorous, and narrow type of civilization to which people are apt to look back as "the good old days." This is the stage of moral fervor, religious zeal, and high political ideals.

Suppose, now, that the towns in such a community begin to grow but have not yet become dominant. That brings the golden age, the time when the older professions and the older type of high moral ideals are still vigorous, but when music, art, engineering, and business also enjoy a healthy development. Opinions differ as to just when this stage begins and ends in a country like Egypt, Rome, or China, but few would question that such a stage is part of the normal course of human progress. Perhaps the United States, England, France, Germany, and Japan are still in this stage. Let us hope so, but the extreme devotion of France and Japan to art, and of the other three to engineering and business may be signs that the best days are past. That, however, is a matter where one man's guess is still as good as another's.

The third stage often seems so glorious that people are dazzled into thinking that it is the culmination of its predecessor. The material and æsthetic aspects of civilization forge to the front. Great buildings, monumental bridges, huge business corporations, fine pictures, and entrancing music dazzle the imagination. But the rural people are likely to have become dull, sodden, and ultra-conservative. Intellectual pursuits, pure science, the discovery of abstract truth and the practice of pure and undefiled religion are forced to the wall by commercial journalism, applied engineering, applied science, and over-organized philanthropy. Education becomes perfunctory, religion loses its fervor, corruption in government becomes rife, and the feverish pursuit of wealth makes men think that money and the power which it brings are the chief ends of human existence. The extreme of this stage of ultra-urban development is found when art runs wild and the artistic temperament is used as an excuse for every sort of self-indulgence and moral weakness. Fifty years ago, according to the indications of our table, the rural districts and smaller towns of the United States were still not far removed from the first of our three stages. To-day, in our larger cities the third stage seems almost to have been reached. Does the second stage still predominate in our villages and smaller cities?

A concrete example will clarify our picture of the three stages. In old New England a country minister of the highest type, both intellectually and morally, stayed fifty years in his first and only parish, even though it was a mere village. His equally able son settled in a village a few miles away, and a grandson came back to the old pulpit when his grandfather stepped out. That might have continued indefinitely, but the cityward drift began. The able grandson was called to a large church in a small city. His son, growing up there, felt the call of science. He became a professor of chemistry in a great university in a town of 100,000 people. His son, in turn, grew up as a city boy, became an engineer, entered business, made a great success, moved to New York, and is a valued leader. Thus a man who in the rural stage of social organization was a moral leader has now become a material leader. He may be just as able as his grandfather, he may do wonderful work in the organization of huge enterprises for commerce, manufacturing, and transportation, and his brother may produce marvellous pictures, dramas, or symphonies. But their efforts are not directed toward the improvement of human character to any such degree as were those of their grandfathers. If other grandsons of the country minister were keeping up the old standards of moral and religious leadership, and of education and science, no harm would be done. In fact, the world would be much better off, because all types of progress would be well developed. But the cityward drift causes a decline in the relative number of able men, and it is the ethical professions which suffer most from this. Where the old minister of the village church had six children who survived to adult life, his chemist son has only four, and his engineer grandson only two. But somebody has to take the lead. If there are not enough young men of the high moral type descended from the country minister, the leadership will pass to men of baser descent, whose training has been along lines of selfishness instead of altruism.

But all this is neither here nor there for the moment. What we are interested in is the general law which seems to be so clearly epitomized in our little table from *Who's Who*. Does this indicate that the processes of the rise and fall of civilization are going on with such rapidity that in three generations we have passed from the pioneer stage to the end of the golden era? Does the sifting power of cities serve as one of the great means whereby the objectives and achievements of a country change from generation to generation? Will a study of this sifting power and of modern migrations to the city enable us to understand history more clearly and change our course to avoid the pitfalls that seem so imminent?

CHAPTER V

THE DOMINANCE OF NOMADS

"THE bad lands dominate the good. Deserts control the fate of the fertile lands around them. Inhospitable regions on the fringes of cultivation overwhelm those where a milder climate fosters a denser and more highly cultured population." Is there any truth in these generalizations? Search history and see. As far back as we can go in history there seems to be a constant see-sawing back and forth between favorable and unfavorable regions. On the whole, the greater, or at least much the more prolonged, tendency seems to be for the favorable regions to spread their dominance over those that are less favored. But during such times the people of the less-favored regions come creeping into the patrimony of their richer neighbors by families, in little groups, or as individuals. Occasionally much larger groups pour in, and sometimes they come as conquering hosts. As a rule, the invaders, especially those who come at the times of more strenuous movement, tend to rise to a position of dominance in their new homes. In many cases they display surprising speed in absorbing the culture, and even the language, of the former inhabitants of the good regions. Thus they are in this sense dominated by their new surroundings. But in a great number of cases they make themselves masters of the new country, seize the best land, and become a ruling class. The Mongols and Manchus in China, the Moguls of India, the Hebrews of Palestine, the Norse of France, the Goths of Italy, the Achæans and Dorians of Greece, the Hyksos of Egypt, the Turks in Asia Minor are only a few among hundreds of examples.

Consider the scanty number of the genuine desert nomads. From time immemorial the deserts of Arabia and North Africa have been peopled by wandering tribes who travel hither and thither, according to the season, in search of water and grass for their animals. In large parts of Persia we likewise find such nomads; in Turkey there are some of them; in Turkestan, Mongolia, Western Manchuria, Tibet, and southern Siberia still others. How many there were in the past is quite uncertain. Even to-day we do not know how numerous they are. We only know that their number is insignificant, but that in spite of this they have dominated the history of the countries around them. Throughout the period since the thorough establishment of agriculture and the development of the first real civilizations in Egypt, Mesopotamia, China, and elsewhere, the actual nomadic wanderers can never have numbered more than a small fraction compared with their neighbors in the oases and in the adjacent agricultural countries. When Egypt, Babylonia, Mesopotamia, China, and North India first appear in history they are already inhabited by a relatively dense agricultural population. To-day the entire country of Arabia, for example, including the Syrian Desert, is supposed to contain about 5,000,000 people. Just how many of them are genuine nomads it is impossible to say. Probably not over half a million, and perhaps only a quarter of a million. The remainder are villagers and city people who inhabit the oases and the relatively well-watered mountainous edges of the country, such as Yemen in the southwest and Oman in the southeast.

The village and city population of the regions immediately surrounding Arabia is roughly as follows: Arabia itself four and a half million; Mesopotamia, three million; Syria, two and a half million; Palestine, half a million. These estimates are conservative, and exclude the few nomads living within the respective areas. Nevertheless, they make a total of ten and a half million settled people, mostly agriculturists, who live in the desert oases, or in the relatively fertile land immediately surrounding the desert. If the nomads in the outlying areas around Arabia bring the total up to half a million, which is probably a liberal figure, we have one nomad for twenty-one settled people. In the Sahara and the Sudan the number of genuine nomads is probably even less than in Arabia. The adjacent settled population in North Africa is above 25,000,000, while the regions to the south also contain large numbers who are in more or less immediate touch with the nomads. Thus here we have, perhaps, one nomad for every fifty or a hundred settled people within easy reach. In the Chinese portion of Asia a similar condition prevails —perhaps a million, or even a million and a half nomads in Turkestan, Tibet, Mongolia, western Manchuria, and southern Siberia, but 100,000,000 or even 150,000,000 settled folk in the adjacent territories. So it is with other regions, such as Persia, Afghanistan, and northern India. Everywhere the true nomads are vastly outnumbered by the agricultural people, and by the villagers and city people who live within their sphere of influence.

The Manchus, as described in *The Character of Races*, illustrate the repeated history of such nomads. The first that we hear of them is in the beginning of the seventh century. Under the name Kitans, which is said to be the origin of Marco Polo's "Cathay," they invaded north China. At the beginning of the tenth century these same Kitans, although driven out after their first inroad, established themselves as a ruling dynasty. Two centuries later they were overthrown by another allied dynasty, the Nuchin or Nuchens, the direct ancestors of the Manchus. A century or so later the Nuchens were expelled from China by the Mongols, under Genghis Khan. Then for three centuries they remained almost unknown in southeastern Manchuria, a wild, barbarous people, but possessed of great vigor and ability. In the middle of the sixteenth century a chief named Nurhachu came into power, and rapidly established a Manchurian kingdom which eventually conquered China.

For our present purpose the most significant fact about the Manchus seems to be the long period of struggle and migration during which they necessarily underwent a rigid natural selection. The Tartar ancestors of the Manchus appear to have been pastoral nomads for thousands of years. Their wandering life, with its sudden calls for exertion and co-operation, as will shortly appear, apparently gave them full measure of that power of leadership which we see so strongly in Arabs, Mongols, and Turks, as well as Manchus, and which may have been evolved in the ancestors of the Nordics under similar conditions of nomadism. When the ancestors of the Manchus invaded China as Kitans and Nuchens, they again apparently suffered selection, especially when they were ejected under the Mongols. Just how they migrated back to their old home in Manchuria we do not know, but judging by modern examples it was quite surely the ablest and most energetic who returned. Many of the leaders were doubtless killed, but on the other hand it is almost universally true that in such cases the weaker, less efficient, and more submissive among a conquered people remain in their old homes. It is the people with initiative and individuality, as well as with physical and mental vigor, who refuse to endure humiliation and are willing to suffer the loss of their property and the hardships of migration in order to escape from their conquerors. It was probably such people who retired to Manchuria after the Mongol conquest. And it was the most competent and active of their descendants who founded the great Manchu dynasty. Nurhachu, their great leader, "though he never entered China, stands as an exponent of the highest qualities of his race, a creative genius not only in strategy but in politics, the founder of a great tradition capably maintained for two centuries by his descendants, the establisher of a line of monarchs which have been surpassed by no other ruling house during an equal period in China. Yet they succeeded through sheer force of character, as the Ottomans have succeeded, during a much longer period in western Asia, in dominating a people that were superior to them in every important quality except that of leadership." (F. W. Williams.)

The Mongols, like the Manchus and Ottoman Turks, were nomadic keepers of cattle, and have dominated other parts of the world to a degree far out of proportion to their numbers. Under Genghis Khan they overwhelmed not only northern China, but a large part of Asia. Genghis Khan himself seems to have been one of the world's greatest leaders, and so was his grandson, Kublai Khan, and the latter's brother, Hulugu. Tamerlane, or

Timur the Lame, was as great a warrior and leader as Genghis. In fact, the Mongols have produced an unusual number of persons of great ability. Think of the Mogul emperors in India, who surged down from the dry interior of Asia in the sixteenth century, under Baber, and subdued northern India with extraordinary rapidity. The kingdom which they established was the most brilliant which India has ever seen. The Emperor Akbar was not only a mighty warrior, but one of the world's great administrators, and perhaps reformers. Among the great buildings of the world which it has been my privilege to see, none has ever given such a sense of perfect satisfaction as the Taj Mahal, built by the Shah Jehan, the grandson of Baber. When this emperor, grieving over the death of his favorite wife, Mumtaz Mahal, decided to build for her a tomb more beautiful than any ever seen before, he placed the whole world in his debt. Here and there from all over Asia, and even from Europe, he procured artists and architects. For twenty-two years, so it is said, he kept 20,000 men at work, without pay, on his wife's memorial. For the materials he paid the huge sum of $20,000,000. No tomb ever cost so much, and none was ever so well worth building.

Other nomadic keepers of animals have shown a similar capacity to dominate other races, and to produce men of genius. The Arabs are especially remarkable in this respect. Even if we exclude the Jews, they have produced a most extraordinary list of great men who have dominated the lands surrounding the deserts. Arab literature, geography, astronomy, mathematics, philosophy, and art are widely famous, and are full of names of men of real genius. The ancient Aramæans, originally Arab nomads, overwhelmed and dominated Syria just as their kinsmen had done in Babylonia. Time and again in later centuries the Arabs poured into the fertile lands on all sides of Arabia, and practically every time the newcomers dominated the old. As a rule, they were quick to adopt the civilization of the people whom they conquered, and in many cases promptly inaugurated eras of brilliant progress. The Jews, as we shall see more fully later, were a marvellous example of this.   The early Israelites were simply nomads of the desert.   They conquered the fertile lands and in a few centuries raised Palestine to its highest pitch of greatness in the days of David and Solomon.   The Nabatæans invaded the same country and built the wonderful city of Petra, with its temples and tombs carved in the many-colored rock.

In Egypt the same sort of conditions prevailed.   How many times Egypt was conquered by people from the desert, it is hard to say.   The Hyksos were quite surely nomadic invaders from the desert, although they may not have been Arabs.   In later days, during the last thousand years, the rulers and leaders of Egypt have systematically been largely of Arab descent.   In the Dark Ages we see people of this same blood and with the same desert background sweeping into Spain under the name of Saracens and Moors.   There they established a great centre not only of political power but of art and literature.   The Alhambra vies with the Taj Mahal.   Nor must the great Mosque of Omar, the Dome of the Rock, at Jerusalem be omitted as an example of the high skill of the people who came out of the Arabian Desert.

Turn now to another kind of cattle-keeping nomad.   All over Europe we find that such people have been responsible for some of the most marvellous achievements.   The Achæan Greeks, and later the Ionians, appear to have been of this type.   After wandering for untold generations with their cattle and sheep in southern Russia, the Balkans, and no one knows where else, they finally came down to Greece.   To them, and not to the old agricultural population that existed in Greece for unknown centuries, we owe the greatest products of that race.   Homer is their early spokesman, while later from the same blood, almost undiluted, as I have explained in *The Character of Races*, there sprang a marvellous line of great men which included Herodotus, Phidias, Socrates, Plato, Pericles, and Alexander.   Farther west a similar condition prevailed.   Not only did the cattle-keeping Goths, Vandals, Huns, and others override large parts of Europe, but they made themselves the founders of a great series of powerful dynasties in many countries.   Charlemagne and many others represent the blood of these invading nomads. The Norse Vikings exemplify the same principle. When they overwhelmed Europe, established themselves in Normandy, and conquered England, they were not cattle-keepers, but they had been through the same type of strenuous selection which we shall shortly describe. Their hard migrations and then their dangerous seafaring life had done for them what the life of the desert and the mountains did for the people there.

Recall once more what was said above as to the small number of nomadic cattle-keepers in comparison with the settled people around them. Down through the generations the story has been the same. Ever since agriculture became well established such nomads have presumably never numbered much more than one for every dozen, score, or hundred of the settled people around about them. Yet practically always they have been victorious whenever they have definitely tried to move out from their old environment. Moreover, as soon as they have established themselves in new countries, it has generally taken them only a few generations to assimilate the new culture. Thereupon they have again and again introduced periods of brilliant achievement. Is not this marvellous? Consider the poverty of their resources. In the nomadic state they cannot build permanent houses, palaces, temples, and fortresses. They cannot be well supplied with blacksmiths, carpenters, armorers, and other artisans able to construct the many appliances which are needed even in the most humble type of settled civilization. Nor can they well amass great wealth except in animals, which are a most precarious resource.

What, then, is the reason why nomadic keepers of cattle and other nomadic people like the Vikings have conquered the world and done its great tasks in a measure so greatly out of proportion to their actual numbers? The reason seems to lie in the nature of the nomadic life, its dangers, difficulties, and its call on all the faculties of every man, woman, and child. The whole matter is well illustrated in the moving picture entitled *Grass*, which perhaps gives greater insight into history than any other moving picture ever made. In *Grass* you see the Bakhtyari nomads of southwestern Persia. They illustrate the most strenuous phase of the pastoral life. In the winter the low hill country east of the plain of the Tigris receives enough rain so that it produces a moderate growth of grass. Agriculture is impossible, for the hills are too rough for irrigation, and too dry without irrigation, but the grass will support many sheep, cattle, goats, donkeys, and horses. If people are to live there, they must be cattle-keepers. But the rainfall amounts to only eight or ten inches per year, and generally comes to an end in April. The summers are intensely hot and dry. Temperatures as high as 128° in the shade have been officially recorded. The grass withers, becomes as dry as tinder, and is soon consumed by the hungry flocks. Worse still, the springs and streams dry up, so that no water is procurable except at long intervals.

East of this parched land rise the high mountains. There at heights of 8,000 or 10,000 feet lie rolling plateaus, snow-clad in winter but covered with deep lush grass and spangled with lovely flowers in summer. If the people from the low lands can climb thither, their animals will grow fat, milk will abound, and the whole tribe will be happy. So each year the Bakhtyari start upward in the spring; the journey is long and tedious, many minor streams and gorges, which would seem formidable if not impassable to the ordinary farming population, are regarded as mere trifles by the hardy Bakhtyari. Even the mighty Karun River with its snow-fed icy floods is approached with laughter and delight. Look at the moving picture and see what a terrible struggle the passage of the river involves. Watch the men inflating their sheepskins and tying them together to form rafts. Watch both men and women throwing the young lambs, calves, and colts upon these rafts and tying the struggling goats in place. Then see how the women and children, as well as the men, mount the rafts and are whirled away, down the river. Round and round they circle, as they paddle desperately to gain the other shore before they are carried too far down-stream into the rapids. Look now at the men and boys as they drive the unwilling animals into the river and then jump in to swim across, each with an inflated skeepskin as a float. No circus performer risks his life more gaily or more desperately than do these boys of twelve when they swim among the struggling sheep, seize those that are on the point of drowning, and drag them to the shore. I have seen this thing myself and know how dangerous it is.

Some of the Bakhtyari, those who are less bold, less strong, or less careful, are drowned each year, but the rest go gaily on, climbing steep precipices, digging paths in the snow, boosting and pulling and beating the weaker and slower animals. Where the highest mountains must be crossed, the people climb cliffs where a fall might easily kill them, or tramp for hours barefooted through the snow. Women, carrying babies in cradles on their backs, wade through glacial streams up to their waists.

Such is one phase of the life of nomadic cattle-keepers. Not all face quite such strenuous difficulties as the Bakhtyari, but the general principle is the same. Death takes a terrible toll among such people. Think what it means when a baby is placed in its cradle early in the morning, tied on the back of a camel, carried twenty miles on the bobbing back of the animal, and not taken from the cradle until afternoon. Yet that is just what happens as a matter of course to a large number of the children of the nomads. Think what it means when every woman, no matter how she feels, must help take down the tents and do her fifteen or twenty miles afoot, or on an animal that leaps and jumps among the rolling stones. Think, too, not only of the training, but of the innate ability needed by boys of ten or twelve years, who must learn to ride any kind of horse and safeguard the cattle, sheep, and goats, no matter how fierce the storm, how icy the flood, or how bold the wild animals and robbers. All this not only furnishes marvellous training in self-reliance, courage, initiative, and bodily strength, but involves a tremendous elimination of those who do not inherit at least a fair share of these qualities. When such people burst from their harsh homes, as did the ancient Kassites, who began to descend on Babylonia from almost the same region as the Bakhtyari, about 2100 years B. C., they are almost irresistible.

Another side of all this has been stressed in *The Character of Races*. Consider for a moment how the peculiar *mores* of the nomads have grown up, and how they, in turn, influence not only culture and training but inheritance. Picture to yourself the main events in the life of an Arab nomad during the course of a year. In the spring, when the camels, goats, and sheep are giving abundance of milk, he lays up a store of sour cheese and curds, dried hard as the toughest hardtack. When the summer comes he exchanges his surplus animals, chiefly the young males, for dates, wheat, and rice grown in the oases or in the border-lands around the desert where agriculture is possible. A few animals may be saved for future use as food, but only the wealthy can afford to eat meat often. In good years the ordinary Arab can lay by enough food to last himself and his family until the following spring. Yet even in good years many of the nomadic Arabs are unable to provide enough to last later than perhaps February, the time when the rains ought to come, and when the young sheep and camels begin to be born, and milk is normally abundant. If all goes well it is possible to live through the spring on nothing but milk. The Arabs do this frequently, although they do not enjoy it. Doughty, in his vivid account of *Arabia Deserta*, tells how the Arabs who have long been living on milk pine for something else. "Give us bread," is their cry. "For two months we have drunk this vile milk. Our stomachs are empty and we cannot fill them. Let us have something we can set our teeth into, something that has substance."

Suppose now that when the time comes for the young animals to be born, and for abundant milk to supplement or replace dates and bread, no rain has fallen. No wonder the Arabs are anxious. No wonder the first question of the tent-dwellers whom Doughty met was:

"Where is the rain? Have showers fallen anywhere? Is there grass in the land? How far to the place of the shower? Did it extend wide over the country? Why does Allah withhold the rain so long?"

Imagine the mental state of people who eagerly pack their

tents and all their crude belongings upon camels, and travel 100 or 200 miles simply because they have heard that a little rain has fallen over an area no larger than that watered by a single summer thunder-shower. Yet this is a common occurrence in Arabia. Often, indeed, the showers are so scanty that the pools are not filled, and the grass springs up so sparsely that to the eye of any but the son of the desert it is almost invisible. Even to him it becomes invisible as soon as its scanty spears, four or five inches high, wither in the scorching sun. When such years come, as they often do, the mother animals can find no fresh pasturage; they may subsist themselves, but they have no milk for their young. Animal after animal dies. The Arabs see that they can lay by no curds and cheese for the winter; but that is far from the worst. They see also that the price of dates and wheat will be high because of the drought, and that they will have no surplus animals to exchange for food of any kind. And worst of all, they see their children hungry and crying for food. This is no overdrawn picture. It is what happens when two or three dry years come in succession.

What is an Arab to do when his camels, his sheep, his wife, his children, and himself are all suffering the pangs of hunger? He cannot go off to some other land and get work. In the first place, the better adapted he is to the nomadic life the more he hates the thought of steady work, and the less adapted he is to it temperamentally. In the second place, there is rarely any work to be had, for when he is in distress the settled regions near him are also usually suffering from drought. And finally, unless he absolutely gives up his old life, he cannot abandon or sell what animals he has left, but must care for them as the basis of any prosperity for which he may hope in the future. The only resource which he sees under such circumstances is plunder. The man who is starving has little thought of right or wrong. To have such thoughts would seem to him fatal. If considerations of humanity or any other moral ideas prevent him from engaging in raids upon the tribes around him, the doom of his family may be sealed, for his children may die of hunger. Thus through the thousands of years since nomads first lived in Arabia the hard conditions of climate have steadily forced the Arabs to frame a moral code which condones violence. Even more significant is the fact that these same conditions have weeded out those who withheld their hands from violence or were incompetent in robbery and raids.

The Arab who would succeed and who would keep his children in health must not only be ready to commit depredations and be utterly dishonest according to our standards, but must also be strong in the endurance of heat, thirst, and the weariness of long rides. Unfortunately, he has little need of steady industry or of strength to endure the gruelling constant grind of labor like that of the farm. Laziness, according to our definition of the word, is no great disadvantage provided a man is able to summon his powers in a crisis when the camels have strayed far away, when they have been driven off by raiders, or when the man himself goes on a foray. Hence the Arab is lazy as well as disregardful of what we call common honesty. Just as he thinks of raids as a part of the ordinary routine of life, so he thinks of steady work as something scarcely to be demanded even of women and as fit only for slaves. "Shame enters the family with the plough." Thus do the Tuaregs, or Berber nomads of Algeria, sum up their idea of agriculture, as Gautier tells us in *The Geographical Review* (January, 1921). To them the towns are "nauseating." An interesting parallel to this proverb of the Arabs is cited by Professor F. K. Morris, who accompanied the Andrews Expedition of the American Museum of Natural History to Mongolia. In the summer of 1925 in western Mongolia, north of the Altair Range, his party found that Tsagan Nor, a salt lake that they had seen in 1922, had dried up because of deficient rain. Part of the Mongol nomads were obliged to move away because the vegetation had also become scanty. Professor Morris and his companions asked the Mongols why they did not give up their precarious wandering life with their flocks and herds, and practise agriculture, as is done by the Chinese not far away. "Impossible," was the answer, and then, when urged for a reason,

"For the Chinese, the loom and the plough,
For the Mongol, the saddle and the sword."

In spite of their almost universal hatred of agriculture and of a settled life, a great many nomads are gradually drawn away from the life of the wanderer and become peasants. But "a nomad tribe ruined by losing its camels and consequently its mobility enters on sedentary life with rancor in its heart. It is the supreme humiliation, an irretrievable loss of caste" (Gautier). The great historian Ibn Khaldun speaks of the degenerate descendants of ancient nomad tribes as "so abased that they pay the impost." The true nomad levies impost and pockets it.

Natural selection is very effective in this process of differentiating the nomads from the villagers. Some nomads may go to the well-watered lands as conquerors, but the ones who become peasants are generally those who either fail in the struggle as nomads, or who have a particular aptitude for agriculture. It may be that they have not enough endurance, and that the thought of having plenty to eat outweighs their dislike of steady work. Or perhaps by reason of physique or temperament the work itself is not so distasteful to them as to some of their comrades. So they leave the nomadic life and go to the oases, or to the fringes of verdure surrounding the desert. Thus through the ages there goes on a steady process whereby one type of character becomes fixed in the desert and another is encouraged in the places where agriculture prevails.

Among the Arabs and among pastoral nomads in general, few qualities are more important than the capacity either to lead or to be led. East of the Caspian Sea, for example, before the Russians put an end to such habits, the regular mode of starting a Turkoman raid was for some one to drive his spear upright into the ground and say: "I am going on a raid. Who will go with me?" Others came forward, thrust in their spears, and said that they too would go. When a raid is once under way three conditions are essential to success: Some one must lead; the rest must obey; and each man must have implicit confidence in his comrades. Failure in any one of these respects may spell not only

disaster but death. To the hunter or farmer it makes little difference whether he can lead other men or not. Nor is it essential
that he should obey on the instant. He usually works alone and
depends almost entirely on himself. But when an encampment of
the desert people is raided, the only chance of recovering the
animals is for some one immediately to issue orders, and all the
rest to obey. The farmers of the oases and elsewhere are sometimes subject to raids, but not nearly so much as are the nomads.
It is far harder and more dangerous to raid a village than to raid
a camp. Then, too, animals—not grain—are generally what the
raiders want.

Again, during the course of a raid it may happen time and
again that the raiders are in sore straits. Often two men ride a
camel. Or if each has his own camel one man may care for several
animals while the rest are busy in other ways. If the one who
has the camels flees at sight of danger, his comrades may perish.
If they escape, the man who failed them is fiercely hated and
driven from the camp. So necessary is it that the comrades in a
raid or in the chase after stray animals hang together that a
nomad scarcely dares come home alone if some accident has be-
fallen his companions.

We have spoken chiefly of the Arabs, but in practically all
desert regions and among mountain nomads, such as many of
the Khirghiz, almost the same habits prevail. Let us sum up
the qualities which make a nomad successful, and which thereby
enable him to marry the finest girls in the community, and to
bring up many healthy, sturdy children. First and foremost
stands the ability to exert himself strenuously, and without stint,
in an emergency. It matters little whether the animals have
strayed, have been attacked by wild animals, or are threatened
by a sudden storm or flood. Or it may be that the man himself
is going on a raid, or his encampment is being raided. In any
case he must not spare himself. He must not think of food, drink,
or his own sufferings. For a while he must do and dare everything, and exert every ounce of his strength. After the emergency
is over he may be absolutely idle. In fact, he generally is. His

wife and children can do the milking and care for the animals so long as there is no emergency. Hence, as already stated, laziness in the ordinary sense of the word is no disadvantage. In fact, the man who is good at steady industry is very likely to be weeded out of the community either because he does not succeed or because he finds the sedentary life better adapted to him. A second great quality of the nomad is the power of leading, and a third is the power of being led. These are, perhaps, as essential as the capacity for sudden and violent exertion. Without them a nomad camp would quickly disintegrate, and its members would, perforce, take to agriculture or become mere hangers-on in other camps.

Another fine quality of nomads is self-reliance. The nomad meets sudden emergencies far oftener than does the farmer. Coupled with this is the necessity of self-reliance on the part of the nomadic women. Little by little the type which is not bold and self-reliant tends to disappear from among the tent-dwellers. Either their children meet with accidents, or they themselves are not wanted as wives by the bolder and more energetic men, and hence are likely to drift with the less adventurous men into the sedentary life. Still other qualities, such as hospitality and faithfulness to one's comrades, are at a greater premium among nomads than among those who live in settled villages, for failure in these respects is much more likely to spell disaster to the nomad than to the farmer. Thus through thousands of years, in North Africa, Arabia, central Asia, and to a less extent in certain other deserts, there has grown up a type of bold, forceful, active, dominating wanderers who, nevertheless, are lazy and have little skill in the handicrafts. They are inherently different from their patient, timid, and submissive cousins who have become inured to the quiet life of the villages, but who are also industrious and skilful. The interplay between these two types, and the repeated conquest of one by the other have been among the outstanding facts of history. In the long run nomads and their immediate descendants have tended to dominate the world out of all proportion to their numbers.

CHAPTER VI

WHAT THE WEATHER DOES TO US

No one doubts the importance of climate. If we know that a region is tropical, arctic, or desert, we also know much about its vegetation, products, occupations, and mode of life. We can even make fairly reliable pictures of the habits and temperament of the people. But is there any definite law as to the relation between climate and history? Can the right kind of people build up an equally high civilization no matter what their climate? "Of course not," says the average reader. "Can the scattered people of deserts make progress as rapidly as the dense population of fertile, well-watered prairies? How can tropical people be energetic when they are always being pulled down by malaria and dysentery? And why should you expect progress in a climate too cold for crops and with practically no resources except seals, polar bears, and reindeer? The idea that people in diverse geographical environments can make progress with equal rapidity or even maintain the same grade of civilization is ridiculous."

But suppose the tropical diseases were subdued and were no more dangerous than those of other regions. Let the same kind of competent people and the same kind of high civilization be introduced all over the world. Assume also that the people of tropical countries, deserts, polar regions, and other supposedly undesirable areas are as well equipped as the rest of the world in respect to transportation, communication, and public service. Give them the best of schools, churches, and banks. Let them have electric lights, water-supplies, movies, policemen, doctors, dances, bridge parties, automobiles, and a hundred other modern conveniences and pleasures. Would the same type of civilization continue to prevail indefinitely everywhere? Or would some of the people go backward, some stand still, and others make progress?

One of the answers to these questions lies in people's occupations. The people in all climates cannot possibly do the same work. Whether our supposed heirs of the whole world be Scotchmen, Yankees, Californians, or New Zealanders, they are practically certain to raise rice in Burmah, wheat in southern Russia, camels in the Arabian desert, corn in Illinois, and reindeer in the far north of Canada. Why? Simply because those things pay. It is foolish to plant wheat in warm, wet rice-land, on a frozen tundra, or in an unirrigated desert. By the same token, woollen factories will not develop in Java, where there is no wool worth mentioning and where nobody wants woollen clothing. Who would establish a huge ice-plant in Nova Zembla, or a great factory for making cotton-machinery in Samoa, or even Utah? We want our ice where the air is warm, and our cotton-machinery where the climate permits cotton to grow or where there are many people to be clothed. Perhaps mankind will some day establish the world's greatest manufacturing centre in the dryest, hottest part of Arabia where there is no water, no coal, no vegetation, and little pleasure in life because of the heat, wind, and dust. All sorts of other strange things may also happen. Perhaps we shall acquire a sixth sense—telepathy—so that we can sit at home and merely open our minds to take in all the wisdom of the world. But such things have not happened yet, and are not likely to happen for a long time. As people are now constituted, the mere fact that the climate differs from one part of the world to another is bound to cause differences in the industries by which people get a living. This in turn inevitably leads to differences in the density of population, in the amount of surplus wealth which can be stored up, and in the development of transportation, commerce, sanitation, public service, education, religion, recreation, and a host of other matters. Unless mankind becomes utterly remodelled, such differences are a necessary consequence of climatic differences, even if all parts of the world were inhabited by people of the same race, culture, and ability.

The differences engendered by the effect of climate on occupations are enormously increased by migration and natural selection. Suppose again that the people in all parts of the world are temporarily alike, not only in race and culture, but in the proportion of different kinds of people. Let each have the same percentage of stupid hod-carriers, patient clerks, cunning criminals, ardent reformers, hard-headed business men, adventurous pioneers, sleek politicians, and eager scientists. How long would the proportions remain the same? Not a single year, one might almost say; and certainly not a generation. Is the keen business man going to remain where the only occupation is herding camels, and where there are no towns? Is the scientist going to spend all his life peering into a microscope in western China, where thick desert dust sifts over his work for weeks and weeks every year? Will the inventor be content to live where only by the most constant care can he prevent his hands and face from being bathed in perspiration, and his drawings from being smudged continually by damp fingers, while he himself feels an almost constant sense of lassitude? And how about the reformer, will his zeal be satisfied if he changes the lives of a few scanty dwellers in the pasturelands of Tibet, or will he be impelled to work among the dense masses who under any type of civilization are almost certain to cover the plains of India?

Mankind is so constituted that certain kinds of people go to certain places, because they have initiative, knowledge, or foresight. Others stay where they are, because they lack the energy, knowledge, incentive, or wherewithal to go elsewhere. This has always been the case. It is true among the beasts. Does not the Bible say, "Wheresoever the carcase is, there will the eagles be gathered together"? Does not the wild goose fly to far islands, while the rhinoceros stays close to his muddy river? Will not this same tendency to divide men into groups according to their tastes, abilities, and temperaments continue to work more and more potently? Civilization increases the tendency. It makes it easier to go from place to place, to gain information about remote regions, to lay up money for transportation and as an aid in getting a start in a new place. All these conditions and many others join with our social fluidity in sorting people out at a tremendous rate. The boy with a genius for painting may never get a chance under the conditions of civilization that now prevail in Central India. He was born a ropemaker, and a ropemaker he must die, in the place where he was born. A similar boy born in the same place, but in the high type of civilization which we are supposing to be established there, will soon be found out. He may be taken to a great city for education, he may paint pictures in the Himalayas, he may go to China, France, or New Zealand to be fêted, and he may settle in a colony of artists at Santa Barbara. If all lands were highly civilized, the wonderful climate and fine scenery might cause an almost incredible concentration of artists on a delightful coast like that of California. Painters would come from every land under heaven. On the other hand, if every one could move freely, how many artists would remain long in far northeastern Siberia, where snow drifts high against the windows seven or eight months each year and a painter may freeze his fingers and forever ruin his future while making the simplest sketch out-of-doors? No matter how high civilization may rise, or how competent the people of northern Siberia may be, is it probable that many landscape-painters will ever choose that region as a home? On the contrary, the tendency will be to weed them out with great rapidity. But as civilization becomes more universal, will not places like the coast of southern California tend more and more to become centres where the artist children of artist parents are born in greater and greater proportions? These illustrations are indeed extreme, but they emphasize a neglected truth of almost universal application. Practically everywhere and always selection is in progress. As civilization grows higher, the selection increases in intensity. And among the factors that cause selection, one of the most powerful is climate.

But occupations, migration, and natural selection are not the only means whereby climate causes the people of one part of the world to differ from those of another. A factor of scarcely less magnitude is the degree of energy imparted by different atmospheric conditions. I shall dwell on this more fully than on the other factors because it is more disputed.

Suppose as before that the whole world is inhabited by the same sort of people, and that all have the same degree of civilization and of innate ability. Suppose that tropical diseases, such as malaria and dysentery, are eliminated. Would people's achievements then differ notably because of climate? This question has long been in debate because we cannot find the answer directly through either experiments or statistics. The trouble is that even when people of the same race live in different climates, we have no assurance that the various groups have been selected in the same way. If especially healthy and vigorous people are selected for a poor climate, and especially weak ones for a good climate, the poor climate will make the better showing. Nevertheless, by one means or another we have now reached a point where it is fairly certain that the ability of European races, and probably of all races, usually differs according to the climate in which they live. This seems to be true even if specific diseases, backward natives, isolation, and other cultural conditions cease to be handicaps. It appears reasonable to the layman, but is sometimes vigorously denied by able specialists in anthropology, physiology, history, economics, and other lines of investigation.

Let us see what actually happens to people who live all the time in one place, but are subjected to different atmospheric conditions from day to day or season to season. So many investigations have now been made that we can speak with considerable certainty. The investigations have been based on deaths, illnesses, amount of work, accuracy and reliability of work, moral behavior, physiological functions, and mental reactions. Some of the studies have been statistical and others have used the experimental methods of the laboratory. Some have compared the human conditions with the air out-of-doors, and others with the air indoors.

In spite of the inevitable differences of detail which arise in every scientific investigation, the final results of these varied lines of investigations harmonize admirably. They are well illustrated in charts prepared by Messrs. Houghten, Yagloglou, and Miller in the Research Laboratory of the American Society of Heating and Ventilating Engineers and the United States Bureau of Mines at Pittsburgh. The charts are based on experiments in two rooms where any desired temperature and humidity can be obtained. The people who are the objects of experimentation enter a room whose temperature and humidity they do not know. They express their feelings as to whether the room is too warm, too cool, too moist, or too dry. They also pass from one room to another where the atmospheric conditions are very slightly different, and express opinions as to which is more comfortable. The human body is so sensitive that differences of no more than one degree Fahrenheit in temperature or of 5 or 10 per cent in relative humidity can easily be felt. This is especially true when the atmosphere approaches the most comfortable conditions.

The central feature of the charts is the so-called "comfort zone" in the midst of which lies the "comfort line." The zone indicates the general range of conditions under which people feel comfortable, while the line shows the conditions of most perfect comfort—the optimum. Of course, the positions of the zone and line vary according to how much clothing people wear, how active they are, and according to their age, sex, health, and personal idiosyncrasies. Nevertheless, among healthy people who are normally dressed and are sitting still the variations in the position of the comfort line are surprisingly slight. Let us consider the case of such persons when they have been quiet long enough so that they do not feel the effect of previous exertions. In perfectly still air the average person of European race, as measured at Pittsburgh, feels most comfortable at a temperature of 64° F. if the air is saturated with moisture. If the air is only 80 per cent saturated he feels best at a temperature of 66°; when the moisture is reduced to 50 per cent the most comfortable temperature is 69½°. Such conditions are like those of an ideal day in May or early June in New York, let us say. If the air is still dryer the most comfortable temperature is, of course, higher.

With a relative humidity of 20 per cent, which is very low for most parts of the United States, the comfort line lies at a temperature a trifle above 72°. Thus on a windless day the optimum for persons in a state of complete inactivity ranges from a temperature of 64° when the rain is falling and the air is saturated with moisture, up to 72° when the air is as dry as that of the desert.

But this is not the whole story. If the air is moving, the most comfortable temperature is higher than if it is at rest, for people's skins are cooled by evaporation. This is shown by Messrs. Yagloglou and Miller in another very clever chart. From this we learn that if the temperature of the air is 76°, for example, and the relative humidity 45 per cent, a movement of 340 feet per minute, which means a gentle drift of the air, will produce approximately the right sensation. In other words, it will cause the air to feel as it would if there were no movement and the temperature were 68° instead of 76°, the relative humidity remaining at 45 per cent as before. At a temperature of 80°, however, and a relative humidity of 50 per cent, the air must move several times as fast as in the preceding example in order to produce the greatest feeling of comfort. Of course, the amount of clothing makes a difference. The unclothed body experiences about twice as great a cooling effect from moving air as does the normally clothed body. But normal clothing is heavier in winter than in summer, so that allowance must be made for this. Again, any sort of work or exercise, even if it be no more than writing a letter, has some effect, however slight, in lowering the comfort line. When people are engaged in the most active kind of exercise, such as playing football or shovelling coal, the comfort line sinks far below the normal level.

Two essential points should be noted in connection with the comfort charts. The first is that they represent an experimental method whereby we can determine with great exactness just what conditions of atmospheric temperature, humidity, and movement are most comfortable for any given type of dress and occupation. The second is that the results obtained by this method agree with those obtained through observations of physiological reactions and through statistical studies of work and health.

The relation between the comfort charts and physiological processes may be judged from the following definition of comfort: "Comfort is a condition where the various physiological functions of the body are carried on with the greatest degree of efficiency and with the least strain, so that the individual is not conscious of their existence." If this definition is correct, we ought to find that physiological processes, such as those which manifest themselves in the rate of breathing, the pulse-rate, and the temperature of the body, function most perfectly under the conditions which give rise to the greatest degree of comfort. Numerous experiments at the Pittsburgh laboratory already referred to, as well as by the New York State Ventilation Commission, the British Industrial Fatigue Research Board, and a number of other organizations and individuals, show that this is the case. For example, the New York State Ventilation Commission found very distinct evidence that when the temperature is much above 70°, any kind of physical exertion raises the pulse-rate, the rate of breathing, and the internal temperature of the body much more rapidly than is the case with similar exertion at lower temperatures. The return to normal is also relatively slow at high temperatures and the feeling of fatigue is correspondingly increased. On the other hand, at temperatures below the comfort zone the body has to exert itself more to keep warm than at higher temperatures, and hence is under a certain strain. Thus the comfort zone embraces the combinations of temperature, humidity, and wind movement which not only give the greatest feeling of comfort but which also impose a minimum strain upon the physiological processes whereby the body is prevented from becoming either too warm or too cool.

The second essential point in respect to the comfort charts is their close agreement with my own studies of factory work, deaths, and diseases. Those studies, as described in *Civilization and Climate, World Power and Evolution*, and elsewhere, show that people in factories from Connecticut to Pittsburgh and Florida

work best when the outside temperature averages from about
60° to 66° F. They also show that the death-rate, as determined
from millions of deaths, is lowest when the outside temperature
for day and night together averages 64° with a relative humidity
of 70 or 80 per cent. An average outside temperature of 64°
and a relative humidity of 70 or 80 per cent mean that at night,
as a rule, the temperature falls to perhaps 60° or 55° and the relative humidity approaches 100 per cent, so that dew falls. By
day, on the other hand, the temperature usually rises to 70° or
75° and the relative humidity may fall to 50 per cent or thereabout. In other words, the conditions most favorable for daily
work among thousands of factory workers, and which are also
best for health as indicated by records covering many years,
many cities, and many countries, fall precisely in the comfort
zone determined by exact experimentation. Thus the evidence
of our senses, the evidence derived from our physiological reactions, and the practical test of daily work and daily health all
agree.

This by no means gives a complete picture of what the air
does to us. Important modifications are introduced by at least
three other conditions, namely, the effect of dust or some other
factor which causes dry air to be harmful, the variability of the
weather, and the seemingly different optima for physical and
mental activity. So far as the mere feeling of comfort is concerned, no experiments, so far as I am aware, indicate any clear
difference between the effect of moist and dry air which have the
same cooling power, although differing in temperature. For example, persons normally dressed find that a temperature of 76°
with a relative humidity of 10 per cent feels the same as a temperature of 65° with a relative humidity of 90 per cent. Nevertheless, the studies of the New York Ventilation Commission as
set forth in Professor C. E. A. Winslow's admirable little book,
Fresh Air and Ventilation, show that the higher temperature is
less favorable. On the other hand, thousands of hospital cases
and millions of deaths, as set forth in part in *World Power and
Evolution*, indicate that dryness as well as high temperature is

unhealthful. Extreme moisture is likewise very harmful at high temperatures, as almost every one recognizes. In other words, there is a distinct optimum or zone of most favorable conditions for moisture as well as temperature. Extensive, but as yet unpublished, studies of work in factories made by the Committee on the Atmosphere and Man of the National Research Council point to a similar conclusion.

Not only do dry regions as a rule show higher death-rates than moister regions of similar character, but in any given region the dry months at practically every season are less healthful than wet months at the same season. In the large cities of the United States from 1900 to 1915, the eight moister Januaries averaged more healthful than the eight dryer Januaries; the same was true of February, and so on in every month of the year. Again, the dry cities of the world generally have high death-rates. Denver, for example, has almost the highest death-rate among the large cities in the northern parts of the United States. This seems to be true even when allowance is made for deaths of persons who go there for their health. Madrid on its high, dry plateau has a very high death-rate in proportion to its temperature, and so does Johannesburg in the cool highlands of South Africa. Mexico City, where the temperature at all seasons comes nearer to the ideal than in almost any other part of the world, has one of the highest death-rates. The rate is higher in the dry season than in the wet, rainy season, although there is not enough difference in temperature to have any appreciable effect. A similar contrast prevails in India. Although the season of the monsoon rains is very damp, sticky, and disagreeable, and comes when the sun is highest, the death-rate falls markedly, especially in the northern parts of India where the winter and spring are very dry. Cairo, in Egypt, even at the end of long years of British rule, still had one of the highest death-rates in the whole world. It is probably the dryest of all great cities.

The evidence as to the harm done by dryness is so overwhelming that it can scarcely be questioned. But why should dry climates be considered health resorts, and why should people actually recover their health there? The answer seems to be that outdoor life is everywhere much more healthful than indoor life. When tubercular patients go to dry climates, the dryness almost invariably makes it possible to live out-of-doors far more than formerly. Moreover, in dry climates people get plenty of sunshine. But outdoor air and exercise and plenty of sunshine work just as well in New England as in Colorado or California, as is proved by several homes for tuberculous children. The youngsters play out-of-doors in the lightest clothing at all seasons. Barefooted and clad only in thin union suits, which do not cover either arms or legs, they frisk about in the snow with the thermometer far below freezing. They return home sound and hearty, and able for a long time to withstand our iniquitous indoor mode of life with its vitiated dusty air and its lack of sunshine. Dry climates make it easy to live out-of-doors, but the dryness itself is not helpful.

Why, then, have the experimenters as yet found no evidence of any measurable difference between the effects of dry air and moist? Part of the answer lies in the fact that even the extensive experiments on school-children conducted by the New York State Ventilation Commission lasted only a few hours at a time, whereas dry weather may last day after day and dry climates last centuries. Moreover, the difference between the dry schoolrooms and the moist was very slight, and the investigators did not test the possible effect of greater variability of temperature in the dry rooms than in the moist. Other important factors may possibly be found in the dustiness of ordinary dry air, or in its electrical condition, although as to this we are not yet certain. It is clear, however, that under natural conditions dry air is much more dusty than moist air, and has a different electrical condition. In climates like those of Madrid, Mexico City, and Cairo every little breeze fills the air with dust, and often the dust is foul with microbes. But regardless of the cause, the fact is clear, the dry regions and dry seasons thus far investigated have higher death-rates than regions and seasons of the same sort which are not dry.

Coming now to variability, we find ourselves faced by a problem which the experimenters have as yet scarcely touched. But, fortunately, there is abundant statistical evidence based on thousands of hospital cases, millions of deaths, and the daily work of thousands of factory hands. This shows that variations of temperature from one day to another produce a marked effect upon health and activity. A moderate drop of temperature at all seasons and under practically all conditions is stimulating and healthful. The low temperature which follows such a drop in winter is by no means healthful. The *change* is what gives the stimulus. This is reasonable. A cold douche gives a pleasant and stimulating reaction even in winter, but let cold water pour over a person for fifteen minutes and he may get a chill that will end his days. On the other hand, a rise of temperature is generally, although not always, accompanied by a high death-rate and poor work. This is readily understandable in summer, but in winter the reasons are not so clear. The secret apparently lies partly in the fact that the advent of a warm day is systematically the signal for overheating our houses and factories. It takes time to adjust our fires and our stokers to the new conditions. Here again we may for the present dismiss the problem of causes and concentrate on the facts. The outstanding fact is that changes of weather have a pronounced and easily measured relation to health and activity.

The net effect of changes of temperature in both directions has not been studied so much as has the effect of individual changes in only one direction. Nevertheless, a study of all the deaths for sixteen years in all the large cities of the United States for which data are available, as explained in the third edition of *Civilization and Climate*, shows that the stormier Januaries, Februaries, and so forth were systematically more healthful than were the same months when less stormy. Storminess, it need scarcely be said, is almost synonymous with variability. Only in the autumn, when people's health is best, does the degree of storminess make no appreciable difference to the health of the northern United States. Of course, a region or a month may be

too stormy as well as not stormy enough, just as it may be too
hot as well as too cool, too dry as well as too moist. Moreover,
there are unquestionably certain types of disease which are unfavorably influenced by storminess, just as certain types are ad-
versely affected by moisture. Perhaps, too, some individuals may
react in a fashion slightly different from the average. Nevertheless, storminess joins temperature and humidity as one of the
three main elements in determining how people's health and
activity vary from day to day and season to season. It does not
appear to be quite so important as humidity, while humidity is
not so important as temperature, but all three are of the same
general order of magnitude.

Before we leave this subject a few concrete examples will help
to make it clear and to explain why the underlying facts still fail
to be universally recognized. In Chapter I we examined the extraordinary effect of unseasonable heat and cold upon the health
of the United States. We saw that a hot spell in 1925 produced
a loss of life which is conservatively estimated as having a value
of $100,000,000, while a cold spell the next winter produced a
greater loss valued at $500,000,000. A recent investigation by
the Committee on the Atmosphere and Man shows that in New
York, when the daily fluctuations are eliminated by the technical method known as ten-day moving averages, the curve of
mortality among persons over five years old regularly goes up
and down with the temperature, as soon as the mean temperature for day and night rises above 66° or 68°. Among children
under five years of age, as soon as this temperature is passed, the
death-rate in New York and Paris has been found to shoot up
as if in an epidemic. After the more susceptible children have
been killed, the death-rate falls off gradually as in an epidemic,
but its rate of fall depends on the temperature. This was pre-
eminently true before the days of sterilized milk and other modern means of preserving the health of children. It is still true,
although less obvious, in our own day.

Even such things as great epidemics like the influenza in 1918
are greatly influenced by the weather. This does not mean that

the weather, so far as we yet know, played any part in originating that epidemic. What happened was that after the epidemic had once started, its severity in one place as compared with another was closely correlated with the weather preceding the onset of the disease and during the main crisis. In places where the weather was cool and invigorating, but not cold, the ravages of the disease were much less than where it was warm. The death-rates during the first ten weeks of the main epidemic of 1918 in all of the thirty-six cities of over 100,000 for which data are available in the United States were as follows:

	Mean Temperature for 30 Days before Outbreak of Epidemic and for 10 Days at Crisis	Death Rate per Thousand from Influenza and Pneumonia
6 coolest cities....................	54°	2.6
6 next coolest cities................	57½°	3.0
6 next coolest cities................	61°	3.5
6 next coolest cities................	63°	4.2
6 next coolest cities................	65°	5.0
6 warmest cities...................	70°	5.2

This little table appears conclusive in itself, but the matter has been studied by the far more delicate method known to mathematicians as partial correlation coefficients. By this method Professor Raymond Pearl, of Johns Hopkins University, compared certain environmental conditions with the destructiveness of the influenza epidemic in the large cities of the United States. He concluded that the severity of the epidemic varied from city to city in fairly close harmony with the death-rate from all causes, and in still closer harmony with the death-rate from organic diseases of the heart. Pearl has such confidence in this method that he states very positively that the biological factor which this death-rate measures is the main factor in "determining the explosiveness of the outbreak of the epidemic mortality. . . . It appears very clearly that of the twelve different factors here studied the normal death-rate of the community from organic diseases of the heart had more to do with determining the proportionate part of the population which perished in the epidemic than any other factor."

Other investigators, such as Professor C. E. A. Winslow, of Yale, and Professor E. E. Grove, of Columbia, agree with this conclusion, but wisely point out that: "We cannot say (as some may perhaps be tempted to do) that the influenza outbreak was severe in a given community *because* the death-rate from organic heart-disease had previously been high in that community. Such may have been the case; but it is equally possible that the high mortality from organic heart-disease, and the explosiveness of the influenza epidemic, manifest in the same communities, may have both been due to some common cause, or causes, affecting both."

This note of caution is well founded. The Committee on the Atmosphere and Man repeated Pearl's investigation, using all the factors employed by him (numbers 1 to 13 below), and also nine others indicated in the following table:

A. Factors of human environment (demography).
   1. Age distribution of the population.
   2. Ratio of the sexes.
   3. Density of the population (persons per acre).
   4. Rate of growth from 1900 to 1910.
B. Factors of geographical position.
   5. Distance from Boston, where the epidemic began.
   6. Longitude.
   7. Latitude.
C. Physiological factors, *i. e.*, normal death-rates, 1915, 1916, and 1917.
   8. All causes.
   9. Pulmonary tuberculosis.
   10. Organic diseases of the heart.
   11. Nephritis and acute Bright's disease.
   12. Typhoid fever.
   13. Cancer and other malignant tumors.
D. Racial factors.
   14. Percentage of Negroes, 1920.
   15. Percentage of foreign-born, 1920.
E. Industrial factor.
   16. Percentage of population engaged in manufacturing, 1919.
F. Climatic factors.
   17. Mean temperature for day and night.

18. Change of mean temperature from one day to the next.
19. Absolute humidity.
20. Relative humidity, or percentage of possible water vapor.
21. Weather—a combination of Nos. 17-20.
22. Climatic energy as defined in the next chapter.

When all these factors were studied by the delicate mathematical method of partial correlation coefficients all the non-climatic factors were eliminated. The weather, which means primarily the weather just before the onset of the epidemic and during ten days at the crisis, is the one factor thus far investigated which shows a clear and pronounced relation to the destructiveness of the epidemic. Even this relationship might also disappear if there were any factor, such as variations in solar energy, which is capable of influencing the weather and the bacterial causes of the epidemic independently, but we know of no such factor.

This investigation of influenza is interesting not only as showing the great potency of the weather in influencing human health and energy, but as illustrating the difficulty which many thoughtful and sincere people experience in believing that the weather can produce such great effects. For example, in his most suggestive book entitled *Studies in Human Biology*, Professor Pearl comments as follows:

Since this work was first published it has been confirmed, so far as it went, by a co-operative study under the direction of Ellsworth Huntington. That study went farther and took into account the weather just preceding and during the epidemic, and reaches the final conclusion that "Among all the factors yet investigated only the weather appears to have had any fundamental significance in causing the destructiveness of the epidemic to vary from city to city." While in a sort of numerical sense this conclusion appears to be warranted by the figures presented, it does not have the backing of common sense, and it will, I think, be cautiously received by thoughtful persons. It involves as one of its major supporting elements in the statistical analysis, a rather high correlation between the *normal*, regular death-rate of the community from organic heart-disease (and also, for that matter, the tuberculosis death-rate) and the state of the weather for ten weeks in 1918 at the time of the epidemic. Now just *possibly* the state of the weather determines the death-rate from organic heart-disease at a particular time. But surely it is difficult to suppose that ten weeks of weather in the autumn of 1918, however bad it may have been, can possibly have influenced the organic heart death-rate of 1915, 1916, and 1917. And equally it is difficult to suppose that both of these phenomena (*normal* organic heart death-rate and weather for ten weeks in 1918) can depend upon a common cause. Yet something like one or the other of these equally difficult statements will have to be accepted by any one who accepts Doctor Huntington's final conclusion.

The answer to Professor Pearl's objection seems clear to the climatologist. The weather for ten weeks in any specific place, especially at seasons other than the summer, is closely correlated with the climate of that place. The climate, in turn, is closely correlated with the death-rate from all causes and from diseases of the heart. Therefore, in cities which are so diverse climatically as those of the United States, it is inevitable that the autumn weather, in any year whatever, should show a significant, even though small, correlation with the average death-rate from diseases of the heart. The normal climate is a potent factor in determining both conditions. It is the "common cause" which Pearl overlooks. A knowledge of climatology does away with most of the objections to the idea that the distribution of health and energy is closely dependent upon climate.

Mental as well as physical health and energy ought also to be considered. Does the weather have any effect upon them? In general, as appears in *Civilization and Climate*, it seems clear that, when the physiological functions of the body are operating most smoothly, the mind also is at its best. Nevertheless, tests made by Lehmann and Pedersen on school-children in Denmark, and my own study of the marks of nearly 2,000 students at West Point and Annapolis, suggest that the greatest mental activity occurs at temperatures averaging about 40° for day and night together. This means that frost occurs at night, but the days are not cold. Of course, the people whose minds were investigated were subjected to low temperatures only when out-of-doors, or when their windows were open at night. Moreover, the temperatures were such that the houses were not hot, dry, and stuffy as they become when the outside temperature is lower. These facts and my own personal observations suggest that an average temperature of about 40° F. is not low enough to do much injury to people who are well clothed and live in good houses, but yet is low enough to provide the maximum stimulus through variations of temperature. Such variations arise not only when people go out-of-doors, but when the windows are open. In colder weather people go out-of-doors less than in the kind we are now discussing, and they also are far more likely to keep their windows shut all the time, even at night in many cases. The exact facts as to mental activity and the weather, however, are so doubtful that we shall not lay much stress on them.

Thus far we have been dealing with people of European origin. How far do our conclusions apply to other races? The scanty data on this point suggest that the same general principles apply universally, although the optimum temperature for tropical races may be higher than for Europeans. Thus in Connecticut and Pennsylvania the best work in factories is done when the outdoor temperature for day and night together averages about 60°, but Cuban cigar-makers at Tampa, Florida, do the best work at temperatures of 65° or more. The optimum for Finns, Swedes, Sicilians, and Japanese, to judge from the death-rate, seems to be nearly the same as for central Europeans and Americans. The optimum for Negroes, so far as has yet been determined from mortality data in the United States, appears to be a mean temperature of 68° and a relative humidity of over 80 per cent. These data and others suggest that among tropical races the optimum temperature is somewhat higher than among Europeans. They also suggest that the differences between the optima are not nearly so great as between the actual climates in which the two types developed. It seems doubtful whether the optimum for any race is higher than about 70° F. with a relative humidity of perhaps 80 per cent, which would mean a temperature of about 80° when the humidity falls to 20 per cent, but perhaps these figures should be raised several degrees for unclothed savages. This, however, makes little difference so far as the interpretation of history is concerned, for the races which have been

most important seem to differ very little in their relation to the
atmosphere.

Here, then, is how the matter stands. We are now quite certain
that among Europeans the most comfortable and healthful outdoor temperature and the one most conducive to active physical
work averages from about 62° to 72° when night and day are
taken together. It is higher when the weather is windy or dry,
lower when the weather is quiet or damp. But even when two
different types of atmospheric conditions feel the same so far as
their cooling power is concerned, the damper, cooler air is more
healthful than that which is warmer, dryer, and perhaps dustier.
Similar, although not such abundant, evidence indicates that frequent variations from day to day are distinctly more healthful
than uniformity. Such variability arises mainly from ordinary
storms. Thus storms rank with temperature and humidity as
potent factors in determining people's health and energy. Finally, there is some evidence, although as yet by no means conclusive, that mental activity is greatest at a temperature considerably lower than physical activity. In the next chapter we
shall be ready to see what these facts mean in respect to civilization.

CHAPTER VII

CIVILIZATION AND CLIMATE TO-DAY

In the preceding chapter we considered what the *weather* does to us. Now we want to find out what *climate* does. How shall we go about it? Shall we compare the health, activity, achievements, and culture of one climatic region with those of another? That would not help much, as is explained in *Civilization and Climate*. How do we know that the contrasts between different regions are due to climate rather than race, food, culture, or some other cause? Shall we try a great experiment whereby we pick out groups of people who seem to be identical, and then see how they differ after living for decades or generations in diverse climates? That would be most instructive, but also most expensive and slow. It is being done after a fashion, to be sure, in Hawaii, the Bahamas, northern Australia, and elsewhere, but unfortunately people thus subjected to tropical climates are not what the mathematician would call a "random sample." They are a special type selected because of fitness for life in the tropics. The selection is unconscious and imperfect, but still effective.

Even though these two methods are impracticable, a reliable way is available. Having discovered by experiment and observation the effect of the different combinations of temperature, humidity, and storminess which occur in any one place upon the people who live permanently in that place, let us use our discoveries as the basis of a climatic map. An example will show how we do this. During the fifteen years which we are here using, we find a number of cases where one or another out of some fifty of the largest cities of the United States and western Europe experienced a month with an average temperature of 60° F., and a relative humidity of 60 to 70 per cent, and was within 200 miles of the centre of three storm tracks. In each case we ascertain the percentage by which the death-rate in that particular month exceeded or fell short of the normal for that particular place. Some cities experienced several such months, and others none. That makes no difference; our purpose is merely to ascertain the average percentage by which the death-rate departs from the normal under those particular climatic conditions, regardless of where they occur. Suppose that the average happens to be 96 per cent. Then wherever we find that the temperature of January, February, or any other month, when taken over a long period, averages 60° F., the relative humidity 60 to 70 per cent, and the number of storms three, we assign to that place a rank of 96 for that particular month. Its rank for some other month may be 82, for still another 112, and the average for the year 98. We do not know, and at present do not care, what the actual death-rate may be. We are concerned only with the relative rates that would prevail all over the world if people's health depended solely on climate, and if every one were influenced by the weather in the same way as are the Europeans and Americans, for whom we have data. Figure 3 is a map of Europe prepared on this basis. It illustrates the distribution of what we may call climatic energy. Its features depend solely on the location of definite combinations of temperature, humidity, and storminess.

The next step is to make a map of health and see whether it is like the map of climate. Figure 4 is such a map of Europe based on official statistics before the Great War. Compare it with Figure 3. Only careful inspection reveals any appreciable difference. There is not one chance in millions that so close a resemblance would arise accidentally. The climatic map cannot possibly owe its appearance to health. There seems to be no alternative except to conclude that the distribution of health and energy in Europe depends upon climate more than upon any other known factor.

A map of climatic energy in the United States, prepared like the one for Europe, is given in Figure 5. A mortality map of the United States like that of Europe cannot yet be made, because no mortality statistics are kept in some of the States, and those

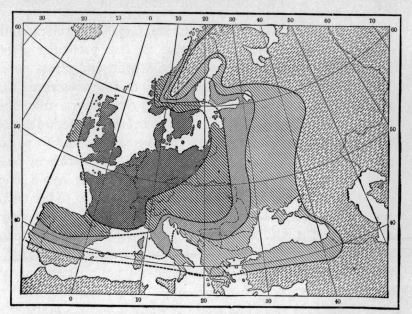

FIG. 3. DISTRIBUTION OF CLIMATIC ENERGY IN EUROPE.
From *The Character of Races*.

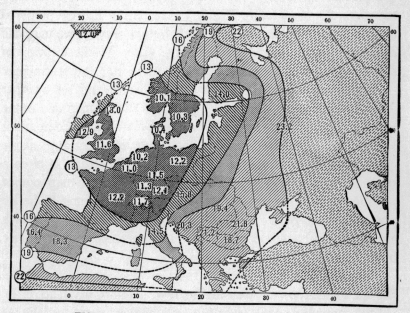

FIG. 4. DISTRIBUTION OF HEALTH IN EUROPE.
From *The Character of Races*.

of certain others are as yet unreliable. Moreover, the recent migration of energetic young people to the Western States is one of several factors which render the distribution of death-rates less regular in America than in Europe. Nevertheless, the statistics of three large insurance companies give a fairly good map of health in the United States, Figure 6. This resembles the climatic map (Figure 5) in the same way that the European map of health resembles that of climate. Incidentally, it is worth noting that as the official mortality data become more abundant and reliable, and as they are corrected to allow for differences in the proportion of children and old people, and for the deaths of non-residents, they provide a map which year by year approaches more nearly to Figure 6. This is especially true when large cities are compared with large cities, and rural districts with rural districts, so that the effect of crowding and manufacturing is partly eliminated. Thus in the United States, as in Europe, the general distribution of health and energy is like that of climate, although the differences between the two are greater.

For the world as a whole it is impossible to make an accurate map of health. No mortality data whatever are available for many countries, and in others the statistics are so inaccurate as to be almost worse than useless. They always err on the side of making the death-rate appear lower than it really is. Nobody takes the trouble to fabricate records of deaths that never occurred, but many people forget to record those that do occur. Look at the littered, dusty, frowsy desk of almost any petty local official in Mexico, Peru, Turkey, or India. Watch him hunt for the blank forms which he ought to use almost daily. Then time him while he spends fifteen minutes in making a record which ought not to take two. Ten to one, he will leave the record unfiled on his desk, and it may get lost. Is it any wonder that the death-rate is almost invariably underestimated in backward countries?

In spite of this, some countries outside the United States and Europe have good records; for example, Canada, Japan, Java, Australia, and others. Their death-rates seem to fit our map of climatic energy quite closely, provided allowance is made for disturbing factors such as density of population in Japan, and recent migration and natural selection in Australia. Thus for the world as a whole, as well as for the United States and Europe, the general distribution of health and energy appears to accord with what would be expected on the basis of climate, even though other factors introduce important modifications.

Having found our maps of health so suggestive, we may well make similar maps of other conditions. How about manufacturing? Does a map of the percentage of workers engaged in manufacturing look anything like the maps of climatic energy and health? It certainly does. Each of the three maps has two dark areas, one in western Europe centering around the North Sea, and another in the United States from New England, New Jersey, and Maryland westward to the Mississippi River. Each has minor areas of relatively heavy shading on the Pacific coast of the United States, in Japan, in southeastern Australia, and New Zealand. All likewise show a greater or less degree of intensity in Chile and Argentina, although there the newness of the countries and the scarcity of statistics leave us in doubt. Yet unquestionably on all three maps these regions rank much higher than practically any tropical region. All the maps likewise show a diminution of intensity in every direction, as one goes away from the high areas. This is especially noticeable in Europe, where the contrast between England or Belgium and the marginal countries such as Portugal, Bulgaria, and Russia is noteworthy. In fact, one of the most surprising features of all the maps is the way in which they decline from the North Sea eastward, even in the same latitude. Russia, Siberia, and China all appear to labor under a climatic handicap which was almost unsuspected before the present studies were made. Japan, on the contrary, ranks relatively high in manufacturing as well as in climate. All over the world the resemblance between climatic energy and the percentage of the population engaged in manufacturing is almost as great as in the United States (Figures 5 and 7).

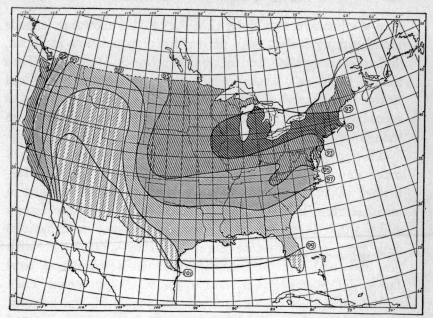

FIG. 5.   DISTRIBUTION OF CLIMATIC ENERGY IN THE UNITED STATES.
From *Civilization and Climate*.   Courtesy of the Yale University Press.

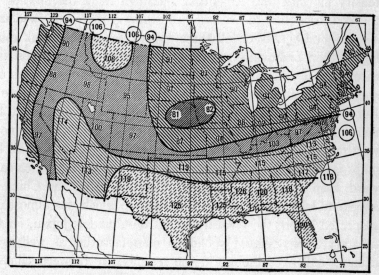

FIG. 6.   DISTRIBUTION OF HEALTH IN THE UNITED STATES.
From *Civilization and Climate*.   Courtesy of the Yale University Press.

Numerous other phenomena are distributed in the same way as climatic energy and health. Outside the United States, however, it is difficult to make maps of them because even in Europe the methods of preparing statistics differ greatly from country to country, and in many cases are defective. So let us concentrate on the United States. Take transportation, for example. Figure 8 is a map based on several factors: namely, the mileage of railroads, trolley lines, and roads per square mile of territory, the amount spent each year per mile of road, and the number of automobiles in proportion to the inhabitants. The States have been ranked from one to forty-eight in each respect; then the scores have been added and used as the basis of the map. The resemblance of Figure 8 to the maps of climatic energy, health, and manufacturing is unmistakable. In fact, all four are almost alike except that the transportation map, as might be expected, shows a more pronounced effect of the Appalachians, Rockies, Sierra Nevada, and other mountains than do the others. It is quite obvious, however, that in general the facilities for transportation are good where the climatic energy is high, and decline rapidly as the climate becomes less energizing. The same appears to be true all over the world, except where the presence of alien races from better climates gives a region, like northern India, a somewhat better transportation system than would be expected on the basis of climate.

Similar conditions prevail as to education, Figure 9. Here, as in the case of transportation, we need to take account of a number of conditions in order to get a fair estimate. Figure 9 is based on the number of days that school is in session, the percentage of children of school age who are enrolled in school, the percentage of the enrolled children who are present each day, the salaries of teachers, and the excess of young men over young women among students eighteen to twenty years of age. The result is a map which has the same general aspect as the maps of climatic energy, health, manufacturing, and transportation. Like each of the others, however, it also displays its own little peculiarities due to conditions which have no relation to climate.

Thus Massachusetts holds the highest rank in education, presumably because of its Puritan background, which seems to be the reason why it still supplies far more eminent leaders than does any other State in proportion to its population. But Utah stands almost equally high, because the Mormons have insisted on universal education. Pennsylvania, on the contrary, stands lower than would be expected, largely because its mines and its laborious and relatively unhealthful industries neither attract nor retain the highest type of workers. But such exceptional conditions do not destroy the general pattern of our maps. They simply give rise to certain interesting details, while the general pattern remains the same as that of climatic energy.

A similar condition prevails in respect to income, Figure 10. The average income is high in the northeast from southern New England and New Jersey to Illinois, and again on the Pacific coast. It declines notably toward the south and to a less degree in the Rocky Mountain region. Of course it is quite possible, and entirely legitimate, to explain the distribution of income as due to the development of commerce and manufacturing, the presence of Negroes, the aftermath of the War of Secession, and the energy of the people of the Pacific coast because they have been selected by migration. Each of these conditions is undoubtedly an important factor in producing the final result. But in practically every case they, in their turn, display a strong tendency toward a distribution like that of climatic energy. Even the location of the colored people in the South, and of an unusually competent type of settlers in California, owes much to climate. The colored people were imported in large numbers mainly because the climate favors cotton, and does not favor white labor. Where the climate is not good for cotton they have never multiplied greatly. On the Pacific coast the delightful character of the climate has had much to do with attracting an unusually large proportion of prosperous and competent people who wish a pleasant place in which to live. A somewhat similar condition causes Florida to stand higher than would be expected, not only in income, but in many other ways. Florida is a remark-

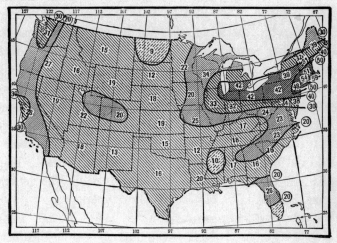

FIG. 7. DISTRIBUTION OF MANUFACTURING IN THE
UNITED STATES.
From *Business Geography*. Courtesy of John Wiley & Sons.

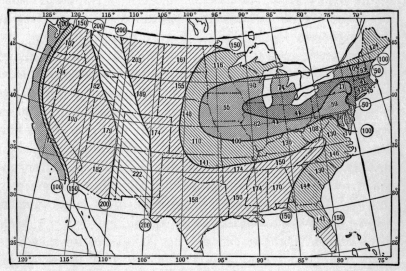

FIG. 8. DISTRIBUTION OF TRANSPORTATION IN THE UNITED STATES.
From *Business Geography*. Courtesy of John Wiley & Sons.

able example of the way in which the selection of an active type
of settler or immigrant raises the cultural level. Such cases
merely prove that other factors as well as climate help in determining the geographical distribution of human activities and
achievements.

Maps of many other human conditions in the United States
display the same pattern that we have already seen repeated
again and again in Figures 5 to 10. Several such maps, in addition to those here given, may be found in the second edition of
Huntington and Williams' *Business Geography*, and in *An Introduction to the Study of Sociology*, edited by Jerome Davis. One
more is here reproduced in Figure 11. It is a map of general
progress, and is based on a combination of eight conditions, each
of which receives the same weight. These conditions are education (Figure 9); health (Figure 6); the accuracy with which ages
are reported in the census; the percentage of illiteracy among
white persons over ten years of age; income per capita in 1919,
1920, and 1921 (Figure 10); the percentage of occupied persons
engaged in professions; the percentage of occupied persons engaged in manufacturing; and transportation facilities (Figure 8).
Another way of ascertaining the general distribution of progress
is by means of the opinions of persons who are unusually well
informed. Figure 12 is based on the opinions of twenty-five
geographers and others, as explained in *Civilization and Climate*.
The most significant fact about it is that it is practically identical with the corresponding map, Figure 11, based on exact
statistics. This suggests that maps of other parts of the world,
based on the opinions of equally well-informed persons, presumably agree very closely with the maps that would be prepared
if sufficiently reliable statistics were available.

In Europe, and still more in the world as a whole, it is almost
impossible to prepare maps of civilization and progress on the
basis of exact statistics. The best that we can yet do seems to
be to prepare maps such as Figures 13 and 15, based on the opinions of a considerable number of men, about fifty in this case,
who live in different countries and continents, and reflect differ-

ent local prejudices. A comparison of Figure 13 with Figures 3 and 4 shows that the distribution of progress in Europe agrees with that of climatic energy and health as closely as in the United States. A similar comparison of Figure 15 with Figure 14, showing the distribution of climatic energy in the world as a whole, indicates the same kind of agreement. Minor differences do indeed occur, and are highly interesting and significant. Nevertheless, the general agreement between climate, health, and human progress is clear. Such an agreement is impossible except on the hypothesis that climate affects health and energy, as we know to be the case, and that health and energy hold an almost predominating place in the determination of the rapidity with which a nation makes progress. Therefore we seem to be forced to the final conclusion that the present distribution of civilization is determined more closely by climate than by any other single factor, so far as is yet known.

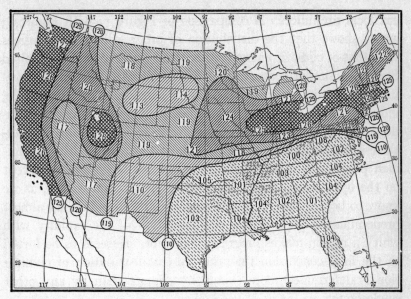

FIG. 9. DISTRIBUTION OF EDUCATION IN THE UNITED STATES.

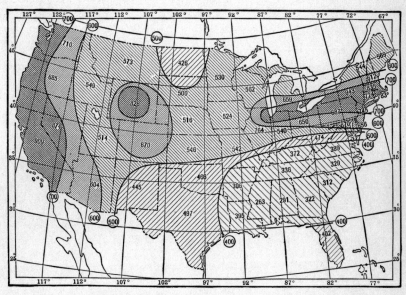

FIG. 10. DISTRIBUTION OF INCOME IN THE UNITED STATES.
From *Business Geography*.   Courtesy of John Wiley & Sons.

CHAPTER VIII

CLIMATIC CHANGES *

BY G. C. SIMPSON

Director of the British Meteorological Service

THE idea that our climate is not stable, but has changed largely in the past and is still changing, is very widespread. It can be traced to three main origins, each of which is independent of the others and is based largely on a different kind of evidence. In the first place, we have the frequent assertions of people, not always elderly, that there has been a marked change in the climate since they were young. In the second place, there are the reports of travellers who have visited regions where, in their opinion, there is every evidence, in deserted towns, abandoned fields, and dry river courses, of a marked and progressive desiccation. And finally we have the incontrovertible evidence produced by geologists, of climatic conditions ranging from tropical to polar at the same place in remote ages. It is the object of this article to examine the significance of this evidence for climatic change and, if possible, to form a rational idea of the causes

* The final conclusion as to the causal relation between climate and the distribution of civilization must be based largely upon our interpretation of the past. How far have past millenniums been characterized by any such intimate relation between civilization and climate as exists to-day? The answer depends, of course, on the much-disputed question of climatic changes during historic times. Just as I was on the point of writing a chapter on this subject, there appeared in the *Nineteenth Century and After* for January, 1926, an article by Doctor G. C. Simpson, Director of the British Meteorological Service. It covers exactly the ground that I had proposed to cover, and does it better than I could have done. Moreover, it has the great advantage of presenting the matured and unbiassed judgment of a climatologist who has had no part in the controversy over historic climatic changes, and has merely looked on without prejudice. Doctor Simpson presents the happy combination of a man who is decidedly progressive in temperament, but who is obliged to be relatively conservative because he holds one of the most important official positions in the whole realm of climatology. His article is presented exactly as it appeared in *The Nineteenth Century and After*, except for the omission of a section dealing with the cause of glacial periods and other "real" changes of climate.

which produce the changes, real or apparent, whichever they may prove to be.

The assertions that there has been a recent change in climate generally take the form that the winters are not now so severe or the summers so warm as they used to be. The advocates of no change in climate explain this as being an example of the tendency of the human mind to remember extremes while forgetting the more normal occurrences. The severe winters which we experience in childhood are remembered much more vividly than the mild winters, so that while the latter are forgotten the former become in our recollections typical of all the winters of that period. Similarly, hot summers stand out in our memory, giving the impression that warmer summers formerly prevailed. There is a great deal of truth in this explanation, but, so far as the present generation is concerned, it is not the full explanation.

Those of us who are now on the wrong side of forty-five have clear recollections of not one or two outstanding winters, but of a period when year after year there was some skating in England and when it was unusual for a winter to pass without some snow.

A study of meteorological records shows that this is not a false impression. The years 1885 to 1892 formed a sequence of eight cold years, especially in the winter. Taking the winter to embrace December to April inclusive, thirty-five out of the forty winter months of these eight years were below the average temperature at Greenwich. At Greenwich the temperature falls to or below the freezing point, on the average, on fifty-four days a year; during these eight years it fell to the freezing point on five hundred and sixty-five days—i. e., an average of seventy-one days a year. In 1887, 1888, and 1892 the number of frosty days was eighty-seven, eighty, and eighty-one respectively. It was this sequence of years which gives us the correct impression of colder winters in our childhood.

This remarkable sequence of cold years was followed by an almost equally remarkable sequence of eight warm years, with abnormally warm summers. Seven of the eight years, 1893–1900,

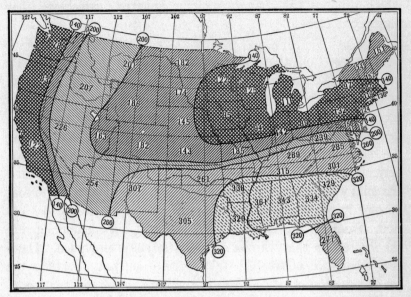

FIG. 11. DISTRIBUTION OF GENERAL PROGRESS IN THE UNITED
STATES, BASED ON STATISTICS.

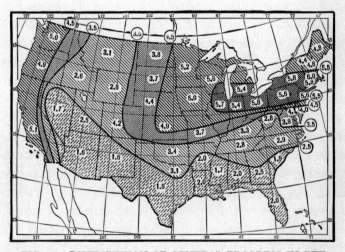

FIG. 12. DISTRIBUTION OF GENERAL PROGRESS IN THE
UNITED STATES, BASED ON OPINIONS.

From *Business Geography*.   Courtesy of John Wiley & Sons.

had at Greenwich a mean temperature above the normal; only thirty-three of the ninety-six individual months failed to reach the long-period average. During this period some remarkably high temperatures were recorded: on the average, at Greenwich the temperature rises to 90° F. or above on less than one day a year—seven days in eight years—yet during these eight years this occurred on fourteen occasions. On August 18, 1893, a maximum temperature of 95.1° F. was recorded, a value which has only twice been exceeded at Greenwich during the last eighty-four years.

Just as the previous eight years have left an impression of cold winters, so these eight years have left an impression of warm summers. Thus we see that there is some justification for the idea that the climate is now different from what it was thirty years or so ago.

The tendency for sequences of years to occur which are warmer or colder, dryer or wetter, than the average is a well-known fact in meteorology. The classical investigation of this tendency was made by Brückner and published in 1890 in a fascinating book entitled *Klima-Schwankungen seit 1700*.

Brückner first took all the meteorological observations then available; these, however, only reached back to 1730 in the case of temperature, 1815 in the case of rainfall, and 1826 in the case of pressure. He found that when he grouped the observations from all his stations between 1766 and 1885 there was clear evidence for appreciable changes in the mean temperature. In this period he could recognize three complete oscillations of temperature with maxima at about 1776, 1821, and 1866. He also found similar oscillations in the rainfall and pressure. The period of observations was, however, too short to make certain of the reality of the phenomenon, and it was essential to find other indications of climatic change which would give information over a much longer period. This he was able to do by employing the indirect evidence given by the changes in water level of lakes which have no outlet to the sea; the records of the dates on which the grape harvest commenced in Europe, which go back to the fourteenth century; the records of the dates on which the rivers of Russia and Northern Europe were closed to navigation by reason of ice, which extend back to 1700; and the records of severe winters which are to be found in literature, and which give information right back to A. D. 800.

By using in this way all the evidence available to him in 1887 Brückner was able to come to far-reaching conclusions regarding the variability of climate. He found that temperature, pressure, and rainfall are subjected to variations occurring simultaneously over the whole earth, and that on the average the variations repeat themselves in thirty-five or thirty-six years. Thus, on the average, seventeen or eighteen years of warm weather are followed by seventeen or eighteen years of cold weather, and similar periods of dry and wet weather succeed one another. On the whole, the dry and wet periods correspond with the warm and cold periods, without, however, being exactly simultaneous during any one period. There is one important difference between the variations of temperature and the variations of rainfall. While the temperature appears to rise and fall simultaneously over all parts of the world, the rainfall changes go oppositely in different regions—that is, while in some regions the dry periods correspond with the warm periods and the wet periods with the cold periods, the reverse is the case in other regions which have the dry and cold and the wet and warm periods corresponding.

During the short period for which instrumental observations are available the mean amplitude of the temperature variations was about 1.4° F. in all parts of the world: the variations in the rainfall are so different in different places, and the record is so short, that it is impossible to give a numerical value for the amplitude of the rainfall oscillation, but the percentage variation appears to be larger in continental than in oceanic climates.

These conclusions are extremely important, for a change in the mean annual temperature of one or two degrees Fahrenheit extending over something like twenty years accompanied by appreciable changes in rainfall is of real climatic significance.

This variation of climate, repeating itself in thirty-five years,

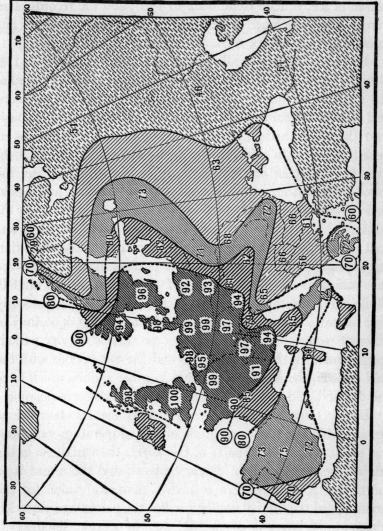

FIG. 13. DISTRIBUTION OF GENERAL PROGRESS IN EUROPE.
From *The Character of Races*.

has received the name of the Brückner cycle, and since Brückner discovered it in 1890 all later investigations have tended to prove its reality. At first sight it would appear that such a discovery would have far-reaching effects on the economic life of the world, for it should be possible to forecast these climatic changes and guard against them or use them to advantage. Unfortunately, this cannot be done to any practical extent, and, so far as I know, no practical use has ever been made of Brückner's discovery. It is important that the reason for this should be clearly understood, for there has been no little misconception, mainly due to the simple way in which the results of Brückner's work can be stated—for instance, as I have stated them above. In my statement I say that the *average* period is thirty-five or thirty-six years, and that the *mean* amplitude of the variation is 1.4° F., and that the wet and dry periods correspond *on the whole* with the cold and warm periods. The words in italics are very significant. In reality, the periods vary largely in length and amplitude; in fact, there is very little of what we usually describe as periodicity. The record of any one place hardly exhibits anything which conforms to Brückner's standard periods; there are variations and sequences of abnormal years; one cannot pick out of a single record—say the temperature of Greenwich—the Brückner variation. It is only when the records from many stations are grouped together, so that inequalities which are local in their incidence cancel one another out, that the Brückner cycle begins to appear. It is probably present in all records, and can be identified by harmonic analysis in most records; but the casual variations from year to year are much larger than the variations due to the Brückner cycle, and completely swamp it. Then, again, even the combined record from a large number of stations shows very little of a regular periodicity. We obtain a curve showing maxima and minima, but they occur at very irregular intervals. For example, the temperatures during the period for which we have observations of thermometers show four complete periods between 1736 and 1885—that is, an average of thirty-six years for a complete oscillation, or an average of eighteen years between successive maxima and minima. The actual maxima and minima occur, however, at the following irregular intervals—ten, twenty, twenty-five, twenty, ten, fifteen, fifteen, thirty years. It is therefore quite impossible to forecast the weather of any one year, or even of a group of years, with any certainty. It is for this reason that it would be better to abandon the idea of a cycle and to say that Brückner's work indicates that warm years and cold years tend to occur in groups, and that the average length of a warm group or a cold group is fifteen or sixteen years.

Brückner reached his conclusion by rigid scientific methods, and his monograph of 324 pages is a mass of records and data all arranged so that his conclusions can be checked and their value appraised. It is remarkable that the same conclusion had been reached by a more empirical method three hundred years earlier, for in his essay *Of Vicissitude of Things* Francis Bacon writes:

There is a toy, which I have heard, and I would not have it given over, but waited upon a little. They say it is observed in the Low Countries (I know not in what part), that every five-and-thirty years the same kind and suit of years and weather comes about again; as great frosts, great wet, great droughts, warm winters, summers with little heat, and the like, and they call it the prime; it is a thing I do the rather mention, because, computing backwards I have found some concurrence.

There is no reason to believe that Brückner knew of this remark when he commenced his investigation.

There is now little doubt that there are climatic changes of small magnitude and of a temporary nature, but sufficiently large to justify the frequently expressed opinion that the climate has changed in the course of a man's lifetime. But from Brückner's work it would appear that these changes are only periodic variations about a mean stable climate. There is nothing in the records of the grape harvest, the frequency of severe winters or the time of ice-free navigation on the rivers of Northern Europe, which would indicate a permanent change in the climate of Eu-

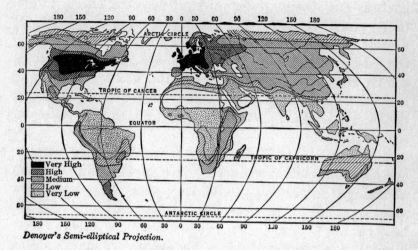

Denoyer's Semi-elliptical Projection.

FIG. 14. WORLD MAP OF CLIMATIC ENERGY.

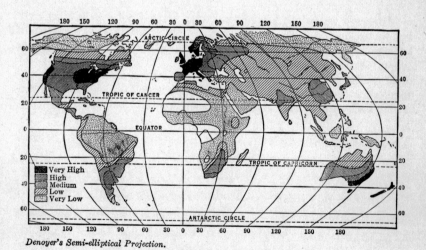

Denoyer's Semi-elliptical Projection.

FIG. 15. WORLD MAP OF CIVILIZATION.
From *Business Geography.* Courtesy of John Wiley & Sons.

rope during the last seven hundred or eight hundred years. Are we, therefore, to conclude from this that in all parts of the world the climate has remained unchanged, except for the small fluctuations described by Brückner, since the last great ice age passed away? This would be to neglect the opinion of some of our greatest explorers and travellers, who are convinced that they have found in their travels clear evidence for a deterioration of the climate over large tracts of the earth's surface. Evidence of this nature comes from many parts of the earth, especially from the borders of desert or arid districts. The Tarim Basin in the centre of Asia, the deserts in Syria, the coast districts of North Africa, the western desert of North America, are all said to show signs of considerable desiccation during the historic period. On the other hand, an ancient civilization in the Yucatan peninsula of Central America appears to have been destroyed by increased rainfall, which has produced such humid conditions that it is impossible for a virile race to survive. Much controversy has raged round this evidence. One school maintains that there has been no change of climate, but that the signs of desiccation, including the abandonment of prosperous towns and villages, can all be explained by such causes as war, disease, indolence, earth movement, shifting sand, changes in trade routes, or bad government. The case of Palestine has been treated as a test case by Professor J. W. Gregory. Much has been written to prove that the change from the prosperous conditions described in the Bible to the wretched conditions of to-day is due to climatic change. Professor Gregory has investigated this evidence, and can find no support for the supposed change of climate. To prove that there has been no appreciable change in the temperature he uses the evidence afforded by the simultaneous existence of the date-palm and the vine in Palestine throughout its history. The palm and the vine are extremely sensitive to changes of temperature. The present conditions are such that Palestine is on the northern limit of the region in which palms can produce fruit and just within the southern limit of the region in which grapes can ripen in the open air. A decrease of temperature of a few degrees would drive the palms from the country, or an increase of the same amount would make the vine unproductive. Yet, according to the records, there have always been palms and ripe grapes in Palestine, but there is no mention of dates in the Bible. There is thus no evidence for a change in temperature. A detailed discussion of the evidence for a change in the amount of rainfall also leads him to a negative conclusion. The rainfall in Palestine was always precarious, so that the greatest care had to be taken in storing the water, every house having its own cistern, and famines were as frequent in the past as at present.

Similar conclusions are reached by Professor Gregory and other writers regarding the supposed changes in climate in Egypt, Greece, Syria, and North Africa. The Tarim Basin is an interesting example of supposed desiccation, and much has been written about it. This low-lying desert in the heart of Asia is bounded on the south by the Kwen Lun Mountains and the great tableland of Tibet. From the high land, rivers and streams flow into the basin, only to be lost in the sand after traversing a few miles of desert. On each of these streams there are now small towns and villages, but there is clear evidence that other towns and cultivated patches once existed in the desert far beyond the ends of the present streams. Existing villages on the rivers, which can now only support a few families owing to the scarcity of water, were formerly flourishing towns.

From the evidence Stein and Huntington are convinced that there was more water in the rivers formerly, while Sven Hedin considers that all the changes can be accounted for by bad government and drifting sand.

It is impossible here to go more fully into the controversy regarding the meaning of these signs of change of climate brought back by travellers. In my opinion, two main facts seem to emerge from the discussion: first, that there have been periods in the past when the rainfall was both greater and less than at present, and secondly, that there has been no appreciable permanent change of climate. Deserts are where they have always been during the historic period, but they have experienced periods when the scanty rainfall was more abundant than at present and also other periods when it was less. This is a similar conclusion to that at which we have already arrived, and which has been demonstrated by Brückner; but the changes to which we are now referring, if not greater than those of the Brückner cycle, continued for much longer periods. Evidence of such long period changes is gradually accumulating. The Caspian Sea affords much evidence. This sea has no outlet to the ocean, but is fed by several rivers. If the rainfall increases in its catchment area, the expanse of the sea must increase until its new area supplies sufficient surface for the increased evaporation necessary to dispose of the increased water supply: this means a higher water level. Similarly, when the rainfall decreases, evaporation from the surface is too great, and the loss exceeds the supply until the area has been reduced sufficiently to restore the balance; this means a lower water-level. That there have been, during the historic period, several important changes of level is clearly proved. There are buildings now entirely submerged which must have been erected on dry land, and Arabic literature contains references to the water invading towns and mosques still standing but now far above the level of the sea. The periods at which the water attained these levels can be inferred from the style of the submerged buildings, and from the dates given in the accounts, and so the periods when the rainfall was excessive or defective determined. Unfortunately, it is not so easy to determine how long the wet and dry periods continued, but that they were not short is clear; a building would not be erected on a site which had recently been under water; and strand marks, still visible, indicate that the water stood at one at least of the high levels for a considerable period.

The individual changes of level of the Caspian Sea have not been definitely correlated with the changes in the Tarim Basin; but there can be little doubt that the periods when the rivers in the Tarim Basin were fuller and longer correspond with the periods when the level of the sea was abnormally high.

The best evidence for changes of this nature is, however,

afforded by the giant trees of California. The rings of annual growth of these trees are very distinct, and have been much studied in America. It is not difficult to count and measure the rings, and this has been done for a large number of trees, some of which have more than 3,000 annual rings. The width of the rings varies greatly, and Huntington, who has done much work on these trees, concludes that the width of the rings is mainly governed by the rainfall, a sequence of broad rings indicating a sequence of years with rainfall above the average, while thin rings, and even the absence of rings, are caused by periods of deficient rainfall.

As a result of measuring 451 trees it has been possible to construct curves showing the average width of the rings for each year, the necessary correction being made to allow for the difference in width due to the age of the tree. In this way the variation in width of the rings has been determined with great accuracy as far back as 200 B. C., and with less accuracy to 1000 B. C. The curves show that the trees grew rapidly for a period and then slowly, and so on in irregular periods. It is possible to pick out periods when the rate of growth was high for one hundred years or so and similar periods when growth was slow. There are still a considerable number of problems which must be solved before we are able to interpret the records of these trees. We do not yet know exactly what factors affect the rate of growth, but we can assume with Huntington that they are mainly climatic, and that the effect of rainfall predominates. We also do not know whether the changes represented by these curves were of worldwide effect or mainly local. These questions will probably not be solved until many years have passed and the rings in trees now growing can be compared with meteorological observations.

Two facts can, however, be deduced. First, no climatic change has taken place during the last three thousand years in California sufficiently large to be fatal to these trees—and the limited region in which they grow shows that they are very sensitive to climatic conditions; secondly, that climatic changes do occur which materially affect the rate of growth, and continue sometimes for periods of a century or more.

It appears reasonable to associate these changes with those which caused the level of the Caspian Sea to vary and the rivers in the Tarim Basin to alter their length. Taking all the evidence into account, there seems little doubt that, while there has been no progressive desiccation or permanent change of climate during the historic period, there have been long periods, much longer than the thirty-five years for a complete Brückner cycle, when the conditions were different from the present—periods of increased rainfall and periods of increased desiccation; but these have been temporary, and the normal conditions have ultimately been restored. It should be remarked that these small variations might have little significance to people living in a climate like ours, but for a people living in arid regions they might be all-important. It is a well-known fact that the percentage variations of rainfall from year to year increase rapidly as the total rainfall decreases, and it is more than likely that a climatic change of a very small absolute amount would make a very large percentage change in the interior of a continent and on the borders of deserts where normally the rainfall is small. Thus, for people already hardly subsisting on the minimum of water the periods of climatic change might well be decisive, and not only cause sites to be abandoned, but a migration of a whole race. Climatic changes have frequently been stated to have been the cause of the successive migrations of the Huns from Central Asia.

We may pause here to consider whether a satisfactory explanation can be given for such periodic changes of climate. To give a full account of the numerous hypotheses and theories which have been propounded would occupy too much space. We can only refer in passing to the theories based on tidal action, changes in the amount of carbon dioxide in the air and volcanic action, none of which have been generally accepted by meteorologists. At present the only theory which is seriously held is that of changes in the radiation given out by the sun. We do know that small variations in the sun's radiation occur, and these changes are now being measured; but the measurements have only extended over a period of about six years, so that we have little knowledge as to how large they may be. There is, however, no known reason why appreciable fluctuations should not take place in the sun's radiation, and it is now widely held that the variations of climate described above are mainly due to changes in solar radiation.

CHAPTER IX

CLIMATE AND HISTORY

THE preceding discussion by Doctor Simpson represents the consensus of opinion among geographers and others who have made a special study of the climate of historic times. The views which he has expressed are greatly strengthened by the abundant evidence of climatic pulsations brought back from northern China and Mongolia by the Andrews Expeditions of the American Museum of Natural History. As this book goes to press Professors Berkey and Morris are completing a book which sets forth a great array of evidence confirming the theory of historic and prehistoric pulsations of climate of greater magnitude and duration than the Brückner cycles. One of the most surprising features of the case is that, although this evidence differs in many important respects from that on which I based my original statement as to such pulsations, it seems to Messrs. Berkey and Morris to agree in the closest fashion with that which I found far to the west in Chinese Turkestan and western Asia.

The most important group which dissents from the conclusions here set forth is found in the United States Weather Bureau. That organization, however, according to the public statement of Doctor C. F. Marvin, its chief, deliberately adopts a policy of ultra-conservatism. Its leaders, wisely perhaps, believe that the mistake of upholding old ideas too long is safer than the mistake of adopting new ideas before they are absolutely demonstrated. Nevertheless, even in the United States Weather Bureau few of the leaders doubt that during the last three or four thousand years the earth's climate has suffered fluctuations of greater magnitude than those observed since accurate records have been kept. It is likewise generally agreed that the fluctuations have differed from region to region. Periods of abundant rainfall in northern California, for example, synchronize with those of low rainfall in Florida. A third point of almost universal agreement is that the curve of growth derived from the rings of growth of the ancient sequoia-trees of California presents the best available long record of historic fluctuations of climate.

The sequoia curve is reproduced in Figure 16. As far back as 800 A. D., the number of measurements of tree rings is so great that there can be comparatively little doubt as to the general reliability of the curve, as is explained in the note which accompanies the diagram. From 800 A. D. to 250 B. C., the curve is fairly reliable, although subject to modification in its details when further measurements are available. Previous to 250 B. C., the curve merely gives a rough sketch of the climatic variations, for, although fifty-nine trees which began to grow before this time have been measured, many of them were then only a few decades old, and the number rapidly declines as earlier dates are reached. The curve of sequoia growth does not represent rainfall, temperature, sunshine, storminess, or any other single meteorological element. It represents the combined effect of all the climatic conditions, together with an unknown percentage of other circumstances such as fires, the ravages of insects, and other accidental circumstances. Nevertheless, the studies made by students of forestry, and by Doctor MacDougal and his associates in the work of the Desert Botanical Laboratory, agree with my own results as set forth in *Quaternary Climates*. They show that at present the growth of the trees in the sequoia region depends upon rainfall much more than upon any other single climatic element. It appears probable, however, that if the effect of storms could be accurately measured we should find that their variations determine the rate of growth more closely than does rainfall. Every storm involves changes not only in precipitation, but in temperature, wind, sunshine, and atmospheric moisture. In the sequoia region, as in large parts of the world, the differences between the weather of one year and another depend largely upon cyclonic storms and upon the general conditions of atmospheric pressure which modify such storms.

From our present point of view storms are even more impor-

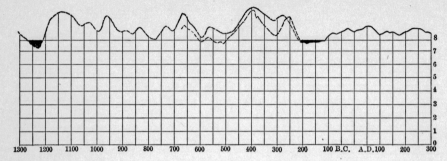

FIG. 16. APPROXIMATE HISTORIC PULSATIONS OF CLIMATE IN

This curve is based on 451 sequoia trees measured by the author and his assistants in 1911 and 1912, in the Sierra Nevada of California. The method of preparing the original curve is fully discussed in *The Climatic Factor*, publication No. 192 of the Carnegie Institution of Washington, 1914. The entire body of material collected by the author was re-examined by Doctor Ernst Antevs in 1924. He made corrections for the different rates of growth of old trees and young and for various other factors by methods entirely different from those employed by the author. His results are described in *Quaternary Climates*, publication 352, and are summarized by him as follows:

"A comparison of all finally corrected curves reveals the remarkable fact that all agree in those parts that are computed from a very large quantity of material. Thus the correspondence is particularly good, partly even detailed, since 800 A. D. . . . .

"The agreement between those parts of the curves that are calculated from a very large quantity of material is particularly significant, since different methods of correction and different age-stages of the trees have been used to construct them. The agreements, consequently, are real, of external origin and almost certainly of climatic nature."

The present author's method of correcting the curves of growth is good because it uses all the material and eliminates all possibility of personal bias in deciding what to use and what to exclude, or how large a correction to apply in any given case. Antevs's method is good because it eliminates very erratic trees or portions of trees, and treats each tree separately. The curve given in Figure 16 is based on a combination of Huntington's final curve without the so-called "Caspian" correction, and two curves of Antevs's based respectively upon trees in dry and moist situations respectively. Huntington's curve is given a weight of 10, and each of Antevs's curves a weight of 3. These weights correspond approximately to the number of measurements in each case. The net result is that the best measurements, that is, those used by Antevs, receive twice as much weight as others. From the present time back to 800 A. D., as appears in the quotation from Antevs, the fluctuations of the curve thus prepared seem to show almost the exact course of climate. From that point back to about 250 B. C., Antevs's curves of trees growing in dry and moist situations, respectively, when *combined*, agree quite closely with Huntington's curve. The agreement is closer than appears from Antevs's diagram, Figure 7, in *Quaternary Climates*, where there seem to be mistakes in curve 3 at certain points.

Before 200 B. C. two curves are given in Figure 16. The one which generally lies lower has been prepared as described above. The upper curve is based only on Huntington's measurements. In spite of the divergence of the curves, it seems quite certain that an important maximum occurred soon after 300 B. C., and a still more important maximum about 400 B. C. Previous to this date the material is too scanty to permit of more than a mere sketch of the climatic pulsations.

In any curve of tree growth the earlier fluctuations, based on only a few trees, tend to appear much more extreme than they really are. This latter difficulty has been overcome, in part, by smoothing the portion from 900 A. D. to 200 B. C. by the formula

$$\frac{a+2b+c}{4}=b.$$

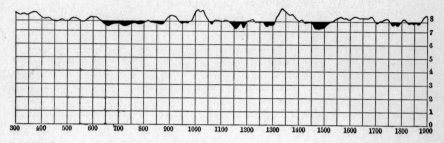

CALIFORNIA AND THE EASTERN MEDITERRANEAN, 1300 B. C. TO 1900 A. D.

From 200 to 1100 B. C. the formula

$$\frac{a+2b+3c+2d+e}{4}=c$$

has been used in order to do away with still more of the minor irregularities. Previous to 1100 B. C., where the curve is based on only two measurements of a single tree, the size of the apparent fluctuations has been arbitrarily reduced.

Another difficulty lies in the fact that although the curve of the trees gives an accurate record of fluctuations of climate from century to century, provided trees enough are available, it does not show how the climate, at the beginning of a tree's life, differs from the climate at the end. In other words, from the trees alone we have as yet no clue as to how far the climate of early times departs from that of to-day. In order to get a measure of this, we have resorted to the fluctuation of lakes. Our main reliance, as explained in *The Climatic Factor*, has been the known levels of the Caspian Sea at different periods. In preparing the present curve we have also relied to a much less degree upon the fluctuations of Owen's Lake, located only fifty miles from the great trees. On this basis the curve has been gently tilted in such a way as to indicate that the seventh and eighth centuries, A. D., and the twelfth and thirteenth were drier than the last century. This is because ruins from these dates lie beneath the waters of the Caspian Sea. Moreover, alluvial fans, which appear to belong to these same dates, descend to, or below, the present level of Owen's Lake.

Although we are not sure how great a degree of aridity actually prevailed in each of the periods indicated by the dark shading in Figure 16, we are quite sure that each period was dry compared with centuries before and after it. It is probable that the seventh and eighth centuries were drier than the diagram shows. On the other hand the second century B. C. may not have been so dry as the nineteenth century A. D., although the diagram shows about the same conditions in both. Nor are we sure that the thirteenth century before Christ was drier than the present time, although we are quite certain that it was relatively dry.

A last point to be considered is why this curve is labelled as indicating pulsations of climate in the eastern Mediterranean region as well as in California. The reason is that the correlation coefficient between the growth of the trees and the rainfall in Palestine, since exact records have been available, rises to the high level of 0.68. This means that while there may be considerable difference between the climate of the sequoia region and Jerusalem in any special month, or even year, the general fluctuations from decade to decade are closely similar. This being so, it is almost certain that the fluctuations from century to century are still more similar. This does not mean that all parts of the world show similar fluctuations. The similarity merely applies to these two regions which have closely similar climates by reason of their latitude, topography, and position in respect to land and sea. In other regions the fluctuations have undoubtedly been quite different, as appears from the fact that in our own day the rainfall of Florida varies in almost the opposite way from that of California.

tant than rainfall, because abundant evidence, which is set forth
in other books, has led to the conclusion that the main features
of the climatic pulsations of historic times arise from variations
in the number, intensity, and paths of cyclonic storms. Hence
Figure 16 may be interpreted as a curve of storminess with all
that is thus implied as to rainfall, temperature, wind, and sunshine or cloudiness.

Having gained an understanding of the general significance
of the sequoia curve, the next question is, for how large a part of
the earth's surface does it supply a climatic record? The curve
given in Figure 16 applies of course primarily to the home of the
sequoias, that is, the central mountains of California. If reversed
so that the high parts are low, it apparently shows the approximate pulsations of climate in Florida, where the rainfall in our
day varies in the opposite way from that of California. For regions half-way between these two places, on the other hand, the
curve affords no clear indication of the climate at any specified
epoch. Judging by present conditions, such a region may agree
with California at one time, and with Florida at another, or it
may be neutral. Thus a given type of climatic variation in one
part of the world may be accompanied by almost any other type
somewhere else. Nevertheless, certain parts of the world belong very definitely to certain types of climate, and the main
fluctuations in a given type of climate appear to be everywhere
similar. Thus the eastern Mediterranean region belongs to the
same climatic type as California. The rainfall of Jerusalem, as
measured since about 1850, actually shows a higher correlation
with the growth of the sequoias than does that of any other place
yet tested, even in California. The correlation coefficient, to use
a technical term, reaches the high figure of 0.68. Abundant evidence from earlier times also indicates a substantial agreement
between these two widely separated regions. Hence we infer that
Figure 16 may be used with considerable confidence as a record of
climatic fluctuations in Palestine and the neighboring regions as
well as in California.

The greatest difficulty with the sequoia curve is that while it reflects climatic variations from one century to the next with considerable accuracy, it does not enable us to determine whether a dry period two or three thousand years ago was more or less dry than at present. We are quite certain, for example, that the second century B. C. was much less stormy than the two preceding centuries, and considerably less stormy than the succeeding centuries. We are not sure, however, whether this period was as dry as the long, arid period in the seventh, eighth, and ninth centuries. Probably it was not so dry. The curve of tree growth as given in Figure 16 has been adjusted to correspond to the level of the Caspian Sea at certain periods when we have historic records as to how high that enclosed salt lake then stood. Similar fluctuations of Owen's Lake, close to the sequoia-trees, have also been used, but less weight has been attached to them because we do not know their exact dates. In spite of these corrections, the left-hand end of our curve ought perhaps to be higher than we have shown it, while the portion centering about 700 A. D. should, perhaps, be depressed below its present position. Nevertheless, the curve appears to offer a fairly dependable picture of the main climatic pulsations during historic times.

If the pulsations indicated in our curve of climate are accepted as real to the extent implied by Doctor Simpson in the preceding chapter, our next effort must be to determine what effect they have had upon man. These effects may be divided into two main groups, the first pertaining to economic and political conditions, and the second to health, energy, and temperament. The first noteworthy feature of Figure 16 is a depression reaching its lowest point about 1230 years before Christ. How much reliance can we place on this? Not much, so far as Figure 16 is concerned, for the earliest two hundred years of the curve there given are based on only a single huge tree which has been measured in three places. But other bits of evidence also point to a dry period about this time. One such bit is the story of the plagues in Egypt, as will be explained in a later chapter. Much fuller information is derived from a considerable series of studies in Europe. These make it quite clear that during the last part of the Bronze Age, and probably at the beginning of the Iron Age, which would be about this time, agriculture in the Alps extended considerably above its present limits, thus indicating a relatively mild climate. Again, in County Donegal, Ireland, the remains of an ancient two story log-house, and of a corded oak roadway, and the stumps of contemporary trees have been discovered half-way from bottom to top in the peat deposits of what is now Drumkelin Bog. The remains and the trees evidently date from a period when the climate was so dry that the bog disappeared. At a later time the region again became so moist that a swamp was formed, and the roof of the hut was in due time covered by twelve feet of peat.

As yet no exact dates can be assigned to these European occurrences. The Irish hut may go back to 1700 B. C., or earlier. Possibly it synchronizes with the period of famines which is said to have driven Abraham, Isaac, and Jacob into Egypt, and which culminated in the exceedingly severe famine attributed to the days of Joseph. At approximately this time northwestern China, which was then the centre of Far Eastern culture, is likewise said to have suffered from seven years of drought in the reign of Yu, first king of the Yin dynasty, not far from 1750 B. C. Chinese writers of later periods frequently extol the great Yu and his prime minister, Yi Yen, not only for having tided the country through the drought, but for mitigating the ravages of floods and introducing irrigation. Thus, although the evidence thus far available is scanty, it is consistent in widely separated areas. It points to two periods of aridity, culminating about 1700 or 1750 B. C., and again between 1300 and 1200 B. C. As to the intervening period we have as yet little evidence, but probably it was stormy and rainy in comparison with the two dry periods.

The normal meteorological conditions at this time . . . resembled those of the memorable drought of 1921, which was characterized by low pressure and stormy conditions in the Arctic Ocean, and a belt of high pressure and persistently fine weather across central Europe.

Thus speaks C. E. P. Brooks, in *The Evolution of Climate*. He is referring to the earlier dry period, but his statements apply equally well to the one in the thirteenth century B. C. He continues as follows:

Although we have no direct evidence, the meteorological conditions suggest very strongly that the dry belt extended from Europe across Russia into Siberia, giving rise to a marked period of desiccation, possibly worse than any droughts of the historic period. At present Siberia receives its rainfall mainly from depressions which cross Russia from the Baltic or Black Seas, and follow a well-marked track north of the central Asiatic mountains. But during the forest period these tracks were abandoned, and the majority of the depressions passed northeastward off the coast of Norway into the Arctic Ocean. The result must have been a great diminution of rainfall over the continent. . . . This period of drought was of extraordinary importance in human history. For during the moist maritime phase central and eastern Europe, and probably also Asia, had become extensively peopled by neolithic nomads of Aryan and Semitic races, while the great river valleys of the south were in the possession of dense agricultural populations in a more advanced state of civilization. As the climate became progressively dryer and the pasture diminished, the land was unable to support such a large nomadic population, and there was a great outburst of raiding and conquering expeditions directed southwards and westwards, resulting in a succession of empires in the rich Mesopotamian regions and neighboring countries, which form the beginnings of our history.

Let us examine more closely these human movements which seem to have been intensified, and perhaps actually caused, in some cases, by increasing aridity. In the eighteenth century before Christ, as I have shown in *Palestine and Its Transformation*, we come upon many evidences not only of invasions of the cultivated lands by people from the desert, but of other changes which would naturally result from a serious diminution in rainfall. From the dry plateau of Persia on the east, or perhaps from deserts still more remote, the non-Semitic Kassites, akin probably to the Tartars and Turks of later days, and like the Bakhtyari in their habits, invaded Media, Elam, and Babylonia, and established a dynasty. From the barren plateaus of Armenia, or Asia Minor, the Mitanni, forerunners of the Hittites, descended to northern Mesopotamia, and there founded a kingdom. In Egypt, at this same time, great internal dissension prevailed, and civil strife was so common that sixty kings ruled in a hundred and twenty-five years. Then, finally, external disaster overwhelmed the peaceful valley of the Nile. "In the time of King Timaus," says the native chronicler Manetho, as quoted by Josephus, "it came to pass, I know not how, that God was averse to us. And from the east there came unexpectedly men of ignoble birth, who had the boldness to make an expedition into our country and easily subdued it by force without a battle. And when they had put our rulers under their power, they afterward savagely burnt down our cities and demolished the temples of the gods, and used all the inhabitants in a most hostile manner, for they slew some and led the children and wives of others into slavery."

These invaders were the Hyksos or Shepherds, who crossed the eastern frontier where the Prince's Wall should have held them in check. "The fearful apparition of this host," to quote the summary of Cormack, "a people coming from unknown regions, strange of speech, uncouth in appearance and bloody in act, dismayed the passive Egyptians. It was not greed of warlike glory, not even the prospect of choice plunder, that prompted the invasion, but a motive far more terrible. The strangers were a landless people who sought a new home. From afar they had made choice of Egypt, a land of peculiar felicity; they had counted the cost, and arranged their plan of action. To appropriate the chosen seat, it was necessary to expel or destroy the existing occupants."

The Hyksos did not come as warriors. They brought their wives and children, and drove before them flocks and herds. It was they, indeed, who introduced the horse into Egypt. They came as did the Sherarat tribe, twenty-four hundred years later, in a similar dry period, which culminated in the days of Mohammed. The Sherarat passed through to Tunis. If they had attempted to stay in Egypt, they doubtless would have fought as savagely as did the Hyksos.

Although we know little of the Hyksos, the great outstanding fact is clear. The period centering about 1750 B. C. was a time of great disturbances in the ancient empires of western Asia and North Africa. Internal dissensions were the rule at home, while invasions overwhelmed all the more settled lands, including

Babylonia, the upper Euphrates region, where the Mitanni settled, Syria, and finally Egypt. Such wide-spread movements among highly diverse peoples were presumably due to some deep-seated and widely distributed cause. The physical evidence of increasing aridity, which has just been sketched, suggests that such a cause was actually in operation. Hence before we appeal to economic, social, and political causes, it would seem logical to inquire how far these causes themselves may have been the more or less direct results of physical causes.

For a century or more the Hyksos held their place in Egypt. Then they moved out once more, expelled by the revival of the native races, and also perhaps attracted back to the desert by renewed conditions of abundant water and pasturage. During the next two centuries, that is, from about 1580 to 1380 B. C., Egypt once more prospered, perhaps in part because of favorable conditions of climate. Then came the first mutterings of a devastating storm of invasion, unequalled in history, or equalled only during the Dark Ages in Europe, and the Mohammedan outburst in Asia. From the confusion Greece and Rome were born, while one of the greatest results was the Aramæan migration, one wave of which cast forth from the Arabian desert and from the borders of Egypt the little tribes of the Hebrews to find a refuge upon the hills of Palestine. Fortunately, the precious Tell el Amarna tablets preserve a full account of the beginnings of the great turmoil. They tell of revolts and raids in Syria. The Hittites from the north forced their way down as far as northern Palestine. The Egyptian governors and officials in Syria were put to direst straits. They appealed to the Pharaoh in Egypt, but succor came not at all, or else in driblets and too late to avail. The trade between Egypt and Babylonia almost disappeared. Caravans could not withstand the raids which the hungry desert folk made throughout Arabia. Egypt had no help for her dependencies. She herself was threatened by uprisings in Nubia. Deep poverty afflicted her. Religious dissensions rent the country and led to civil war. In other regions equal distress prevailed. The kingdom of Mitannia was overthrown in northern Mesopotamia by Hittite invaders from the neighboring highlands. The Mitanni themselves, forced from their homes in the north, came into conflict with the Assyrians on the east, while the Aramæans of the desert probably scourged them on the south. The Phœnicians experienced an impulse which drove them forth from their narrow strip of mountains to colonize North Africa and the Mediterranean islands as never before.

In the midst of the distress and chaos a brief lull preceded the final storm. About 1330 B. C., according to the monuments, the shattered rule of Egypt was reinstated in Palestine. Then came the reign of that famous monarch Rameses II. He restored Egypt to its old position. He held it firm against the Empire of the Hittites, which had grown great in the north. Down to about 1250 B. C. civilization maintained its own. Then came the last great crash. About that date famines played an important part in international affairs. In a time of scarcity, Merenptah, king of Egypt, went so far as to send grain to Syria for the relief of his Hittite allies. The mention of this fact is highly significant in view of what follows. Soon after, in the fifth year of his reign, the Libyans of North Africa and the "peoples of the coasts of the sea" combined to invade Egypt. A great migration of the races of Italy, Greece, and Asia Minor was in progress, induced, it would seem, by a movement from regions farther north or east, a movement which finally brought the Dorians into Greece.

Other events agree with the famines in suggesting that extreme drought played a part in causing these wide-spread migrations. About 1250 B. C. an official report addressed to King Merenptah, states that permission was given to certain Edomites to pass the Egyptian frontier. The report runs thus:

A further matter for the gratification of my lord: We have permitted the Bedawi tribes of 'Aduma (Edom) to pass the fortress of King Merenptah in Thuku (Succoth) to the pools of Pithom of King Merenptah which are in Thuku, so that they may obtain food for themselves and for their cattle in the field of Pharaoh, who is the gracious sun in every land.

This peaceful admission of the nomads is supposed to have been a matter of policy on the part of the Egyptians. The country had just emerged from one of the worst wars for centuries, a war that racked it to distraction. The Libyans, who had invaded the country in great force from the deserts west of the Nile at the time of the famines, had been repulsed only with the greatest difficulty. Now, by permitting the Edomites to enter within the wall and obtain food for their cattle, the government apparently thought to add to its fighting resources a warlike clan hostile to the Libyans. The peaceful admission of the nomads from the east, however, did not end the matter. Tribe after tribe pressed in without the consent of the Egyptians, and threw the land more and more into distress. Religious dissension continued to add to the bitterness of life in Egypt. Or, perhaps because life was so bitter, religious differences assumed a more sombre aspect. The last straw was added when the Arabs joined hands with the Libyans and the nations of the Ægean, and the three rivalled one another in devastating the little strip of fertile land beside the Nile. For fifty years Egypt was in dire confusion. Then better days appeared. The first sovereign to enjoy them was Rameses III, who began to reign 1204 B. C.

It is only by inference that we connect this decay of civilization and this turmoil of the nations with the pronounced aridity which seems to have prevailed during those times. One reason for the inference is that in our own day drought almost invariably drives nomads out of the desert and causes them to invade the better-watered border-lands. Another reason is that each of the major periods of aridity shown in Figure 16 has been characterized by similar historic events. This was true in the second century before Christ, the seventh and eighth of our era, the twelfth and thirteenth, and even the fifteenth. Still a third reason is the general parallelism between periods of migration and confusion in the Mediterranean lands and in those farther east, even as far as China. Only some widely acting cause, such as climate, seems likely to produce similar effects at the same time in regions so remote.

Let us examine the arid period culminating in the second century before Christ. Rome may serve as an example. We shall not dwell on the physical evidences of a dry period. They resemble those already discussed, but are much stronger and more numerous, and have been fully considered in other books. Nor shall we dwell on economic conditions and migrations, although these played a basic part in the history of that period of widespread decay. Let us, rather, focus our attention on an apparent change in national character which I have described in *World Power and Evolution*, and which runs closely parallel to what appears to have occurred at about the same time in Greece, and probably in China. The change is much like that which appears to have taken place in Egypt during the dry epoch which culminated eleven hundred years earlier.

In the pristine days of Rome, during the epoch of abundant storminess which culminated about four centuries before Christ, even the patricians, the most wealthy part of the Roman population, possessed what we have elsewhere called the pioneer quality. They "were peasants like their fellows, and not above handling the pick and the plough," as Ferrero puts it in his fascinating *History of the Rise and Greatness of the Roman Empire*. Similar conditions, so far as we can gather, prevailed among the neighboring tribes. "The cause of (Rome's) success," continues Ferrero, "lay in the vigorous discipline of her constitution, which was strong enough to control that spirit of self-indulgence which is the most powerful solvent of national life. It was this that maintained a pure and simple morality among her rich and powerful class, which would have been the first to succumb to the vanity and vice that too frequently attend on the pride of conquest. The Romans were a primitive people without the defects peculiar to a primitive people." They accustomed their boys "to reverence and purity, to labor and sobriety, to the careful observance of laws and customs, and of a narrow but tenacious patriotism." They taught the girls to "be gentle, obedient, and chaste, attentive only to housework and children." Every one knows how democratic was the form of government among the early Romans. Officials were judged by their deeds, and the slightest dereliction from duty was severely punished. No offi-

cials were paid, but it was deemed sufficient honor to be allowed
to serve the state. Ancient Rome was, in many ways, remarkably like the early Puritan colonies in New England.

Between 450 and 250 B. C., the Romans extended their power
over most of the peninsula of Italy. This brought them great
wealth. "But this increase of wealth did not at first tend to
weaken the ancient traditions, nor was it immediately followed
either by a change in manners or by political revolution. The
thrift and simplicity of the old times were still the proudest virtues of every noble family."

The basis of this sturdy, simple life of the early Romans was
intensive agriculture. We are told that in the days of the Roman
republic seven jugera, or about four and a half acres of land, sufficed to support an average family. Agriculture was so intensive,
and perhaps the climate so propitious, that farms of this small
size, supplemented presumably by pastureland, supported a con-
tented and self-respecting population.

So much for the period from 450 to 250 B. C. That period
ended in a great decline in rainfall and storminess, as appears in
Figure 16. Up to 250 B. C., the climate still appears to have been
highly favorable. Then by 220 or 210 it had apparently fallen
to about the present level. Such a change might be expected to
help in producing at least three kinds of results: first, economic
difficulties; second, political upheavals; and third, a decline in
health, energy, and moral fibre. History shows all of these results, but I shall not attempt to keep them separate. During the
second half of the third century before Christ, that is, at the very
time when the climate was changing most rapidly, the whole
tone of Roman society became changed. Through the "increase
of wealth and the continuance of victory, this spirit of discipline
and rural simplicity" had already begun to show symptoms of
decline, as Ferrero puts it. Social simplicity had begun "to be
impaired and domestic discipline to loosen its bonds. The family
council was more rarely summoned; sons, thanks to the proceeds
of campaigning, became more independent of their fathers,
women less submissive to husbands or guardians; the nobility

neglected its duties toward the middle class. . . . The new spirit was fatal to the old friendly co-operation between class and class. A selfish and grasping nobility that looked to Carthage for its model inevitably provoked popular opposition."

In political, as in moral and social, life, we find a change in Rome at the end of the third century B. C. "In the Gallic War (225-222), for the first but not for the last time in Roman history, the people, not the nobles, were the aggressors. It was the democracy that cast its eyes upon the great plain that stretches at the foot of the Alpine barrier—a plain rich in fresh and fertile soil, covered with immense oak forests and huge tracts of marsh and lake-land, dotted with Celtic villages, watered by hurrying streams."

The eagerness of the common people for a war against the Gauls in the Plain of the Po sounds as if poverty and distress might have been prevalent. With a decline of rainfall such as is indicated in Figure 16, how could it be otherwise? It is extremely difficult, however, to distinguish between the effects of different causes. In 218 B. C., the Second Punic War introduced seventeen years of bitter fighting. How far this war was due to the economic and political stress arising from diminished rainfall in both Italy and Carthage we cannot tell. It is equally difficult to determine how far it was war, climate, or other factors which, about 200 B. C., "hastened the advent of the commercial era in a society which had hitherto been military and agricultural." Certain it is that Italy now needed food, and had to import it from abroad. The year 196 saw the first public distribution of grain in Rome. It is also certain that in spite of this demand for food, farming became less profitable. Especially in southern Italy, where the effect of a climatic change would be greatest, land fell to a low value. Speculation became rife, the peasants fell into debt, their lands were bought by capitalists or large proprietors, and the cultivation of wheat gave place in large measure to the raising of sheep and goats. Many country people flocked to the cities, huge wooden tenements were erected, and bakeshops were established to furnish bread to the many unmarried tradesmen and laborers who could not get it at home. So great was the influx of country people to the cities that, in 187 and 177 B. C., the Latin towns lodged complaints with the Senate. At the same time, "there grew up, even among the aristocracy, a generation of arrogant and ambitious politicians, who transformed the reasoned and moderate liberalism of Scipio and his followers into a revolutionary movement at variance with all the ancient principles of social discipline, and destined to set public and private life at the mercy of passion and self-seeking (Ferrero)."

This disgraceful state of affairs lasted through the second century. "At the first symptoms of its decadence," in the third century, "the Roman public had burst out in a passion of pride and savagery which swept Carthage and Corinth clean from their foundation." Then followed other wars which were less successful, as might be expected from so decadent a people. The Spanish War, from 153 to 133 B. C., was "a costly inglorious campaign, which lasted twenty years, and almost reduced Rome to bankruptcy." When the great Slave Revolt took place in Sicily, from 139 to 132, the government had real difficulty in suppressing it. In this revolt, as in many other occurrences, we see signs that the trouble lay chiefly in the southern part of the country. The healthy growth of the Roman Empire came to an end during this sad century. Expansion, to be sure, still took place, for other countries were suffering even more than Rome, but it was, at best, a sickly growth.

Far away in China this same period was equally disastrous. The half century of increasing aridity from 250 to 200 B. C. was a time of constant invasions on the part of the barbarian nomads of the north and west. In consequence of this the Great Wall was begun. At first isolated sections were built here and there at points of special danger. Then, just as the curve of Figure 16 reaches an especially low level, conditions became so bad that the whole wall was united into a single great defense, the main work being completed about 215 B. C. It was a defense not merely against the barbarians, but against the effects of increasing aridity upon people "hardly subsisting on the minimum of water," as Doctor Simpson puts it, "in the deserts of Central Asia." Greece, too, especially Attica, is in the same way a marginal land, by reason of its scanty rainfall, and it suffered even more than Rome or China.

What caused this second century to be so disastrous? The wealth and luxury that came from foreign conquest doubtless played a part. The importation of slaves and the increasing sterility of the upper classes of Rome must have had a deplorable effect upon Rome's biological inheritance. It should be noted, however, that a similar decadence took place in Greece, Egypt, Carthage, Syria, and many other countries. So far as wealth and slavery were concerned, many of those countries were the opposite of Rome. They were plundered and not plunderers; they lost slaves instead of gaining them. Yet the general course of events was the same. Nevertheless, they may have suffered greatly through a declining birth-rate of the upper classes.

Many historians have thought that agricultural decline was one of the chief elements in the fall of Rome. Such a decline unquestionably occurred. Some authors ascribe it to competition with other countries, such as Sicily and Spain. That does not seem quite reasonable. The Italian soil is as fruitful as that of the other countries, and the farmer who lives nearest the market has a great advantage, especially where transportation is as primitive and hence relatively expensive, as it was in the Mediterranean region two thousand years ago. Others, like Liebig, who was a student of history as well as of chemistry, hold that the depletion of the soil by constant cropping was the main factor. This idea seems untenable, however, because it clashes with the long survival of China and Japan. It is also rendered improbable by the suddenness of the decline of Roman agriculture, and by the fact that a similar decline occurred at the same time in many neighboring countries. It is scarcely possible that the soil of all these countries reached a stage of sudden exhaustion at one particular time. Moreover, the theory of chemical exhaustion of the soil does not explain the revival of agriculture

during the days of the Roman Empire. Finally, there is no need
of such a theory, for almost everything which may be attributed
to exhaustion of the soil may also be ascribed to aridity.

The agricultural decline in Italy may have produced dire results not only in the field of economics but in politics. The Slave
Revolt in Sicily was probably closely connected with it. Even in
the better years of the second century B. C., Rome was never
entirely immune from partial famines. Little by little the troubles
of the farmers became the greatest political problem. Finally, in
133 B. C., Tiberius Gracchus tried to remedy them by a series
of laws for the redistribution of the land. He paid with his life
for his attempt to change the old order. Ten years later his
younger and greater brother, Caius, took up the problem once
more, but without permanent success. Yet at that very time relief was in sight. Pliny states that in 121 B. C. Rome became
aware through the cheapness of wine that a change had taken
place in the methods of agriculture. Vines and olives, so it appears from Cato and others, had been substituted for grain in
many places at the beginning of the century, that is, immediately
after the climate became driest. Now, nearly a century later,
there is evidence of further agricultural change. Perhaps this
was due to improved methods, but may not the new methods
have been due partly to improvement in the rainfall? Figure 16
shows that about 120 B. C. an amelioration of the climate began
to make itself felt. A decade later, in 111, Spurius Thorius succeeded in enacting a land law which is supposed to have been
much better than those proposed by the Gracchi. Thus he received credit for the solution of the great problem which had been
vexing Rome for a century. But does he deserve the credit?
Agricultural disturbances certainly declined and the price of land
rose rapidly after the law was enacted, but look at Figure 16
and see how the rainfall, and hence the crops, improved at just
this time. Nature often does the work which man thinks he has
done.

At the end of the second century before Christ, Rome was
in the state of a sick man who is just beginning to be convalescent.

As he grumbles, so she grumbled. "There were interminable discussions on the diseases from which Rome was suffering," says Ferrero. One of these diseases was a deluge of crime. "Murder, poisoning, theft, assassination, even family tragedies, became alarmingly frequent. A large category of crimes committed by women and young persons went entirely unpunished, being still outside the cognizance of the law and no longer dealt with by the family. Even recognized offenses, when committed by Roman citizens, often evaded a penalty." Another disease was anæmia. "No one tried the remedy of action. Men frittered away their energies in a morbid inertia, pouring vain encomiums upon a golden past, and childishly appealing for the intervention of some heaven-sent deliverer."

Rome's later history is no less consistent with the curve of the Big Trees than is the earlier. Ferrero's picture of the mixture of the old forces of decay and the new forces of revival, about 100 B. C., is most suggestive. The great proletarian uprising, or Social War, was approaching, the disorder of the past century was gathering itself together for a final attack on the established order, and "the day of reckoning was felt at last to be at hand. Yet it would be a mistake to imagine that decadence and ruin filled the whole picture. Even amid the chaos of society and politics there were promising symptoms of intellectual advance." Reformers like the Gracchi, strong, if misguided, spirits like Marius and Sulla, and great men like Julius Cæsar were beginning to arise. Roman law was taking shape, handsome houses of imported marble were beginning to be erected in the metropolis, sculptors and painters were developing their art, and the literature of the Augustan Age had its first forerunners. We have already seen signs of an agricultural revival. A little later, almost on the morrow of the sanguinary struggle of the Social War, B. C. 90 to 89, there was "a marked increase in the general luxury and comfort." By the time when Varro wrote his *De Re Rustica* in 37 B. C., some of his characters could say that Italy was the best-cultivated land in the world, and had become almost entirely one vast garden. Another states more modestly that

Italy was better cultivated in his time than in preceding centuries. Many other indications point to a return of prosperity and also of vigor. The period from 75 B. C. onward was marked by a high degree of luxury and affluence. Though vice and sensuality abounded, they did not play such a part as in earlier times. In their place came more desire for the graces of life, for art and literature, for serious studies in science such as the work of Varro just mentioned, and the more poetic Georgics of Virgil. This was the time of Cicero and of the men who made the succeeding Augustan Age the most famous epoch in Roman history.

Turn again to Figure 16 and see how the climate improved from the end of the second century B. C. until after the birth and death of Christ. This period corresponds closely with what is often called the greatest age of Rome. It was an age when the Roman arms were once more invincible, and the city by the Tiber was the mistress of the world. It was an age when the ideas of the earlier Roman republic flowered and bore fruit in the great system of Roman law which still so largely guides modern jurisprudence. Yet this was not really Rome's greatest period. It was a vast improvement over the second century B. C. but it lacked the idealism and the high moral purpose of the earlier, simpler days. It was like the health which a man enjoys after a deadly illness—something to be devoutly thankful for, something that may enable him to achieve the master stroke of his life, and yet not equal to the young vigor with which he laid the foundations of his career.

It is easy to see that in communities whose main support is agriculture, as was the case in practically all the nations of antiquity, a decided diminution of productivity by reason of prolonged drought must lead to grave economic results. It is almost equally clear that economic distress is one of the most potent causes of political discontent, and even of revolution and war. Nor does it require much argument to prove that economic distress, political unrest, and wars are among the strongest of the factors that lead to migrations. Sometimes such migrations occur en masse, but far more often merely a few individuals or families move unostentatiously from the country to the city, from one part of a country to another, or from one country to another. Such migrations appear to have taken place on an especially large scale during times of increasing dryness in practically all the countries where civilization was highest in the era before Christ. Because these facts are so well recognized, the preceding statements regarding the effect of dry periods are probably open to little criticism *qualitatively*, although there may be ground for wide differences of opinion as to whether the pulsations of climate during historic times have been great enough to cause all the results which I have attributed to them. That, however, is not the main question at present. I fully recognize that no one yet knows how great the effects of climate actually are in comparison with those of other factors. The important point is to recognize that physical conditions, together with the racial changes which are emphasized in this book, deserve exactly as much attention as do the more familiar economic, social, and political causes of the events of history.

CHAPTER X

CLIMATE AND TEMPERAMENT

In the preceding chapter the main emphasis was placed on the economic and political effects of climatic changes. We also saw, however, that in Rome such changes were accompanied by pronounced alterations in the character of the Roman people. In Greece a similar change in national character took place at this same time. Moreover, the same thing seems to have occurred in Egypt, Mesopotamia, Persia, China, and other countries under similar conditions. Is it possible that climatic changes have a deep-seated connection with changes in human temperament? The answer to this question is doubtful. Yet there is enough evidence to create a presumption that such a relationship may actually exist.

The example of Athens as set forth in part in *Civilization and Climate* illustrates the matter. About 400 B. C., when Greece was in its prime, the general climatic conditions appear to have been approximately as follows: (1) The *average temperature* for the year, as a whole, was probably a little lower than at present, but it is doubtful whether the difference amounted to more than two or three degrees at most. (2) The temperature of the *seasons* may have varied somewhat more than that of the year as a whole. The greater mixing of the air from wide areas by means of the winds that accompany storms presumably lowered the average temperature a little over the lands in summer, and raised the winter average, although the winter extremes may have been increased. (3) The amount of *rain* was apparently considerably greater than now. Doubtless the rain then, as now, came chiefly in winter, while the summers were very dry just as at present, but the length of the rainy season appears to have been increased. That is, the rains began earlier in the autumn and lasted longer in the spring than at present. (4) The amount of *atmospheric moisture* over the lands was presumably greater than now. This would arise partly from the increased cloudiness and rainfall, and partly from the fact that the winds were presumably more efficacious in bringing moisture from the neighboring seas. (5) The *winds* were apparently stronger than at present, and varied in direction much more than now because of the frequent storms. (6) The greater storminess and the more frequent changes in the winds, as well as their greater strength, must have caused great, or at least frequent, *variability of temperature* as well as variations in other respects. Such variability would occur even in summer when the storms passed to the north of the lands that were most progressive, two or three thousand years ago; it would be still more pronounced in the rainy season.

Let us apply these generalizations to a specific case. Suppose that from 500 to 400 B. C. the climate of Athens differed from that of the present in the following respects:

1. Temperature of July, 77° F., instead of 81° F.; January, 48° instead of 46°. Mean temperature of the year 62.0° instead of 63.1°.

2. Relative humidity at all seasons, 10 per cent higher than now; January the moistest month, 84 per cent instead of 74 per cent; July the driest month, 58 per cent instead of 48 per cent. As a matter of fact, the change was probably not the same at all seasons, but I wish to keep our example simple.

3. Annual rainfall 22 inches instead of 15, ranging perhaps from 3.3 inches in November to 1.0 in July, instead of 2.9 in November and .03 in July.

4. Number of storms twice as great as now.

Such a change seems conservative. It is scarcely more than the normal variation from one year to another. Nevertheless, when we calculate its effect upon health in the same way that we have calculated the data for our map of climatic energy based on the effect of the seasons in American cities (Figure 5), the result is astonishing. From a climatic level only equal to that of Augusta in Georgia, and Vicksburg in Mississippi, Athens rises to a level practically the same as that of New York and Chicago, the best regions in North America aside from the coast near Newport; a slight further increase in storminess or a further lowering of the summer temperature two or three degrees more would make Athens rival Paris and Berlin; and if the storminess should be three times as much as at present, which would be a small matter compared with the differences between one year and another at places like San Francisco, the healthfulness and stimulating qualities of the climate of Athens would rival those of southeastern England, which seems to be well-nigh the most favored place in the whole world. When we recall that according to Figure 3 the estimated death-rate in Greece is nearly twice that of England, such a change becomes highly significant. It would presumably get rid of malaria to a large extent; it would stimulate the Greeks to a degree of persistent activity quite foreign to the country at present; it would raise the economic level and correspondingly improve the diet of the people; and it would give to the Greeks a spirit of enterprise, a physical vigor, and a mental activity which would probably soon enable them to take advantage of all sorts of modern discoveries which they now use half-heartedly and ineffectively, if at all.

The slightness of the variations necessary to give rise to important results is one of the most surprising features of recent investigations of the relation between health and the weather. We have already referred to a recent investigation of the relation between the weather and the daily death-rate at New York, among persons over five years of age. This was carried out by the Metropolitan Life Insurance Company in co-operation with the Committee on the Atmosphere and Man of the National Research Council of the United States. It shows that in New York City at temperatures above a daily average of about 68° F., every major fluctuation of temperature upward or downward in each of six consecutive years was followed by a corresponding fluctuation in the death-rate. In addition to this, a hot summer was found not only to be accompanied by a high death-rate, but to be followed by a relatively high rate during the autumn, especially if the heat lasted a long time, and there were hot spells late in

August or in September. A similar phenomenon came to light in my investigation of the rate of work among factory operatives, although the year, place, and subject of study were all different from those of the committee. Thus there seems to be ground for supposing that in a country like Greece, where the winter is mild, the general level of activity is closely dependent upon the length and character of the summer. If the steady, monotonous heat of summer were broken by cool spells due to winds arising from cyclonic storms farther north, the debilitating effect of the hot season would apparently be much diminished, and the vigor of the people in the autumn and winter would likewise be increased.

Another phase of the climatic problem is suggested by Doctor E. G. Dexter's book entitled *Weather Influences*. In this pioneer work he gathered daily statistics as to crime, sickness, deportment in school, errors in banks and the like, and compared them with the weather. In previous studies of the climate of the past, I have failed to grasp the significance of what he has to say as to the effect of wind. The reason probably is that I have supposed, and still suppose, that the effects which seem to be associated with the wind are due largely to the conditions of temperature, moisture, and sunshine which the winds bring with them. It is quite probable, however, that the winds themselves also produce some definite effect. However that may be, one of the most distinctive features of the climate at times when the curve of tree growth stands high appears to have been increased windiness, as I have shown in *The Climatic Factor* and elsewhere. Therefore, it appears probable that four centuries before Christ Greece was distinctly more windy than now. Many classical references seem to bear this out. If such were the case, Dexter's studies suggest that the relative windiness, together with the other meteorological conditions which accompany it, may have had a genuine effect upon the Greek temperament. Here is a fairly close paraphrase of what Dexter has to say:

None of the meteorological conditions which I studied rivals the wind in the clearness with which its variations are accompanied by corresponding variations in human phenomena. Nor does any meteorological condition present more anomalous and unexpected effects. Particularly is this true for atmospheric movements of less than 100 miles during twenty-four hours. These I characterize as calms. During such calms I found that the following types of human phenomena made their appearance ,to the following extent, 100 per cent being the degree of prevalence for all days when averaged together.

TABLE SHOWING PREVALENCE OF VARIOUS PHENOMENA DURING CALMS

(One hundred per cent equals the normal or expected number)

Insanity (female)............	34%	Assault and battery (male)....	89%
Assault and battery (female)..	45%	Death.....................	104%
Schools: deportment.........	50%	Policemen off duty...........	105%
Suicide....................	62%	Banks, errors in.............	105%
Insanity (male).............	67%	Sickness (hospital)...........	114%
Drunkenness (male).........	78%	Schools: absences............	314%
Penitentiary: deportment.....	80%		

This indicates that on calm days the number of females arrested for insanity was only 34 per cent of the normal, while the number arrested for assault and battery was 45 per cent of the normal. Misconduct in public schools rose to only half the normal level, while suicide, drunkenness, cases of insubordination in penitentiaries, and arrests of men for assault and battery were also well below the normal. These eight classes of crime or delinquency constitute a distinct group characterized by an abnormally low occurrence during calms. With the death-rate, the next in the list, we have the beginning of a group of an opposite type. Deaths, cases of illness, errors among bank clerks, and absences from school all rise above the normal on calm days.

Another way of bringing out the relationship between human actions and the wind is to plot the curves showing how the human activities vary as the velocity of the wind increases. The most striking thing about such curves is the sudden change which takes place in nearly all of them when the wind increases even slightly. Arrests for assault and battery, and for insanity (both among males and females), and misdeeds in the penitentiary, all of which are deficient during calms—rise above the normal when the wind movement rises even to so low a level as 100 to 150 miles per day. Misdemeanors in the schools do the same thing before a movement of 200 miles is reached. On the other hand, policemen off duty, cases of sickness, and deaths, all of which are excessive in number during calms, take a sudden drop when the wind rises, and show deficiencies when the wind movement is 100 to 150 miles per day. Only suicide, drunkenness, and clerical errors show a gradual change with the wind.

The appearance of the curves as a whole is such as to lead me to place calms in a class by themselves as far as wind influences are concerned. High winds seem to have an influence peculiarly their own, gradually merging into that characteristic of moderate and slight movements, but when an aerial stagnation of 100 miles per day, or less, is reached, a sudden change takes place, and certain phenomena suddenly increase in numbers while others drop almost to the vanishing point. Which are the ones in excess? Absence from school, absence from police duty, clerical errors, sickness, and death. But absence from school means sickness, absence from duty the same, clerical errors the same in milder forms, and death the same at its maximum. It would seem to be true that: *during calms, those life phenomena which are due to depleted vitality are excessive.*

But let us return to those phenomena which are deficient during calms. They are misdemeanors in public schools and penitentiaries, cases of assault and battery, insanity, drunkenness, and suicide. In the schools the misdemeanors are usually sins of commission, rather than sins of omission. As a rule it is the active, energetic boy, the one with vitality to spare, who gets the demerits. The anæmic youngster may never stand at the head of his class, but he is very likely to delight his fond mamma with a mark of 100 in deportment. If that be so, and I speak with authority upon this point, if upon no other, disorder in the school-room is an active thing, and an evidence of excessive vitality. With the penitentiary inmate I have had less experience, but upon *a priori* grounds would argue that what is true for the child in questions of deportment would not be radically different for the adult. In fact, the wardens expressed the opinion that the prevalence of disorder bears a pretty close relation to physical health, and varies directly with it. Order is only observed through evidence of superior force on their part; a sick person is always a good one, but with a return to health, the conditions are frequently very different. We may, then, conclude that in the penitentiary misdemeanors are evidences of excessive vitality.

With persons arrested for the crime of assault and battery the same is, I believe, demonstrably true. One may feel like fighting, and perhaps more frequently does feel so, when possessed of "that tired feeling" which makes the fortunes of patent medicine vendors, but to *feel* like fighting without doing so, never brought a man before the police judge for the crime which we are considering. There must be both the inclination and the consciousness of strength to back it up before one would be likely to figure in this class of data.

As to arrests for insanity, we shall take the word of the psychiatrist that acute mania increases with any condition which tends to augment the output of nervous energy. The daily fluctuations in strength which we all experience are not so much those of physical, as of nervous, energy, if the distinction may be made. Among persons having tendencies to mania an increase in nervous energy leads to just the kind of conduct that would lead to arrests for insanity, which our records show to be especially numerous when the wind is strong.

Drunkenness and suicide are not so plainly manifestations of superabundance of vitality but, with these possible exceptions, we can say that *during calms those life phenomena which are due to excessive vitality are deficient in number.*

The significance of all this for our present problem is obvious. The climate of Greece, Rome, and practically all the other great empires of antiquity *at the time when they reached their greatest dominance* appears to have possessed much more than the present degree of those qualities which Dexter finds associated with excessive human vitality. On the other hand, in the dry periods of relative economic decay and political disintegration the climate tended to be of the kind that brings into prominence the human qualities arising from depleted vitality. This accords with our findings as to health during the two phases of a climatic pulsation. It adds a highly important element in its suggestion that the general temperament of a community varies in response to variations in its climate, even if all other factors such as heredity and culture remain constant.

Still another factor may be concerned in this matter. The temperament of a community depends somewhat upon the diseases to which it is subject. Malaria is especially important in this respect, as I have shown in *Civilization and Climate*. Any one who has lived in a malarial country knows its ravages. The form which prevails in countries like Italy rarely kills people. Most persons who suffer from malaria continue their daily work, except when actually having a chill. But watch the work of such people. See how feebly they act, how irritable they are, how careless, and how ready to leave a task half finished. Note, too, how soon such conduct becomes habitual with people who suffer frequently from malaria.

Malaria is pre-eminently a disease of tropical and subtropical countries whose climate is characterized by alternate wet and dry seasons. Except in the perennially moist portions of the tropics, the streams of such regions are subject to seasonal floods which spread over wide areas for a short period and then disappear, leaving innumerable stagnant pools and swamps, ideal breeding places for the anopheles mosquito. Permanent bodies of water usually contain fish which eat the mosquito larvæ and reduce their numbers, or else the water moves sufficiently to carry away most of the eggs that are laid in it. When the climate of a subtropical country becomes drier, the conditions which favor the mosquito are intensified. This is due in large measure to the fact that a diminution of the rainfall lessens the amount of vegetation upon the slopes and thus allows the soil to be washed away rapidly. The streams are thereby overloaded and begin to fill the valleys with sand and gravel. This causes the flowing water to wander hither and thither over broad flood plains in innumerable channels, which form pools when the floods assuage. Or it may be that the water loses itself in marginal swamps. The streams also become intermittent, and no longer contain large quantities of fish. Thus many conditions co-operate to reduce the number of streams which flow steadily throughout the year, and to increase the number of bodies of stagnant water in which the mosquitoes may live. This in itself may produce most wide-spread effects. How great they are may be judged from the success of the United States Government in eradicating malaria at Panama by the opposite process of reducing the number of places where mosquitoes can breed.

At present malaria is endemic in Greece and Rome. That is, it is always there, and is looked upon as one of the necessary diseases of childhood, much as we look upon measles. Sir Ronald Ross of the Liverpool School of Tropical Medicine is responsible for the statement that nearly half the people of Greece have suffered genuine injury from malaria, and in Italy the case is scarcely better. Up to the age of puberty children are attacked by it every autumn. They grow weak and sallow, their spleens are permanently enlarged, and their vitality is lowered for life. No one who has known much of malaria will question the severity of its results and the length of time which elapses before they are eradicated, even in the case of adults. In spite of quinine, which has come to our aid in modern days, malaria is one of the most insidious of diseases. Every traveller who is really familiar with the Orient knows how the sufferers from malaria lie and groan for days, and may have little energy for months. They go languidly to the necessary tasks, and as soon as possible sit down to rest with open, stupid mouths. Physicians agree that it is impossible to expect much initiative or energy from a nation in which, for centuries, almost half of every generation has been devitalized by this baneful disease.

From a painstaking study of classical authors, W. H. S. Jones* has concluded that up to about 400 B. C. in Greece and 200 B. C. in Rome, malaria was almost unknown. Then it appeared, and during the succeeding century or two became common. At first it attacked adults, which shows that it was a relatively new disease, which was still epidemic and not endemic, or else, we would add, that Greece was on the very border of its habitat. Later it became permanently located in the respective countries and attacked chiefly children, the older people having become immune after suffering in childhood. It is noticeable that the introduction of malaria coincides with the beginning of the weakening of Greece and Rome, and the time when it became endemic, in Greece at least, is synchronous with the epoch when the lustre of the ancient names became irretrievably dimmed.

Ross and Jones are of the opinion that, along with various other factors, malaria was one of the important causes of the fall of Greece and Rome. The growing effeminacy and lightness of the Greeks, and the brutality of the Romans, are just the effects which they think would be produced upon people of the respective temperaments of the two races. The case is so strong that one can scarcely resist the conclusion that this pathological factor may have played an important part in the psychological changes which appear to have accompanied the decline of civilization, and of population, in both Greece and Rome. It would be unwarranted to assert that the increase in the amount and severity of malaria was due wholly to climatic changes. Other influences, such as contact with Egypt and the introduction of slaves, may have been equally effective. Nevertheless, it seems probable that the spread of the disease in both Greece and Rome

---

*Malaria: A Neglected Factor in the History of Greece and Rome. Cambridge, England, 1907.

proceeded most rapidly when a change of climate not only rendered the topography of the valleys and the behavior of the streams more favorable than hitherto to the propagation of the anopheles mosquito, but likewise weakened the physique of the people so that they readily succumbed to disease.

Natural selection presents a still more insidious way in which the change from relatively moist, stormy, cool conditions to those of aridity may have affected the Greek, Roman, and other races. In the opinion of many scholars, one of the most important factors in the greatness of these powers was the presence of a race of blond northern invaders. Take the case of Greece. The Achæans apparently came into the country in the thirteenth century B. C., and were followed after a century or two by the Dorians. The coming of these two branches of the same family may have been influenced by the dry period of which we find some evidence at that time, both in America and Asia. After their arrival the climate, on the whole, although with many fluctuations, appears to have become more propitious. Up to the third century it continued to be favorable. Then it became more arid. We have seen how sensitive people are to climatic environment. The Negro would apparently disappear in the northern United States were he not replenished from the South. The Scandinavian does not seem to prosper greatly in the dry, sunny portions of the United States; he is there subject to diseases of the skin and nerves which appear seriously to deplete his numbers in a few generations; whereas in the rainy Northwest, which resembles his native habitat, he thrives greatly, both in body and estate. It was probably the same with the northern invaders in Greece. So long as the climate was propitious they flourished and lent strength to the country. Then, when conditions became less favorable, the unseen ravages of malaria and other diseases presumably attacked them with especial severity, and in the course of centuries they gradually disappeared. To-day blond Greeks are almost unknown, although classical literature and many fair-haired old statues demonstrate their presence formerly in considerable numbers.

We are now in a position to appreciate the full effects which may arise from climatic pulsations. We have spoken mainly of the change from moist to dry, but the opposite effects are equally strong. In fact, during the fourteenth century a brief but strong climatic wave, which appears to have benefited dry regions, caused England to suffer from a series of rainy and cold summers which well-nigh ruined agriculture. Northern Scandinavia at that same time was almost depopulated because crops could no longer be raised in sufficient quantities to support the farmers. But we must confine ourselves to the change from moist to dry conditions in regions like those surrounding the eastern Mediterranean. There the onset of the dry phase of a climatic pulsation seems to produce the following effects: first, it diminishes the crops, and thus creates economic distress. This leads to political troubles, partly because mankind is prone to attribute all its troubles to political causes, and partly because taxes and other governmental requirements which are easily borne when people are prosperous become highly burdensome in times of distress. Such conditions often lead to uprisings; they provide fruitful soil for agitators. They also tend to exaggerate whatever difficulties there may be by reason of racial friction, religious rivalry, class distinctions, and many other social phenomena.

The combined effect of all these causes is to furnish a great stimulus to migration. Occasionally this leads to the swift and irresistible migration of great masses of people, as in the case of the Mongols under Genghis Khan and of the Arabs in the Aramæan invasions. In the early days of Mohammedanism religious faith seems to have reinforced economic distress, thus giving rise to a peculiarly violent outburst. Oftener the migration is slow and consists of a sort of seepage whereby thousands upon thousands of people gradually drift to new homes. Both types of migration tend to be highly selective. The more adventurous parts of the community, and those with the pioneer spirit, are likely to migrate farthest. Those with a more conservative spirit, and those who have less physical energy, are, on the whole, more likely to stay where they are, and wait for better times.

In addition to these external results of periods of diminished storminess, there are certain more intimate results. First among these is the effect of aridity and lack of storms on health and energy. Other things being equal, a dry climate is less favorable to health than is a fairly moist one. Storms, too, are an important element in bringing health to a region, and so are winds and variability up to a certain point. A falling off of the climate in these respects is almost certain to lower people's vitality, diminish their initiative, reduce their productivity, and increase their death-rate. But these same conditions, according to Dexter, have a measurable influence upon temperament, for the stormier type of climate fosters the qualities which arise from an excess of nervous energy, while the less stormy climate fosters those which accompany depleted vitality.

Diseases act in the same way, for such afflictions as malaria increase under the influence of diminished storminess. This, in turn, not only saps people's energy and raises the death-rate, but, according to Ross and Jones, has the added effect of fostering a less hopeful, more brutal, and more pliable type of temperament. Moreover, disease as well as migration tends to exert a selective effect. The peasants of a country, those who are closest to the soil, who live out-of-doors, and whose ancestors have dwelt longest in a region, appear to be the most likely to survive. The types that have arrived recently, and which usually form the sheltered upper classes and city-dwelling population, are less likely to be well adapted to the new conditions, even though they may possess the pioneer qualities of energy, initiative, and progressiveness.

The significant feature of the whole matter is that in marginal regions of the drier type practically all the main factors tend to be unfavorable when a change from fairly moist to dry conditions takes place. In marginal regions of the other type, such as Ireland and Norway, the opposite is true, for the drier phases of the cycles are most favorable. If these results were confined to the marginal regions, their influence upon history, though important, might not rise to the first rank, But through selective migrations, wars, invasions, and the dislocation of trade the disorganization of the marginal regions tends to pass over into the more favored regions where the climatic changes in themselves do relatively little harm. This, perhaps, is the greatest of all reasons why such changes must be considered if history is rightly to be understood.

CHAPTER XI

THE EVOLUTION OF RACIAL CHARACTER

THE principles set forth in this book help to explain why mental characteristics vary from race to race. But do the mental characteristics of the races really vary because of biological inheritance, or merely because of differences in physical environment and cultural development? Negroes obviously differ from Chinese not only in outward appearance but in mental activity and aptitudes; Semites differ from Malays, and Nordics and Eskimos display similar differences. It is equally obvious that many of these differences are due to environment and culture. The inland Chinese villager, for example, would probably drown if set afloat in an Eskimo boat; the Eskimo might starve in the midst of fertile rice-land. This is merely because Chinese culture trains a man to cultivate rice in accord with his physical environment, while Eskimo culture trains him to use a tipsy little boat of skins on rough cold seas. Reverse the physical environments and cultures of the two races, and the Chinese could undoubtedly manage kayaks, while the Eskimos could raise rice. But would any amount of training ever make the *average* Chinese as good a boatman as the *average* Eskimo, or could the average Eskimo by any possibility be as careful and patient a farmer as the Chinese? *Selected* Chinese might indeed rival the best Eskimos as boatmen, and selected Eskimos might be wonderful horticulturists, but we are talking about racial averages. Selection may sort out people with all kinds of abilities, for every race contains a great variety of people, but has not selection already given a special character to each of the world's main races? Can that character be changed except by further selection, or else by wholesale mutation?

The answers to these questions depend upon the answer to the broad question of whether races do actually differ in their inherited temperaments and intellectual abilities. Each reader can perhaps give concrete expression to his own beliefs in this respect by analysing the following example. Assume that we have a hundred average Negroes from the plateaus of central Africa, or from Georgia, if you choose. Assume that we have also a hundred average Chinese from the villages near Peking, a hundred average Englishmen born and bred in London, and a hundred Lapps from Norway. Assume likewise that no member of any of these four groups has any personal knowledge of the care of horses, cattle, or sheep. Place the four groups with their wives and children on exactly equal terms in the plains of north-western Argentina, and set them to raising those three kinds of animals. At the end of thirty years how will the four groups compare, economically and socially? All have changed their occupation quite radically, although the Lapps have changed far less than the others, and the Londoners have changed most of all. All have also changed their physical and cultural environments to about the same degree; all are living in a climate quite different from that of their old homes, and all have had to learn a new language and new customs. How well has each group adapted itself to the new conditions? Which group, if any, is dominant? Which is most prosperous? Which the poorest? Does any of them supply servants habitually to the others? Is any of the groups habitually looked down upon? Do all four show equal capacity to adapt themselves to the new surroundings? Answer these questions thoughtfully, and you will have given your own answer to the great question of whether there is any such thing as innate mental differences between one race and another.

Perhaps your answer is wrong, but never mind. The vast majority of people believe in biological differences in the mentality of different races. The people who chiefly question this are a relatively small group of scientific men, especially those who belong to races that are not dominant, and a rather large group of persons with strong philanthropic and religious tendencies. Nevertheless, even the scientists who believe in racial differences of mentality recognize the impossibility of any clear demonstration as yet of exactly what parts of the character of a given group of people are due to heredity and what parts to physical and social environment. Such a demonstration for a race is vastly more difficult than for a small group of people or for a few individuals. The larger the groups that are compared, the less clear is the evidence of inherent mental differences. This does not mean that the *reality* of such differences is any less in the large groups than in the small. It simply means that the *degree* of inherent difference is less, and that *other factors*, such as the social and physical environments, play a relatively larger part.

Consider the degree of mental difference between individuals as compared with nations or races. Suppose that two equally healthy infants with equally good physiques are deposited in an orphan asylum at birth. At first there is practically no difference between them so far as evidence of mentality is concerned. Soon, however, they begin to pull apart; at five years of age one is much brighter than the other; at ten there is a still more noteworthy contrast; at twenty the contrast is painful; at forty one is a famous inventor, the other is still a moron. Both had the same environment from birth to the age of twelve, except as they themselves altered their own environment. But one was born with an uncommonly good mind and a highly persistent, flexible, and courageous temperament; the other was born with a subnormal mind and a weak, cowardly, vacillating temperament. The difference in inheritance is so obvious that no reasonable person questions it.

Now take two fairly homogeneous groups, such as the university professors of the United States, and the adult miners who have no chance of ever becoming bosses or foremen. The difference between these groups is very clear. Few would deny that even though training and opportunity play a part, the difference is based on a profound inherited difference of ability. It is like the difference between the inventor and the moron, though it may not be so great. Next take all teachers and miners everywhere. The difference between these two large groups is of the same kind as the difference between the inventor and the moron, or the professors and the unsuccessful miners; but it is far less intense. The reason is that now we are including many very stupid teachers and some very bright miners. Moreover, we are including people in many lands and with many kinds of training, so that the inherent differences are partly masked. Yet those inherent differences still remain. The brightest miner may be the equal of a large number of teachers, but a good many miners are morons, while practically no morons can be teachers. Moreover, the teaching profession contains a large percentage of the world's most brilliant scientists, authors, historians, and other thinkers; the mining profession contains only a few such men.

It would be easy to carry this analogy further, but the essential point is clear. Even though differences in intellect and temperament exist between one race and another, those differences are far smaller than between individuals. They are also so mixed with other differences due to social and physical environment that they cannot easily be detected. Nevertheless, they seem to be real, and to be of profound importance.

The present position of this whole question of inherent racial differences is well exemplified in a book called *Temperament and Race*, written by Professor S. D. Porteus with the assistance of Miss Marjorie E. Babcock. The book is likely to live long because it sets forth a new and illuminating method of studying an old and perplexing problem. Hawaii forms an especially good racial laboratory. Anglo-Saxons, Portuguese, and Porto Ricans have come from the West; Japanese, Chinese, and Filipinos from the East. All except the Anglo-Saxons came as laborers in the sugar plantations; "they started from the same mark," and their position at the end of the race "will be determined by the mental, temperamental, or character traits" which each possesses.

The method employed by Doctor Porteus in attempting to separate innate qualities from those due to environment is to begin with the general impressions of employers, chiefly on sugar plantations, and then to grade the races according to social efficiency, school work, the size and growth of their brains, intelligence tests, and tests of temperament. Here is a summary of the impressions of employers as to the qualities of four of the races:

"The Chinaman plodding away at his allotted task, accepting the burden which centuries of use have laid upon his shoulders, unwilling or unable to follow new leads or fearing to face new situations, hating notoriety and the unaccustomed, and clinging fast to old traditions and ways—essentially the feminine temperament. . . . The Japanese—self-assertive and anxious for a larger place in the sun, eager for any adaptation that will advance his ambitions, selfish in outlook and not given to over-scrupulousness, sensitive as regards his self-conceit, yet exhibiting wonderful tenacity of purpose and self-control in meeting new difficulties—essentially masculine characteristics. . . .

"The Portuguese volatile, impulsive, quick-tempered, rather obtrusive, suggestible, and poorly inhibited. Their general temperament thus has in it some elements of instability. On the other hand they are sober, hard-working, and respectable—a decided acquisition to the permanent population of the Territory. Marital infelicities and divorce are common, but nevertheless the social morality of the Portuguese is good. . . .

"The Filipinos represent a fine example of a race in an adolescent stage of development. Their departure from the normal balance of maturity [appears] in their egocentric attitude, in their rather obtrusive habits and desire for personal recognition, in their supersensitiveness, poor emotional control, and unstable moods, in their alternate obstinateness and suggestibility, in their impulsiveness, love of display, and noisy self-expression."

A Filipino who entered the University of Hawaii, but did not graduate, explained that he had "too much engine for his steering gear." His people, he said, have "powder enough but a crooked barrel. . . . The fields on the other side of the river look always greenest, and so we damn fools spend most of our time in the river."

The next step taken by Porteus in comparing the races of Hawaii is based on his "social rating scale." From a study of mental defectives in New Jersey he came to the conclusion that the most important social traits are planning-capacity, resolution, stability, self-control, prudence, self-determination, dependability, and tact. When rated along these lines by teachers and others, the Japanese and Chinese compete for first place. They are almost equal in stability, self-control, prudence, and self-determination, but the Japanese lead in planning-capacity and resolution, and the Chinese in dependability and tact. The Portuguese and the mixed Hawaiians compete for third place, although the Portuguese have the advantage; the Filipinos and Porto Ricans stand together at the bottom. The man from China "is an almost ideal immigrant." He possesses "all the virtues of a useful citizen without the embarrassing ambition to become one. . . . The Japanese is a horse of the same color but of a very different disposition. He is restless, ambitious, enterprising, antevert (looking toward the future), in contrast to the retrovert Chinese (who look toward the past), willing to forego the immediate advantage for the larger end. Much more outwardly adaptable than the Chinese, he tends to identify himself with his adopted people and to demand the rights of citizenship."

Measured by their tendency toward crime, the Japanese have far the best record in Hawaii; the Portuguese and Chinese stand next; while the Hawaiians are twice as bad as the Chinese, and the Filipinos and Porto Ricans are still worse. Turning to another criterion, the ages of the children in comparison with their degree of advancement in school put the races in nearly the same order as that just mentioned, namely Japanese, Chinese, Hawaiians, Filipinos, Portuguese, and Porto Ricans.

Thus far we have been trying to determine whether the *behavior* of one race or another is better adapted to promote civilization. Now let us use the more subjective method of mental tests. According to the standard Binet tests and others, Porteus finds that the races in Hawaii occupy essentially the same position as in his estimates of social value. But such tests show nothing as to temperament. A wonderfully industrious, well-balanced temperament may be associated with a rather dull intellect, while a most brilliant intellect may belong to a person whose value to the community is almost completely destroyed by his irresponsible, lazy disposition and his lack of self-control, tact, and the ability to plan for the future. Accordingly Porteus tested his various races by means of an invention of his own, the Maze test. In this the subject who is being tested has to follow the windings of a more or less complicated maze, which is printed on a sheet of paper. The degree to which the subject plans out his course before marking it on the paper, and the degree to which he repeats himself, persists in the face of frequent failure, or becomes discouraged and exasperated are believed to indicate his planning ability, persistence, and other temperamental traits. Here, too, the Japanese come out ahead, with the Chinese near them and the other three non-Anglo-Saxon races trailing behind.

This brings us to the most original and significant part of *Temperament and Race*. Is the position of the various races dependent on any measurable physiological condition? Porteus believes that it is. The weight of the brain may have something to do with the ability of a person or race, but is relatively unimportant compared with the complexity of the cerebral corrugations, and the development of the outer cortical portion in proportion to the inner and less important parts. A careful series of measurements suggests that another factor is also highly important, namely, the time at which the brain stops growing and the rate at which it grows after puberty. In other words, Doctor Porteus and Miss Babcock come back to an old idea which is ably set forth in one of John Fiske's essays. The idea is that the level to which any individual ultimately rises is closely related to the length of the period of immaturity. A horse is physically immature during scarcely a tenth of his normal life; his mental immaturity may be of even shorter duration. An eagle or a sparrow apparently knows how to perform all the functions of life and has reached the acme of its powers before it has lived more than perhaps a twentieth of the span which it might enjoy if not killed by accident. On the other hand, at least a fifth of the life of the ordinary human being has passed before it becomes even moderately mature; full maturity such as the horse enjoys at the age of four is not reached by man till the age of about twenty-five. But the moron reaches full mental maturity—that is, his low type of maturity—before the age of ten; the stupid day laborer is as competent and valuable at twenty-one as at fifty, and perhaps more so; but a genius like Lincoln keeps on developing new powers until he is thirty, forty, or even fifty years of age. He may be much more valuable between the ages of fifty and sixty than between twenty and thirty.

Porteus now finds that this old idea is apparently based on a biological fact. Some brains stop growing at puberty or thereabout; others keep on growing for many years. The growth seems to consist mainly of a thickening of the cortical layers, especially the supra-cortical portion which appears to be the most important from the point of view of mentality. The rate at which the brain grows after puberty is greater among boys than among girls, as is well illustrated in certain curves of growth where the line for the girls flattens out more quickly than the curve for boys. Porteus connects this fact with the difference between the sexes in temperament and achievement. Even more important for our present purposes is the fact that similar differences are found among the brains of the different races. The Japanese brains, for example, although not growing quite so fast as those of Anglo-Saxons, grow more rapidly after puberty than do the Chinese brains. This may account for the "masculine" character of the Japanese compared with the relatively "feminine" character of the Chinese.

It cannot be too strongly emphasized that this whole matter of racial mentality and its relation to the physical qualities of the brain is still in a very nebulous condition. Nevertheless, the temperamental differences between one race and another are so pronounced that they can scarcely be the result of mere external circumstances. Climate, for example, may make one race seem less persistent than another, but it could scarcely make a race artistic or tactful. Even to one who, like myself, is primarily a student of environment some non-environmental factor seems necessary. Porteus's argument hangs together so closely and is supported by so many extraneous facts that it appears to suggest this necessary factor. His groups of people in Hawaii seem not only to show measurable differences in social value, but those differences appear to be inherent, and to be associated with differences in the brain which may be sufficient to account for the intellectual and especially the temperamental differences among the races.

But even if this be granted, are the differences which Porteus measures really racial, or do they pertain merely to the small groups of each race which happen to live in Hawaii? In other words, are the inhabitants of Hawaii average samples of their races, as Porteus insists, or are they selected samples? I doubt whether they are average samples, but this does not invalidate Porteus's argument, for essentially the same mode of selection appears to have operated among all of them, and especially in the cases of Japan and China. The *average* Japanese or Chinese laborer does not leave his home and travel thousands of miles across the water. Unusual determination and energy, a high degree of the spirit of adventure, or ambition, and a good endowment of physical courage and strength are required to pry a man loose from his home, his family, his language, and his ancestors. Among the Chinese we seem to have independent evidence that those who have come to Hawaii tend to be of this type. In *The Character of Races* I have shown that the Hakkas are a very competent and highly selected little section of the Chinese people. They appear to have been selected by strenuous migration. Now, Hakkas are proportionally far more numerous in Hawaii than in China. They seem to be relatively still more numerous among the school children in the higher grades. For example, in the only graduating class at the University of Hawaii as to which I have knowledge, four of the five Chinese were Hakkas. Such facts suggest that the Japanese, Chinese, Filipinos, Porto Ricans, and others in Hawaii may not be fair representatives of their races. But this does not alter the significance of the facts that have just been set forth. That significance lies in this: In

Hawaii, for the first time, a scientific study of racial groups which have been subjected to a similar selective process suggests that certain widely recognized and important intellectual and especially temperamental differences are associated with physiological differences in the brain. Much further study is needed before this conclusion is finally verified or rejected, but it agrees with so many other lines of evidence, and is so reasonable, that we may well accept it as a working hypothesis.

Accepting this working hypothesis, but recognizing that it is still under investigation, let us inquire how differences of racial temperament have arisen. To make the problem concrete let us inquire why civilization first developed rapidly around the Mediterranean Sea and later in northwestern Europe. Why did the people of those regions possess almost unrivalled energy, initiative, persistence, and inventiveness which caused civilization to advance with extraordinary rapidity? What we shall say is avowedly speculative, even though for the sake of brevity and clearness we shall have to state it somewhat categorically. Nevertheless, it seems to illustrate a great principle so clearly, and to spring so logically from that principle, that it is worth considering.

The origin of racial differences, both physical and mental, is doubtless found in mutations. The cause of mutations still remains as much a mystery as ever. After mutations have occurred, however, it seems clear that they are preserved or eliminated according as they render the organism better or worse in its adaptation to the environment. All parts of the environment play their part in the natural selection which thus occurs, but paleontologists and students of prehistoric man are practically a unit in holding that previous to the development of civilization, by far the most potent selective factor was climatic pulsations, especially those of glacial periods. In *World Power and Evolution* I have summarized some of the facts which show how great were the evolutionary steps associated again and again with periods of climatic extremes. For our present purpose it must suffice to outline the events of the Permian Glacial Period, which appears to have been the most severe of all the epochs of climatic stress through which the earth has passed. Then we will turn to the Pleistocene glaciation, during which man took the final steps in mental evolution.

Previous to the Permian Period the vegetation of all parts of the earth, including high latitudes, was much alike. In general, according to Professor Charles Schuchert in his *Textbook of Geology*, the lands were covered with forests of soft, rapidly growing trees with soft or even spongy wood, among which evergreen trees with needle-like leaves were prominent. Associated with these were thickets of rushes, also of very rapid growth, which resembled modern cane-brakes and bamboo thickets in appearance. Here and there there stood majestic tree-like ferns, while many smaller ferns and similar plants thrived in the shade below. Flowers of a certain sort were sparingly present, but of insignificant size and unattractive color. Spores took the place of seeds to such a degree that when the trees and ferns were liberating them the entire forest was covered with a greenish-yellow or brown dust. The Permian Glacial Period with its sharp transitions from warm to cold and from moist to dry, and with its prolonged periods of great extremes, practically eliminated these ancient types of vegetation. Conifers much like those of to-day came into existence; seeds largely replaced spores; the plants showed a wide-spread reduction in size and variety; they tended to become hardier, and to have thicker and less ornate leaves.

During the climatic stress of the Permian Period, animal life suffered an even greater transformation than plant life. Previous to that time the insects, for example, were of astonishing size. The smallest of the 400 forms yet known had wings over a third of an inch long. The wings of more than twenty species were six inches long; six attained a length of eight inches, and three were giants of twelve inches. Imagine a spore-dusted forest full of insects as large as crows! The cold and changeable climate of Permian times apparently extinguished all these forms. Their place was taken by small species resembling those of to-day. A change still more profound occurred at this time through the introduction of metamorphosis. Previously the insects had merely grown gradually from egg to adult. Now the creatures emerged from the eggs as maggots or caterpillars, then passed into a resting stage, and finally were transformed from maggots to flies, or from caterpillars to butterflies and moths. At the same time insects acquired the power to become dormant, and thus persist for months without food or activity. All these changes were apparently due to the necessity for enduring long, cold winters. Thus the climatic variability of the Permian Period not only caused a wide-spread remodelling of the earth's garment of vegetation, but reduced the size of insects and introduced a unique stage in their life history.

Another change which occurred at this time is even more important. That change was the preliminary step in the evolution of our direct ancestors, the warm-blooded mammals. Extreme aridity and low temperature both prevailed during certain epochs of the Permian. Among the more progressive types of land animals aridity has a tendency to accelerate development. It places a premium upon the power to travel, and especially upon speed. As Professor Richard S. Lull puts it in *The Evolution of the Earth and Its Inhabitants*, "not only are food and water scarce and far between, but the strife between pursuer and pursued becomes intensified—neither can afford to be outdistanced by the other. This means increased metabolism, which in turn generally implies not only greater motive powers but higher temperature. With increasing cold a premium would be placed upon such creatures as could maintain their activity beyond the limits of shortening summers, and this could be accomplished only by the development of some mechanism whereby a relatively constant temperature could be maintained within the animal regardless of external conditions." In other words, the extreme climatic conditions were efficacious in placing a premium upon warm blood, so that there arose the first animals whose temperature was more or less independent of the surrounding air. Among birds this forced the mother to protect the eggs and even the fledglings from cold. Among mammals it led to the production of the young within the body of the mother instead of from eggs in which the mother took little or no interest. Thus the relation of mother and child became firmly established. The later development of this relation has been the chief source of all that is best in mankind. The whole evolution of warm-blooded animals and of real motherhood was by no means completed in a single geological period. In fact, it reached its culmination only after many millions of years. Nevertheless, the first great step was taken under the stress of an extreme climate, just as the vegetation was remodelled and the insects revolutionized.

The last of the great glacial periods, the one known to geologists as Pleistocene, had as great an effect upon primitive man as the Permian had upon plants, insects, and mammals. It exterminated an extraordinary number of species, genera, and families of animals, but it was chiefly notable for the evolution of the human brain. When the mammals had reached a condition of complete dominance over all other forms of life, the stress of climate suddenly wiped them out wholesale. In North America the whole family of horses was destroyed; the elephant tribe, including the mammoth and mastodon, disappeared; the camel, which had formerly been abundant, passed away, leaving no trace except his bones. Still other families, such as the giant beaver, the sloth, the tapirs, and the so-called glyptodonts, were likewise exterminated. Europe likewise experienced a wholesale and appalling destruction of life. All of this arose directly or indirectly because of the severity of the climate and the frequent and great changes.

Just how, or when, or where man first came upon the scene no one yet knows. According to the majority of authorities he originated in Asia, and came into existence at about the time when the first premonitory waves of the last glacial period were beginning. However that may be, we are quite certain that he existed in Europe and Asia, and perhaps in Africa, during the four main epochs of glacial advance and retreat into which the last glacial period was divided. During these epochs and during the various glacial stages of alternating severity and mildness which have ensued since the last glacial epoch, he was buffeted most fearfully by the alternations of good conditions and bad. During that time occurred the main evolution of the human brain. Moreover, during the last of the four glacial epochs, when the climatic conditions were much worse than during any other, the brain evolved much faster than ever before, as I have explained in *World Power and Evolution*. During this same epoch the races which later peopled Europe gradually forged ahead.

All this, as it seems to me, was closely connected with a repeated process of migration and natural selection. The cause of this process was apparently the alternate expansion and contraction of the ice-covered area of Europe on the one hand and of the deserts of Asia and Africa on the other. When the climate became cold and stormy, Europe became practically uninhabitable almost to the Alps, while northern Asia was likewise extremely cold and inhospitable. At the same time the deserts of western and central Asia and of north Africa became relatively rainy and habitable. The inhabitants of the regions that became unduly cold were forced to migrate southward or eastward. Naturally they came into conflict with their neighbors in better climates, and either pushed through them into the formerly desert areas which now had become habitable, or drove the other tribes ahead of them into the former deserts. At the same time the former deserts attracted the people who lived near them, for game and other food must have become abundant as soon as the climate became moist.

When the climate changed in the other direction, an opposite process must have taken place. Of course this is an inference based on only the meagrest facts. But it is an unusually reliable inference, because it simply assumes that before we have records people did exactly what we know that they almost invariably have done since records have been available. In our own days habitable regions which easily supply plenty of food, and which are pleasant and healthful, never remain long unoccupied, provided people can get to them. On the other hand there is almost invariably a migratory tendency away from poor regions into those that are more attractive. Thousands of examples of such movements here occurred in the past century. If a region deteriorates seriously, as apparently happened to Greenland in the fourteenth century and to the dry parts of central Asia in the seventh, the exodus becomes relatively great, until the population is reduced to the point where it can find sustenance. Not all the people necessarily migrate under such circumstances. Some may remain in the old homes, but they are almost sure to diminish in numbers or else to be forced to lower their standards of living. The adults may not die, but the death-rate among the children becomes so great that the population declines in numbers. This is the sort of thing that we may confidently assume to have happened in parts of Europe and in the deserts of Asia and Africa time after time. It must have happened not only during the four main glacial epochs which compose the last glacial period, but on a smaller scale during the post-glacial stages which were like the epochs but less intense. It certainly happened during the climatic pulsations of historic times, for of that we have clear records.

Migrations are practically always selective, especially among primitive people. As a rule the more conservative people, the old, the weak, the stupid, and those who lack the spirit of adventure and progress tend to remain behind when a region becomes less fertile or less favorable for some other reason. The young, vigorous, ambitious people tend to move out. Those who have the best minds are the most likely to know where to go and to have the foresight to migrate far enough to locate in good places. While they are on the move the weeding process is very severe. As soon as people leave their accustomed haunts, the mere search for food becomes especially difficult. If hostile people have to be fought or circumvented, as is usually the case, the situation becomes far harder. If the journey is prolonged because the migrants can find no place where they can settle in peace, as frequently happens, the death-rate, especially among the women and children, may rise to huge proportions. It is the weaker, the more stupid, the more incompetent who are most likely to die. The brave, the strong, the wise are the survivors.

Any race which goes through this process of selection time and again is almost sure to display a rapid evolution of mental ability. If mutants, or variants from the normal type, display more than the usual energy, initiative, adaptability, and capacity to cope with difficulty they are especially likely to survive. More important still, under such circumstances they are likely to find mates of their own kind instead of mates of lower quality. Thus these favorable mutations are especially likely to be preserved. That is what seems to have happened under the stress of the climatic changes of the glacial and post-glacial epochs, thus helping the human brain to evolve rapidly.

Consider now the geographical location of the areas into which selected migrants are likely to have been driven during the glacial and interglacial epochs. The lands around the eastern Mediterranean and to the east of that sea through Mesopotamia to Persia, together with certain narrow strips in central Asia, form areas which have again and again been squeezed, as it were, between the deserts on the south and east and the glaciated and cold regions on the north. Selected migrants appear to have been forced into those areas again and again, first from one side and then from the other. At other times, the descendants of the migrants have moved outward to China, India, North Africa, and Europe.

Consider now in detail what must have happened after the culmination of the last glacial epoch, the Wisconsin epoch as it is called in America. As soon as the storminess which appears to have been one of the main causes of glaciation began to decline, as I have explained in *The Character of Races*, the interiors of Asia and of North Africa, which seem to have enjoyed a fine climate at the height of the glacial epochs, apparently began to return toward the present condition of vast deserts. The population there, to judge by the stone implements scattered far out in the now uninhabited deserts, was large and progressive as measured by the standards of people of the Stone Age. If our hypothesis is correct, the population was also unusually competent because it was descended from the survivors of numerous strenuous migrations which came from more northerly regions while the snow and ice of the Wisconsin epoch were gradually mantling northwestern Europe and making vast regions uninhabitable. Moreover, during the earlier glacial epochs this same process of migration and selection had doubtless gone on again and again, thus enabling the evolution of man's brain to proceed faster in the regions of stress than in regions like the tropics or southeastern Asia where the physical conditions appear to have varied relatively little even during the extremes of the glacial period.

If space permitted we might well amplify what is said in *The Character of Races* as to the relative uniformity of the environment in lower latitudes, and to a certain extent in very high latitudes. We might point out that migrations and other selective processes have there been rare and ineffective, or have had a repressive effect by eliminating the more active types of people. Such a discussion would suggest that in a broad way the progress of any part of the world is closely related to the amount and recency of selective migration, and to the consequent introduction of energetic types of people. Combine this factor with the present degree of climatic energy and with the possibilities of obtaining food, and we seem to have an almost complete explanation of the fundamental conditions which determine the rate of human progress. Social, religious, political, and commercial institutions and all the other complex paraphernalia of civilization are not the cause of progress; they are merely the tools by which progress is attained, or perhaps better the stairs by which men climb to higher levels. They are built by people who possess the qualities of initiative, energy, adaptability, persistence, and inventiveness, and those qualities appear to be selected and isolated by migration more than by almost any other agency.

To return now to the end of the last glacial epoch, the relatively large and progressive population which had apparently become established in what are now the deserts of Asia and North Africa must have been put under great stress by the return of the climate toward aridity. The population must have been too great in proportion to the food-supply. Large numbers presumably perished because of recurrent famines or droughts, or else failed to bring up enough children to replace themselves. Others, who were especially clever, doubtless devised new ways of increasing their food-supply, and thereby survived. Still others migrated, especially those who were especially energetic or had an unusual share of what we now call the pioneer spirit, or who perchance were wise enough to gain information about distant regions. A few of the migrants may have gone northward, but that would do them little good, for the northern lands were still extremely cold. Southward the lines of migration were more or less blocked by the plateaus and mountains of Tibet and the Himalayas, and by the deserts of Arabia and Sahara, the southern parts of which were doubtless already very dry even in the times that we are now discussing. Some migrants doubtless broke through the mountains into India, as has happened repeatedly during historic times. Others presumably followed the lofty and relatively well-watered western side of Arabia, and found a way into Africa at the southwestern corner of Arabia. A much stronger tendency must have been to migrate eastward into China and adjacent regions such as Chosen and Japan. The strongest of all tendencies was probably westward into the relatively well-watered and highly attractive border-lands of Asia such as the Caucasus, Mesopotamia, Asia Minor, Syria, Egypt, and northern Africa. In those regions some of the lands which were available for occupation were especially attractive by reason of broad fertile plains and opportunities for agriculture when once that means of obtaining food came into use. But thus far, be it noted, much of northern Europe was still shrouded in ice, while large areas in the central parts were still too cold and stormy to attract immigrants.

The process of migrating out of the deserts into the adjacent regions where the rainfall was greater was by no means steady.

It must have been marked by great fluctuations corresponding to the post-glacial climatic stages of which there is abundant evidence both in Europe and Asia. Thus movements out of the deserts must have alternated with movements in the other direction as the climate swung back toward the glacial type. The presumable result must have been that western Asia and North Africa, and to a less extent China and northern India, experienced one of the most strenuous periods of migration, selection, and racial mixture that can well be imagined. Tribe after tribe, we may well believe, or perhaps family after family and group after group, moved out of the desert into the lands with more water, then their descendants moved back again, only to be driven out once more by a recurrence of still severer drought. During the process a large share of the weaker, less intelligent people must have perished or failed to replace themselves. Almost everywhere the migrants must have come into conflict with the previous inhabitants; and the hardy remnants which remained on both sides must frequently have amalgamated. In western Asia and the Mediterranean region the previous inhabitants presumably contained a large infusion of the picked remainder of the peoples who at an earlier time had been driven out of northern and central Europe by the approach of glaciation. Thus in the very region where early civilization made its greatest strides the pressure of the deserts on one side and of glaciation on the other appears to have created the acme of the conditions that produce races with high powers of mind and with the high physical activity which is needed in order that the powers of the mind may fully express themselves.

In view of all these circumstances it is not surprising that the world's greatest early civilization arose in the region extending from Persia through Mesopotamia and Syria to Egypt, Rhodes and Greece, while similar but less notable developments took place in India and China. Nor is it surprising that from this same general region, as the climate ameliorated and the ice retreated from Europe, there came the tribes which peopled that continent after the ice had passed away. Some moved northward from the Mediterranean regions, others westward by the route through Asia Minor, and still others passed to the north of the Caspian Sea. By whichever route they came they represented a new selection from races that had already been through the same selective process time and again. As they poured into the new continent, renewed by its long rest under ice and storms, the various streams met and fought, and the rigors of a sterner climate also killed off the weak and inefficient. Still another strenuous selection and great mingling of races took place. Thus here, even more than in western Asia and North Africa, we should look for the development of races among whom high intelligence and restless activity are highly developed.

When Europe had begun to grow old according to our standards, although still young compared with most parts of the world, another great migration began. This differed from the others because it was not set in motion by stress of climate or by gradual increase in population, but by a clearcut "cultural" cause, the discovery of America. Yet the effect was the same as in the other cases. A great wave of migration ensued. The migrants were again a selected type, selected primarily because of energy, the pioneer spirit, and the capacity to adapt themselves to new circumstances. The proportion of weaklings and of those who were socially and intellectually undesirable was doubtless greater in this migration than in any other, because new motives, such as the philanthropic desire to help the weak, and the industrial desire for cheap labor, came into play. Yet taken as a whole, the migrants in the American migration, the latest and greatest of its kind—appear until the last few decades to have been mainly of a peculiarly energetic and progressive type, and to have contained relatively few who were physically or mentally weak.

This is as far as we can go in our attempt to explain how racial and national differences have arisen. Again we must emphasize the fact that no man yet knows how or why new types of human beings arise. We only know that there are mental differences between one person and another. If we select a given type which differs from the average and segregate that type so that it does not intermingle with the old type, a new variety may arise. Among the selective factors climate appears to have been far the most important all through geological times and even during the human period so long as man remained uncivilized. Thus the climatic stresses of the glacial period, with its four epochs and its many stages, seem to have been the greatest of all selective factors in hastening the development of the human brain, and in differentiating the relatively inactive races of low latitudes, or of very high latitudes, from the highly active races of middle latitudes. The selective process was most potent in a great belt from China to Gibraltar. There, too, occurred an almost unrivalled mingling of races and the consequent production of new types which gave the selective processes a new opportunity to exert their effect. In this same belt, moreover, during the change from glacial conditions to those of to-day, the climate was especially stimulating. Then when the climate reached its present condition, further migrations with their attendant selection brought the centre of power into northwestern Europe, where the climate is even more stimulating than in the Mediterranean region. Lastly, a continuation of the same process has now carried the centre of human wealth and influence across the Atlantic to America, where a new type of humanity is evolving by reason of still further natural selection and racial mixture. In these later migrations a wholly new factor has gradually intruded itself, until in our day the cultural causes of migration overshadow the physical causes, with results which as yet we cannot clearly discern. This, however, is merely a new phase of the same old process. Throughout the course of evolution and of history the results of migrations, racial mixture, and natural selection seem to stand next to mutations as the main reasons why one race, one stock, or one nation differs from another in both intellect and temperament.

CHAPTER XII

THE ORIGIN OF A GREAT RACE

THE Jews are probably the greatest of all races. Has any other so persistently produced an almost ceaseless string of great men for three or four thousand years? Has any other produced so many great men in proportion to its numbers? Certainly no other, unless it be the Chinese, has so consistently maintained a prominent position for millennium after millennium. At any given epoch, to be sure, unless it be the time of Christ, some other group may have surpassed the Jews in the production of genius. The extraordinary fact about the Jews is the constant succession of notable leaders from Moses, David, and Isaiah through Jesus, John, and Paul to Mendelssohn, Disraeli, Einstein, and many others whose Hebraic origin is often overlooked. The history of this unique race furnishes one of the most notable examples of the principles set forth in preceding chapters. The early history, to be sure, is obscure, but it suggests such interesting possibilities and provides such an extraordinary example of racial selection and eugenics that it would be a pity not to discuss it. The later history is clear, and reinforces many of the conclusions based on the early period. Careful students now seem to be almost universally agreed that "the Old Testament does not furnish a history of Israel, though it supplies the materials from which such a history can be constructed." *

The reconstruction takes many forms. Some students say that Abraham, Isaac, Jacob, and the twelve sons of Jacob are merely personifications of tribes. The more common view is that the main biblical personages from Abraham to Samuel were real people, and that their personal biographies as given in the Bible

* W. Robertson Smith, Preface to Wellhausen's *Prolegomena to the History of Israel* (1885), p. vii. Quoted by S. A. Cook in *The Cambridge Ancient History*, vol. II (1924), p. 352.

are founded on facts. But the biographies have become greatly distorted and confused. They are full of repetitions, contradictions, mythical perversions and accretions, so that it is often impossible to separate fact from fiction. Many traditional events, for example, have been ascribed to the patriarchs, even though they occurred centuries earlier; the same experience has sometimes been ascribed to two persons; and people with similar names have been confused. Moreover, tribes *are* often personified as individuals, which adds to the confusion. Thus many blood relationships described in the earlier books of the Bible may mean merely that certain tribes are related. The degree to which the supposed ancestors of the various tribes are asserted to be the children of inferior wives, or to be illegitimate, is an excellent measure of the esteem in which they were held by the later Hebrews.

Stripped of excrescences, the kernel of truth seems to be that the beginning of Hebrew history was a migration. A Semitic family migrated five or six hundred miles northwestward from Ur of the Chaldees, near Babylon to Haran, in northern Mesopotamia; thence part of them went on to Palestine. Perhaps many families thus migrated, but the Bible is concerned with only one. These people were nomadic keepers of camels, sheep, and asses, and it was easy for them to move long distances. They were not distinguished, nor were they numerous, so that it is not surprising that no records of them are found on the monuments. The surprising thing would be to find such records.

After the first migration, the Patriarchs wandered back and forth more or less freely between Haran and Palestine. They also went down to Egypt, or at least to the borders of that country. Although the general region through which they passed contained in the aggregate a considerable population of fairly civilized people, there must then, as now, have been large areas where the dryness of the climate and the ruggedness of the hills caused the population to be so sparse that a small company of nomads could pass back and forth without attracting much comment. This would be especially likely to be true if the original migration occurred in one of the recurrent dry periods of which there seems to be evidence. If the right of the Hebrews to pass back and forth with their animals were once established, it would persist for a long time. Even in Spain, and far more in Turkey, one can to-day see such migrations regularly every season. But the right of the Patriarchs to drive their flocks and herds did not pass wholly unchallenged, for the herdsmen of Isaac had strife with those of Abimelech concerning the wells of Beersheba, and there are other stories of conflict.

A period of drought appears to have been the reason for this strife. Droughts and famines play a prominent part in the story of the Patriarchs. Abraham and Isaac are both said to have been forced to travel to Egypt to buy food. Jacob likewise sent his sons to Egypt in search of food in the days when Joseph had become a great ruler. Finally the prolonged drought drove him and his family out of Palestine. At the invitation of Joseph they settled on the borders of Egypt, just outside the zone of irrigation, but near enough so that they had frequent intercourse with the Egyptians and could easily buy grain and clothing in exchange for animals and cheese. Doubtless some of the poorer Hebrews went into the irrigated regions to find work. Ultimately most of them were forced to do task work under unkind Egyptian slave-drivers. Such conditions, together with the prolonged and repeated droughts, which other evidence suggests as occurring at this time, finally led the Hebrews to leave the unhappy Egyptian border-land and try to find a new home elsewhere. They dared not attempt to oust the Egyptians from the well-watered lands of the Nile. They were too few in number, and they had experienced the crushing might of Egyptian oppressors. The only feasible course was to migrate in a more or less easterly direction. They probably tried to go eastward, but found the country too dry. Then they tried to go northeastward and to penetrate Palestine from the south, but were turned back by the inhabitants of the towns. Next they went farther east between the Dead Sea and the Gulf of Akaba. Then they turned north and gradually drifted past the Dead Sea on its east side, and thus to a point where they again turned westward and made another attempt to enter the western plateau of Palestine by crossing the Jordan north of the Dead Sea. This time they succeeded, and entered the "promised land."

The descendants of Abraham were probably only a small group. How many they numbered it is impossible to tell, for the numbers given in the biblical narratives are impossible. The band which came up from the Egyptian borders can scarcely have numbered more than a few thousand. Even three or four thousand would have to split into many small bands in order to find sustenance in the desert, unless the climate was far moister than at present. But the Egyptian group of Hebrews was apparently by no means the only one that entered Palestine at that time. All over the eastern world a great spirit of unrest and migration prevailed. Tribes from the desert pressed into the well-watered area of Palestine from all sides. These tribes were of the same racial stock as the descendants of Abraham, Isaac, and Jacob, and amalgamated with them more or less after entering the new land. Those who became most closely amalgamated were reckoned as tribes of Israel, and in later days were considered descendants of the sons of Jacob. Tribes that were a little more remote or hostile, like the Edomites, Moabites, and Ammonites, were said to have been descended from Abraham by an inferior wife, or from Isaac and Jacob in some fashion that implies inferiority.

So much for the bare skeleton of early Jewish history. Now let us clothe it with flesh and blood. But first let us get clearly in mind the central feature of the whole history. That central feature as interpreted by Cook in his excellent chapter on "The Rise of Israel," in the *Cambridge Ancient History*, is that up to the time when the Israelites joined with other Hebrews in entering Palestine, the biblical story is concerned merely with a single family group which never numbered more than a few thousand souls. Could such a group preserve its identity? It doubtless could, and in view of the social customs which we shall shortly describe it almost certainly would do so. Even under much less favorable social conditions, a family like that of Confucius can trace its ancestry two and a half milleniums. A few thousand Parsees in India have preserved their racial integrity in the midst of millions of Hindus for more than a thousand years.

Although it is easily possible for a family group or small tribe to retain its identity as long as eight centuries, I doubt whether this is what happened in the case of the Israelites. It is generally supposed that Abraham lived about 2100 B. C., and that the Exodus from Egypt occurred about 1230 B. C. The date for Abraham is set by the story of four kings who made a raid on Palestine and carried away Lot and his family. Abram, for that is what he is then called, is said to have collected three or four hundred men and pursued the plunderers. He put them to flight and recovered all the loot, which he gave back to Lot in spite of Lot's selfishness. One of the kings is called Amraphel. Many authorities believe that this is the great Hammurabi, who framed a famous code of laws. They point out, however, that the fourteenth chapter of Genesis, where the story occurs, is Midrashic and uncertain. That is, it was incorporated in the book of Genesis at a relatively late date, being taken over from the Midrash or traditional records which were framed long after the original materials which form the older parts of the earlier books of the Bible. Moreover, it is generally agreed that the way the raid was made and the persons with whom Amraphel was associated do not seem consistent with what we know of Hammurabi from the monuments. Thus the identification seems doubtful, but the biblical critics still discuss it, because this is the only clue whereby Abraham can be connected with the monuments.

Even if Amraphel really was the great Hammurabi, there is no certainty that Abram was really Abraham. Nothing else in the story of Abraham seems consonant with his warlike dash after the invaders. Moreover, the names Abram and Abraham appear to come from different roots in spite of their seeming similarity. Paton and others have plausibly suggested that in this case, as in others, the editors of the old Israelite traditions confused two similar names. Although the bearers of those names lived centuries apart, they put the two stories together without even altering the names. But later some critical editor, with a philological turn of mind, was disturbed by the obvious inconsistency. So he added a gloss to the effect that God changed Abram's name to Abraham. Then he went back through the parts of the narrative previous to the story of Amraphel and changed "Abraham" to Abram in order to be consistent. Such things were certainly done. In fact, the main reason why the Bible is not a history, but merely a book of materials for history, is that the uncritical authors and editors repeatedly made such additions, putting together two diverse accounts, confusing the identity of different persons, altering the numbers to fit the facts of their own day, and in general trying to create harmony. Fortunately for us, however, they had too much respect for the written word to make more radical alterations and rewrite the stories according to their own interpretation. Thus the original and conflicting accounts often remain intact, even though set in a frame of later interpretation.

In addition to all these doubtful matters, we are confronted by the fact that according to the genealogies in the Bible there are only seven generations from Abraham to Moses. Of course it would be easy for a chronicler to leave out some names in a genealogy, but it scarcely seems as if enough would be left out to explain the difference between the two or three centuries covered by seven generations and the eight centuries covered by the period from Hammurabi to the Exodus. Moreover, the book of Genesis says that the Israelites stayed in Egypt only three or four generations. Another record gives the period as four hundred and thirty years according to the text followed by the English version of the Bible, but the Samaritan and Septuagint versions make this only two hundred and fifteen years. The fact seems to be that if Abraham was a real man, as seems to be the consensus of all except the critics of the more extreme type, he probably lived between 1700 and 1500 B. C. Aside from Amraphel or Hammurabi, a date as late as 1500 seems to fit the rest of the biblical story better than does 1700. At any rate, if we omit the Hammurabi story, our task is merely to trace the history of an inconspicuous nomadic family which, in three or four centuries developed into a small tribe.

The first matter that now concerns us is Abraham's migration away from the rest of his family. It was that which made the original Israelites, if we may use that name so early, a separate people. Why did Abraham migrate? The Bible says nothing about it. The Talmud says it was because Abraham wanted to get away from the irreligious practices of the people around him but, of course, the Talmud is of late origin, and we have no means of knowing where the writer of this particular portion got his information. The modern critics of the more destructive type say that Talmudic statements of this kind amount to nothing because the later Jewish writers made all sorts of assertions in order to emphasize the religious character of their ancestors. It seems to me that such critics go too far, for the whole story of Abraham suggests that he was a deeply religious reformer. People of that type, as we saw in studying *Who's Who in America*, are just the sort who migrate farthest.

But let Abraham's story speak for itself. He is pictured as a believer in a tribal god called Jehovah. He is also pictured as a reformer who set his face against human sacrifices. This is how it happened. Being a man of deep religious feeling, Abraham thought that he heard the voice of God bidding him "Take now thy son, thine only son, whom thou lovest, even Isaac, and get thee into the land of Moriah; and offer him there for a burnt-offering upon one of the mountains which I will tell thee." (Genesis, 22.)

Then the beautiful and simple biblical account goes on:

And Abraham rose early in the morning, and saddled his ass, and took two of his young men with him, and Isaac his son; and he clave the wood for the burnt-offering, and rose up, and went unto the place of which God had told him. On the third day Abraham lifted up his eyes, and saw the place afar off. And Abraham said unto his young men: Abide ye here with the ass, and I and the lad will go yonder; and we will worship, and come again to you. And Abraham took the wood of the burnt-offering, and laid it upon Isaac his son; and he took in his hand the fire, and the knife; and they went both of them together. And Isaac spake unto Abraham his father, and said, My father: and he said, Here am I, my son. And he said, Behold, the fire and the wood: but where is the lamb for a burnt-offering? And Abraham said, God will provide himself the lamb for a burnt-offering, my son: so they went both of them together. And they came to the place which God had told him of; and Abraham built the altar there, and laid the wood in order, and bound Isaac his son, and laid him on the altar, upon the wood. And Abraham stretched forth his hand, and took the knife to slay his son. And the angel of Jehovah called unto him out of heaven, and said, Abraham, Abraham; and he said, Here am I. And he said, Lay not thy hand upon the lad, neither do thou anything unto him; for now I know that thou fearest God, seeing thou hast not withheld thy son, thine only son, from me. And Abraham lifted up his eyes, and looked, and, behold, behind him a ram caught in the thicket by his horns; and Abraham went and took the ram, and offered him up for a burnt-offering in the stead of his son.

Up to the point where the angel appears the story sounds real. From that point onward would we come any nearer the truth if we were to rewrite the biblical account as follows?

And Abraham spake unto Jehovah, "Is it right, oh Jehovah, that a man should slay his son, his only son whom thou hast given him? Art thou not merciful and loving? Spare, I beseech thee, this little lad created in thine own image." As he spake he raised his hand to slay the sacrifice, but turned away in anguish. And lo, in the bushes, caught by the horns, a ram. "It is the work of Jehovah. He spareth my son. He giveth his pledge that he is not pleased with human sacrifice."

No man can say what occurred on that momentous day, three or four thousand years ago, but many things are clear now that were not clear even a generation ago. The way in which the interpretation of such a story varies from generation to generation is well illustrated by the experience of the committee in charge of the international Sunday-school lessons. For a long time the story appeared under the bald caption: "Abraham Sacrifices Isaac." At length the more progressive members of the committee wanted a title which expressed the spiritual meaning of the story. One group suggested "Abraham Obeys God," and another "The Test of Abraham's Faith." But a radical member stood out for "Abraham Learns a Better Way of Worship." The committee could not agree, and the lesson was omitted. The next step might logically be to include it as "Abraham, the Reformer, Opposes Human Sacrifice."

One of the most significant facts about the Patriarchs is the succession of great men in generation after generation. If our interpretation of Abraham is right, and its general spirit is borne out by the whole account of him, he was a truly great reformer; he falls in the group with Confucius, Buddha, Mohammed, Paul, and Jesus. The mere fact that to this day Abraham is a hero and saint to millions of Jews, Mohammedans and Christians is in itself strong evidence that he was one of the world's great characters.

Abraham's son, Isaac, to judge by the biblical story, was by no means so great as his father, perhaps not great at all. Yet he appears to have been by no means a nonentity. Nevertheless, he holds his place in history almost wholly because he was Abraham's son and Jacob's father.

With Jacob the case is different. In his own right he stands out as one of the world's noteworthy figures. He may have been tricky and deceitful; but he shows abundant evidence of real greatness. Only a man of fine qualities could have such visions as he had at Bethel. Of course, that bit of the world's great literature wherein he is made to bless his sons must be the work of some unknown later author, who had seen what the twelve tribes became. Probably there never were any such twelve sons, for at least part of the twelve are almost certainly the mere personification of tribes. But even so, there remains the fact that Jacob has impressed himself upon the world as only a few hundred men have done. That in itself is a strong claim to greatness.

By the same token, Jacob's son Joseph was another of the world's great benefactors. He alone among the so-called sons of Jacob does not represent a tribe. He is also the one about whom we have the fullest and most exact information. Therefore, he stands out as an unmistakable historic personage, far more clearly than any of the others. The story of Joseph's interpretation of dreams illustrates a common practice of his time, and is a tribute to his mental acumen. The story of his sale to the Midianite merchants by his brothers is typical of what happened in those barbarous days. His contributions to the economic and social system of the Egyptians are the chief proof of his greatness. Son and great-grandson, as he was, of two of the world's great citizens, he was sold as a slave to Egypt through the jealousy of his brothers, but speedily made himself a power in the land. Finding that the crops were very erratic, by reason, as we suppose, of a period of climatic stress, he sets himself to work to devise an economic remedy. He works out a system of public storehouses in which a large reserve of food is gradually accumulated. His foresight proves warranted. One of the worst and most prolonged of Egyptian famines ensues, and the people are desperate. They flock cityward seeking food; they sell their land and themselves. Pharaoh and the favored priestly class become all-powerful. Aside from Joseph's unique contribution, the course of events closely resembles that which occurs again and again during periods of scanty crops and famines. In China, Rome, India, and Russia, periods of drought have repeatedly sent hordes of people cityward, and caused them to sell their land to large landholders, who have reduced the remaining peasantry to serfdom.

In later generations Moses and Aaron continued the line of great men. According to one of the biblical genealogies they were great-grandsons of Levi, the brother of Joseph. On this basis, as we have seen, the period from Abraham to Moses comprises only seven generations, or perhaps two hundred and fifty years. Of course, there is no certainty that the genealogies are correct even in their main statements, and they certainly are wrong in details. Nevertheless, they show that in spite of the figures in other chapters, the writer of this particular genealogy believed that the whole period of Israelite history previous to Moses was relatively short. Moreover, they show that it was almost universally believed that Moses was in the direct line of descent from Abraham and Jacob. Now Moses is almost universally considered one of the world's greatest religious teachers. Almost no one doubts that he was the original leader who gave shape to the early Jewish religion. Nor does there seem to be much doubt that he was a descendant of Jacob. With him were associated other leaders of no small ability, including his brother Aaron, and his lieutenant Joshua. They, too, were of the same kinship, descendants of Jacob.

This line of closely related great men extending through many generations brings us to one of the most extraordinary facts as to the beginnings of the Hebrew people. This fact remains unaltered in its essence, even if the genealogical material in the Bible is much more doubtful than would appear from what we have said. The Bible may make mistakes as to individual genealogies, it makes no mistakes in depicting the main social customs of the times. A unique social custom is what we shall now illustrate. According to the biblical account Jacob, Joseph, Moses, and the other early Israelites originated by the same biological process which produces the finest types of domestic animals. There lies before me at the present moment the pedigree of Laet, probably the greatest prize-winner among Percheron horses in the first quarter of the present century. In all essential respects the pedigree is identical with the genealogy of the Patriarchs and the early Israelites.

In the days of Abraham and onward until long after the Israelites had settled in Palestine, the marriage of near relatives was apparently as common as among the Egyptians. In later days there was a strict Jewish law that an heiress must marry her cousin, the son of her father's brother, in order to keep the property in the family. That in itself would produce relatively limited lines of descent in many of the richer and more powerful families, especially if monogamy was practised, as in the later days. In early times even more intimate marriages were permitted, and marriages outside the family or clan were looked upon with disapproval. Thus Sarah, the wife of Abraham, was also his sister, the daughter of his father, but of a different mother. When the time came for Isaac to be married, his father was very unwilling that he should marry an outsider, as his half-brother, Ishmael, had done. Inasmuch as there were no near

relatives living in Palestine, Abraham sent a trusty servant back
to Haran to get a wife for his son. He found Rebecca, the daughter of Isaac's cousin, Bethuel. But she was much more than her
husband's first cousin once removed. Her father, Nahor, had
married his own niece, Milcah. Moreover, the marriage customs
of that time make it highly probable that Milcah's mother was a
close kinswoman of her husband. In the next generation Isaac's
son, Esau, like Ishmael, is said to have married outside the immediate family, but Jacob, the favorite son and heir, was not
permitted to take a wife among the "daughters of the land."
He was sent back to Haran, where he married his two cousins,
Leah and Rachel, daughters of his mother's brother.

The relationships become so complicated, and different generations intermarry to such an extent that it is hard to follow
the genealogies. The net result, however, is that Jacob's sons
by Rachel and Leah were of nearly the same blood as their great-
grandfather, Abraham. Along two lines they were the sixth
generation from their ancestor Terah, who was Abraham's father,
and the original migrant from Chaldea, along two others the
fifth, and along two more, the fourth. If there had been no intermarriage of relatives, they would normally have derived from
Terah either one, two, or four sixty-fourths of their inheritance,
according to which line of descent we follow, and an equal amount
from his wife. As a matter of fact, even the incomplete genealogy
in Genesis ascribes fourteen-sixty-fourths of their ancestry to
Terah, ten-sixty-fourths to the one of his wives who was the
mother of Abraham, and four-sixty-fourths to the wife who was
the mother of Sarah. How much intermarriage there was along
the unrecorded lines of descent representing the unknown thirty-
six-sixty-fourths of the ancestry, we do not know, but probably
a good deal. Marriages of near kin were especially probable in
such a case, for if Terah and Abraham migrated as recorded in
the Bible, their descendants presumably formed a small group
widely separated from most of their own people. Therefore, the
choice of wives was very limited unless the young men married
aliens. Moreover, the biblical account suggests prosperity among

the whole kinship, so that heiresses were presumably obliged to marry their cousins very frequently. In addition to all this, it is quite probable that there were other marriages between brothers and sisters, or uncles and nieces, like those recorded in the case of Abraham and Milcah. Even as the genealogy now stands, Joseph, for example, who was Abraham's great-grandson, derived three-eighths of his inheritance from the same parentage as Abraham, although normally he would derive only one-eighth if there were no marriages of kin. But since other kin marriages doubtless occurred in the unrecorded part of Joseph's ancestry, Joseph's germ-plasm presumably resembled that of Abraham at least as much as that of a son resembles that of his father.

This does not end the matter, for Amram, the father of Moses, is said to have married his father's sister, that is, his aunt. If this sort of thing persisted through all the period when the Jews were in Egypt, as presumably it did, the germ-plasm of Moses, Aaron, and Joshua, and of Moses's gifted sister, Miriam, must have been much the same as that of their ancestors, Jacob and Abraham, especially if the period covered by the history is as short as seems probable. But even if the period stretches well beyond three hundred years, and even up to seven or eight hundred, the principle remains the same. Marriages within the immediate circle of relatives were the rule; the Israelites were a small group among an alien people; in Egypt they despised the Egyptians, and the Egyptians looked with scorn upon the rude herders of the desert. Thus the chances of marriage with outsiders were slight. Nevertheless, we must not carry the argument too far. The general principle is all that is important. The principle is that the early Israelites were accustomed to marrying their cousins, sisters, aunts, and other near relatives. They also objected strenuously to having heirs and heiresses marry any one but near relatives. Other children might marry outside, but they had to go off to other lands, as in the stories of Ishmael and Esau. Even as late as the days of David, the story of Amon and his infatuation for Tamar suggests that it was considered proper for a man to marry his half-sister, if not his sister.

But is not such close inbreeding the very way to create a weak and imbecile race? Not if the original strain is strong. There are hundreds of examples of this kind among animals. In a good strain the good qualities tend to become intensified. In fact, the intensification of qualities is the great danger as well as the great recommendation of close inbreeding. If the qualities thus intensified are bad, the results of inbreeding are disastrous, which is one reason for the well-grounded prejudice against it. If the qualities are high, and there are no serious counteracting qualities, successive generations may show no diminution of the original ability, or even an increase.

In the human race it is often supposed that the marriage of brothers and sisters, or even of cousins, results in feeble-minded offspring, epileptics, deaf-mutes, and other degenerate types. But Charles Darwin married his cousin, and had five sons, four of whom attained fame because of sterling character and high scientific achievement. Many similar cases could be cited. The well-founded prejudice against the marriage of close kin, especially of brothers and sisters, arises largely from the fact that experience has proved that it is socially unwise. Accordingly, in our own day it rarely occurs, except among degenerates. Naturally, the union of a degenerate brother and sister, or of a degenerate father and daughter, is practically certain to produce degenerates —in many cases worse than the parents. On the other hand, if marriages of brothers and sisters occur among people of especially high ability, that same ability is likely to be perpetuated.

Cases like that of the early Israelites, where close kindred intermarried for many generations, have occurred frequently, but only among the pharaohs of Egypt have they been carefully studied. Sir Marc A. Ruffer, in his *Studies in the Paleopathology of Egypt*, has made a most interesting investigation of a notable example of this kind, which occurred at the very period when the Jews were in Egypt. In ancient Egypt the woman was the legal head of the house. She owned the property, including the throne, and it passed from her to her daughters. Nevertheless, the men of Egypt, like the men everywhere else, assumed most of the responsibility. If they were to remain in power, it was necessary to exclude other families by having the crown-princess marry her brother or some other near relative. The case was much like that of the Jewish law compelling an heiress to marry her cousin. In many Egyptian dynasties the marriage of brothers and sisters continued for generation after generation.

Doctor Ruffer has selected for special study the Eighteenth Dynasty, which ruled Egypt in the sixteenth, fifteenth, and fourteenth centuries before Christ, a period when Egyptian power reached one of its highest points. The dynasty began when the Hyksos, or shepherd kings, were driven out of Egypt after ruling there for one or two hundred years. The Israelites perhaps went to Egypt while the Hyksos were ruling, and were well received because the rulers, like themselves, were nomadic keepers of cattle. Ahmose I, the founder of the eighteenth dynasty, was a vigorous, sturdy man, who drove the foreign pharaohs out of the kingdom, and made the land relatively secure against further invasion. He undertook a systematic restoration of the great architectural monuments of Upper Egypt. He married his sister. Their son, Amenhotep I, according to Popenoe's summary,* extended the empire by reconquering Nubia, repelling the Libyans, and invading Syria as far as the Euphrates River. So much was he venerated that divine honors were paid to him for six hundred years after his death. This monarch, like most of the pharoahs and most of the Jewish patriarchs, had children by several wives, one of whom was his sister. Her daughter, Aahmes, married a half-brother, Thutmose I. Their kinship was like that of Abraham and Sarah. Thutmose, like his father, was a man of parts. He consolidated his father's work in Nubia and Syria, and was a noted builder at home. Queen Hatshepsut, a daughter born to Thutmose I and his half-sister, was so strong a character that she overshadowed her husband and half-brother, Thutmose II. She was the actual sovereign, a wise ruler of far-reaching influence—the greatest queen of Egypt.

Hatshepsut was succeeded by her daughter and by a stepson,

* Popenoe, Paul, "The Marriage of Kin," *The Scientific Monthly*, vol. 17, November, 1923.

Thutmose III, who was not only half-brother, but apparently cousin, to his sister-wife. This monarch's character, says J. H. Breasted, "stands forth with more color and individuality than that of any king of early Egypt, except Akhnaton. We see the man of a tireless energy unknown in any Pharaoh, before or since; the man of versatility, designing exquisite vases in a moment of leisure; the lynx-eyed administrator, who launched his armies upon Asia with one hand and with the other crushed the extortionate tax-gatherer. . . . His reign marks an epoch, not only in Egypt, but in the whole East as we know it in his age. . . . He built the first real empire, and is thus the first character possessed of universal aspects, the first world hero."

And he was the product of five unbroken generations of brother-sister marriage. This great king married his half-sister. Their son Amenhotep II was a man of extraordinary physical strength, who claimed that none of his subjects could bend his bow. His reign was marked by energy and military success. He married Tias, whose pedigree is uncertain, although she has been called his half-sister.

Their son, Thutmose IV, was an energetic lion-hunter in his youth, and a successful leader in war after he ascended the throne. His marriage to a Babylonian princess resulted in a son, Amenhotep III, whose ascension to the throne broke the line of brother-sister Pharaohs. As there were no more kingdoms within easy reach to be conquered, and the king's tastes were pacific, or perhaps because prosperity was wide-spread, his reign is marked by great development of the pursuits of peace—by expansion of commerce and patronage of the fine arts. He took a Syrian princess as his bride. Their son, Akhnaton, bearing in his germ-plasm a quarter part of the long brother-sister inheritance, is generally accounted the greatest of all Egyptian sovereigns. He was an ardent religious reformer, of transcendant enthusiasm, the highest courage, and the highest moral standards. He brought the dynasty to an end, for he was succeeded by his stepson, the young Tutankhamen, the finding of whose tomb attained great notoriety from 1923 to 1925.

The salient characteristics of the Eighteenth Dynasty, as summed up by Doctor Ruffer, are, first, tireless energy, which enabled Egypt to resist its foreign foes, carry the Egyptian flag abroad, and establish wise government at home; second, an enlightened taste for the fine arts, most forcibly shown in the artistic reforms of Akhnaton. In these nine generations, issued from consanguineous marriages, there is no diminution of mental force. The energy characteristic of Ahmose I is found two hundred years afterward in Akhnaton, used, it is true, for different objects and higher ideals, but as intense in 1375–1358 as in 1580–1557 (B. C.).

The subject of consanguineous marriages is so interesting and so germane to our topic of how a great race originates, that I shall summarize Doctor Popenoe's conclusions a little further. One of the specific evils popularly attributed to such marriages is infertility. Data are lacking to compare the fertility of the members of the Eighteenth Dynasty with that of other families of the same period, but it is certain that the fecundity of the royal family was not below normal.

Again, children born of consanguineous unions are sometimes said to be short-lived. While the average duration of life in ancient Egypt is unknown, it is easy to ascertain the longevity of the male rulers of this dynasty. Eight of them show an average of forty-four years, which is not bad, considering the stress to which a military ruler is subjected.

The physical proportions of these rulers, as measured on their mummies, are good—many of them were men of notable strength. Doctor Ruffer finds no evidence that idiocy, deaf-mutism, or other diseases generally attributed to consanguineous marriage ever occurred among the members of this dynasty, and as far as can be ascertained from mummified bodies, masks, and statues, the features of both men and women were fine, distinguished, and handsome.

The result of this inquiry is that a royal family, in which consanguineous marriage was the rule, produced nine distinguished rulers, among whom were Ahmose, the liberator of his country; Thutmose III, one of the greatest conquerors and administrators that the world has ever seen; Amenhotep IV (Akhnaton), the fearless religious reformer; the beloved queen Nefertari, who was placed among the gods after her death; Aahmes, the beautiful queen, and Hatshepsut, the greatest queen of Egypt. . . . There is no evidence that the physical characteristics or mental power of the family were unfavorably influenced by the repeated consanguineous marriages.

The kings and queens of the Nineteenth Dynasty, which followed, were probably lineal descendants of the Eighteenth. "Rameses II," says Ruffer, "the great historical figure of this dynasty, married two of his sisters and had four children by the first and three, or possibly four, by the second. He is said to have married two of his daughters, but the evidence on this point is not conclusive. By other wives and concubines the king is said to have had 106 other sons, and 47 daughters, therefore this descendant of a long line of consanguineous marriages cannot be said to have been infertile."

A thousand years later another dynasty is cited by Ruffer and Popenoe as of wholly different race, but offering additional striking evidence as to the marriage of near kin. This is the dynasty founded after the death of Alexander the Great by his bold and patient general, Ptolemy Soter. The first four Ptolemies were not sprung from consanguineous marriages; it is, therefore, particularly useful to compare them with the later rulers, among whom brother-sister matings had become customary.

The general reputation of the Ptolemies is, of course, bad; morally they were the conventional type of Oriental despot, wicked and unscrupulous. But they were not weaklings; whatever their moral defects (for which environment must receive some credit, as well as heredity), they displayed abundant physical and mental energy. The direct line of the Ptolemies came to an end with the twelfth ruler of the dynasty, "not because the women had become barren, or the men unable to beget children, but because all the male descendants born in legitimate wedlock had been killed or exiled."

The sceptre was taken up by Auletes, an illegitimate son of Ptolemy X, and was finally laid down by his daughter Cleopatra

VII, whose fame in history is sufficiently great, although not altogether spotless. It must be remembered, however, that public opinion as to her character has been based either on the accounts of her contemporary enemies, or on those of a long line of romancers, ranging in calibre from William Shakespeare and John Dryden down to the latest writer of vaudeville songs, or "Sunday Supplement" thrillers. Here is Doctor Ruffer's summary:

> The Ptolemies born from consanguineous unions were neither better nor worse than the first four kings of the same family issued from non-consanguineous marriages, and had the same general characteristics. Their conduct of foreign affairs and internal administration was in every way remarkable and energetic. They were not unpopular in their capital, and the Alexandrians rallied round their ruler when the Romans entered Egypt and resisted the foreigner. Though much has been written about the awful sexual immoralities of the Ptolemies . . . their standard of morality was certainly not lower than that of their fellow townsmen. The children from these incestuous marriages displayed no lack of mental energy. Both men and women were equally strong, intelligent, capable, and wicked. Certain pathological characteristics doubtless ran through the family. Gout and obesity weighed heavily on the Ptolemies, but the tendency to obesity existed before the consanguineous unions had taken place. The male and female effigies on coins are those of very stout, well-nourished persons. The theory that the offspring of incestuous marriages is short-lived receives no confirmation from the history of the Ptolemies. . . . Omitting those who died violent deaths, the average length of life of the Ptolemies was sixty-four years. Sterility was not a result of these consanguineous marriages. No case of idiocy, deaf-mutism, etc., in Ptolemaic families has been recorded.

Turn back now to the Hebrew patriarchs. According to the book of Genesis their biological history was almost identical with that of the contemporary pharaohs. Starting with Terah, of whom we know nothing save that he is said to have migrated 600 miles and was the father of Abraham and Sarah, and the grandfather of Lot, a long line of closely consanguineous marriages is reported. Even if the stories of the patriarchs are largely traditions, there is every reason to suppose that such marriages were well-nigh universal among the people from whom sprang the Israelites. The result was three of the world's greatest leaders,

Abraham, Jacob, and Joseph, almost in successive generations; then a gap of uncertain length, and finally Moses, a man of perhaps even higher calibre, and around him others like Aaron and Joshua, whose talents also rank high. Such a family history, joined with the evidence of the Eighteenth Dynasty and the Ptolemies, suggests that it is relatively easy to build up a group of competent people by choosing parents of uncommon ability and then guarding the marriages of the children. But that is neither here nor there, so far as our present purpose is concerned. We are interested in the fact that the great Jewish race appears to have originated in the same biological fashion as great strains of race horses or cattle, and that some of the most steadily powerful and original lines of Egyptian rulers originated in the same way. Here is an almost unknown historical process whose ramifications may be most interesting in the interpretation of the past, and perhaps helpful in building a higher type of progress in the future.

CHAPTER XIII

THE PURGING OF THE HEBREWS

IF a racial group is to achieve great things for century after century, it needs a good inheritance and must preserve that inheritance. One way to accomplish this is by strict regulations as to marriage, and by weeding out all individuals who do not conform to a certain standard. Among the Hebrews these methods were rigidly employed, although they themselves had no idea of it. How long the Children of Israel stayed in Egypt we do not know. Perhaps only a few generations, as suggested by the genealogies, perhaps much longer, as suggested by the four hundred and thirty years mentioned in the Bible. We do know, however, that while they were there they tended to keep apart from the Egyptians. The Hebrews were keepers of cattle. They lived in Goshen on the borders of the delta, apparently beyond the limits of irrigation. To the Egyptians they were an unclean people; they, on their part, scorned the Egyptians, as is apt to be the case among keepers of animals, especially nomads, when they come in contact with plodding, settled, agricultural people. "Shame enters the family with the plough," say the Arabs. Of course there must have been more or less intermarriage, but Israelites were more likely to be absorbed by the Egyptians than were Egyptians to become Hebrews.

When "there arose a king that knew not Joseph" the Hebrews were regarded with less and less favor. They were perhaps tolerated only because they could be used as slaves. But at length a series of great disasters fell upon Egypt, and led to the departure of the Israelites. In the Bible the disasters take the form of plagues which Jehovah brought upon the Egyptians because of their oppression of the Hebrews. Only seven are mentioned in the earliest of the documents that compose the book of Genesis, but the other three are inserted in such a way that they

194

conform very closely to the sequence that a geographer and climatologist would expect. Moreover, in this case, unlike some others, the discrepancies between one account and another are insignificant.

It is universally agreed that the plagues are a more or less distorted version of natural disasters connected with the annual floods of the Nile. One favorite idea is that they represent the successive phenomena of the seasons. If this is not the case, the only alternative is that they represent a season or period of special aridity, when the Nile fell to a phenomenally low level. The only apparent objection to this hypothesis is that the Bible says nothing about the famine which would inevitably follow. But the Israelites were on the point of leaving Egypt, and therefore did not experience any trouble from the failure of the crops in the Nile valley. But they had plenty of trouble from dryness, bad water, and lack of food. In fact, they are represented as finding the desert far worse than they anticipated, and its waters salty and undrinkable at places where they had expected to find them good. All this agrees with many other scattered bits of evidence indicating that the thirteenth century before Christ saw the culmination of a pronounced period of climatic stress characterized by extremes of drought in the dry regions around the Mediterranean. Part of the evidence has been given elsewhere, and we have seen how it appears to have set many nomadic tribes in motion, thereby almost wrecking civilization. This period is so critical in ancient history and had such a profound effect upon the history of the Israelites that we shall relate the story of the plagues in some detail. Moreover, that story is in itself most interesting.

According to the book of Exodus, Aaron and Moses performed a series of signs or miracles in order to persuade the Egyptians to let the Israelites escape from oppression and take refuge in the desert. In the first of these Aaron casts his rod upon the earth, and it becomes a serpent. The Egyptian magicians do likewise, but Aaron's serpent eats the others. Since serpents frequently figure in supposedly miraculous events in many religions, we are probably safe in dismissing this first "sign" as merely a mythical introduction to the real events which follow.

The first and most important of these is that "all the waters that were in the river (Nile) were turned to blood. And the fish that were in the river died; and the river became foul, and the Egyptians could not drink water from the river; and the blood was throughout all the land of Egypt. . . . And all the Egyptians digged round about the river for water to drink; for they could not drink the water of the river."

Aside from the word "blood" this is a scientific description of what happens when the Nile falls to a phenomenally low level. At such a time the river suggests blood, for it becomes a sluggish, dark, dirty, repulsive stream, with a bad odor and full of slimy, decaying fish and weeds. From such a river the frogs would naturally depart in search of a better habitat. So Jehovah said to Moses: "Go in unto Pharaoh and say unto him, Thus saith Jehovah, Let my people go, that they may serve me. And if thou refuse to let them go, behold, I will smite all thy borders with frogs; and the river shall swarm with frogs, which shall go up and come into thy house, and into thy bedchamber, and upon thy bed, and into the house of thy servants, and upon thy people, and into thine ovens, and into thy kneading-troughs: and the frogs shall come up both upon thee, and upon thy people, and upon all thy servants."

Here again we have a faithful description of what would actually happen if the river fell to a very low level. It is well known that when the water in which they live becomes too bad and too scanty, frogs leave their homes en masse, and hop across the country to find a new home. Any one who knows the habits of the frog can well believe that they hopped into the Egyptians' kneading-troughs, into their mud ovens with round, open tops, and into their beds lying on the floor. The vast majority of them must have died ere long, thus adding their decaying corpses to the fetid river as a source of atmospheric pollution. Here is what the Bible says about it: "And the frogs died out of the houses, out of the courts, and out of the fields. And they gathered them together in heaps; and the land stank." The writer of Exodus certainly knew how to make his descriptions vivid.

The next plague is just what one would expect. "Aaron smote the dust of the earth, and there were lice upon man, and upon beast; all the dust of the earth became lice throughout all the land of Egypt." Why not? There are always lice in Egypt, some of them in almost every family and upon almost every beast. If the water became so bad and scanty as the story indicates, neither man nor beast would be able to wash, and the lice would thrive till they became a perfect torment.

Meanwhile the frogs were decaying. Flies settled upon them and filled them with millions of eggs. "I will send swarms of flies upon thee," is the way the words are put into the mouth of Jehovah, "and upon thy servants, and upon thy people, and into thy houses; and the houses of the Egyptians shall be full of swarms of flies, and also the ground whereon they are. And I will set apart in that day the land of Goshen, in which my people dwell, that no swarms of flies shall be there. . . . And there came grievous swarms of flies into the house of Pharaoh and into his servants' houses; and in all the land of Egypt the land was corrupted by reason of the swarms of flies." All this is thoroughly scientific, even to the exception of the land of Goshen. That land was excepted because it did not lie near the river, it was not irrigated, and hence was not overwhelmed by the frogs to any great extent.

Now comes a still more terrible affliction. Moses speaks again to Pharaoh: "Let my people go, that they may serve me. For if thou refuse to let them go, and wilt hold them still, behold the hand of Jehovah is upon thy cattle which are in the field, upon the horses, upon the asses, upon the camels, upon the herds, and upon the flocks; there shall be a very grievous murrain. And Jehovah shall make a distinction between the cattle of Israel and the cattle of Egypt; and there shall nothing die of all that belongeth to the children of Israel."

Doubtless the flies that afflicted the land included not only the ordinary housefly, but horse-flies, and others that would help in carrying disease. The domestic animals must have been weakened by bad water, they must have been weak from lack of food; and it was natural that disease should break forth violently. But the animals of the Israelites would escape in large measure, for they would not be bothered with flies, their water supply may even have been about the same as usual, and the dry grass on which they pastured beyond the limits of irrigation would not suffer at first, even though a series of dry years might greatly reduce it.

The same conditions which weakened the cattle of the Egyptians also weakened the people. And dust must have filled the land, for the fields became dry, and there was no means of keeping down the fine dust which forms all the fertile land of the Nile valley. Small wonder then that the story next takes this turn: "Take to you handfuls of ashes of the furnace," says Jehovah, "and let Moses sprinkle it toward heaven in the sight of Pharaoh. And it shall become small dust over all the land of Egypt, and shall be a boil breaking forth with blains upon man and beast, throughout all the land of Egypt." It is easy to picture the ashy gray dust. It was doubtless whirled a thousand feet into the heavens by great dust whirls such as any one who has lived in the desert has seen again and again. Under their influence I have seen the air become so full of dust that one could see only a short distance. When one of them passes over a house, or tent, it blows the suffocating dust into every nook and corner, the eyes smart, the lungs are choked. No wonder boils and blains broke out on man and beast.

The next plague, "hail, such as hath not been in Egypt since the day it was founded even until now," may seem out of place in the midst of a great drought. But a low Nile does not arise from lack of such scanty rain as commonly falls in Egypt. It arises from lack of rain in the mountains of central Africa, fifteen hundred miles farther south. All the rain that falls in Egypt would make scarcely a trickle in the bed of the Nile. A terrific thunder storm in Egypt giving rise to tremendous hail is not at all inconsistent with extreme drought in Abyssinia, a few months earlier, at the time when the Nile ought to have been replenished. In fact, it is what one would expect. Such storms are characteristic of periods of extreme climatic stress, and tend to be more severe in proportion to the severity of the drought. Witness the deluges of rain that fell on an almost rainless portion of the west coast of South America, in 1925, when the ocean currents suffered a temporary derangement. We may well believe that "Jehovah sent thunder and hail, and fire ran down upon the earth; and Jehovah rained hail upon the land of Egypt. So there was hail and fire mingled with the hail, very grievous, such as had not been in all the land of Egypt since it became a nation. And the hail smote throughout all the land of Egypt all that was in the field, both man and beast; and the hail smote every herb of the field, and brake every tree of the field. Only in the land of Goshen, where the children of Israel were, was there no hail."

Except for the fact that the words of Jehovah and the instrumentality of Moses are invoked at every turn, we seem to be dealing with a faithful record of the actual phenomena of nature. So, too, with the next affliction. It seems that in spite of the lowness of the river some of the crops had made a start. Perhaps the flood rose as usual, but not very high, and then receded rapidly to a very low level. At any rate, after the great storm it appears that "the flax and the barley were smitten; for the barley was in the ear, and the flax was in bloom. But the wheat and the spelt were not smitten; for they were not grown up." But they did not last long, for Jehovah said: "I will bring locusts into thy border. . . . Then Jehovah brought an east wind upon the land all that day, and all the night; and when it was morning, the east wind brought the locusts. And the locusts went up over all the land of Egypt; and rested in all the borders of Egypt; very grievous were they; before them there were no such locusts as they, neither after them shall be such. For they covered the face of the whole earth, so that the land was darkened; and they did eat every herb of the land, and all the fruit of the trees which the hail had left; and there remained not any green thing, either tree or herb of the field through all the land of Egypt."

I have seen just such an affliction in the desert of Transcaspia. I know of few things more irritating than the steady hop, hop, hop of an army of invading locusts. And never have I seen the temper of a people change more rapidly from gay and happy to dark and morose than when the locusts "did eat every herb of the land and all the fruit of the trees." Just such swarms of locusts are one of the best known and most dreaded of the evils which afflict the majority of dry regions, especially in times of scanty rain.

As I read this account of the plagues of Egypt I am filled with astonishment at its exact accordance with facts. After the locusts had stripped the land of the last traces of vegetation there arose "an exceedingly strong west wind, which took up the locusts, and drove them into the Red Sea. . . . And Moses stretched forth his hand toward heaven, and there was a thick darkness in all the land of Egypt three days; they saw not one another, neither rose any one from his place for three days." Do you believe that such a thing is possible? I might not believe, had I not lived in the desért. I remember vividly a day in Chinese Turkestan when a violent wind stopped our progress in mid afternoon. The air was so full of dust that we could see only a few feet; the sand cut our faces. The only thing to do was to seat ourselves back to the wind and wait till the wind had blown itself out. Night shut in long before the sun had set, and not till late the next morning did the sun appear as a faint red ball through the dense cloud of dust. Two days later "the air was still so full of dust that we could scarcely see half a mile. In the dense haze the larger dunes loomed like distant mountains; again and again we were amazed to find ourselves suddenly at the foot of a small hill, which we had felt must be a mountain, miles away." At Broken Hill, in the desert of Australia, I was told that the dust is sometimes so thick that automobile lights are useless. They cannot pierce the murky air more than a few feet. If such conditions were magnified a little, a west wind from the desert might bring to Egypt almost exactly the conditions described in the book of Exodus.

All this leads naturally to the last and greatest of the plagues.

"And it came to pass at midnight that Jehovah smote all the first-born in the land of Egypt, from the first-born of Pharaoh that sat on his throne unto the first-born of the captive that was in the dungeon; and all the first-born of the cattle." Barring the fact that others as well as the first-born doubtless died, this seems to be merely a way of saying that the culmination of the afflictions of Egypt was pestilence. Perhaps it was the terrible scourge known as the Black Death in the Middle Ages. Perhaps it was famine-fever, or typhus, diseases which are common when people have been weakened by hunger, boils, and other kinds of distress. Some such disease is just what would be expected as the climax of the horrors arising from an extraordinarily low Nile. And through all these horrors the Israelites would largely escape because as keepers of cattle and dwellers in tents on the borders of Egypt, they were not especially affected by the vagaries of the great river. This remarkably full picture of the results of a climatic condition whose occurrence is suggested by other conditions at this period does much to give confidence in the general reliability of the biblical narratives.

Now let us turn to the wanderings of the Israelites in the desert. In our childhood, if we studied the story of the Israelites, we generally thought of the Exodus as a great march of orderly bands of thousands of people. Many of us have seen pictures of the pillar of fire by night, and the cloud by day. We have imagined it as passing to the rear of the column when danger threatened from enemies. But few of us have pictured the Israelites as they really were. In ancient days the deserts of Sinai and Arabia appear, for the most part, to have been better watered than now. They presumably had more springs and water-holes, and more water in each spring. Oases also were probably more numerous and larger than at present, and cultivation spread farther into the desert. Nevertheless, there is every reason to believe that the desert in those days was very terrible. In fact, in the days of the plagues it may temporarily have been as dry as now.

Naturally then, one of the first difficulties of the Israelites was a spring of bitter water at Marah. Any one who has travelled in the desert knows how common such salty springs are. I have travelled where for weeks we drank water which tasted so salty that it was good for nothing except soup. It gave all of us indigestion. In eastern Persia, after a night spent at a waterless camp, I have the next day approached a spring and heard the men wondering whether we could drink it. In summer, they say, the water is scanty and absolutely undrinkable, but we were there in winter and happened to find it drinkable. The Israelites, on the contrary, when they reached the bitter waters of Marah found them undrinkable.

Later they came to Rephidim, where there was no water at all. "Give us water that we may drink!" cried the people. And Moses smote the rock with his magic rod and water gushed forth. In a small way an experience of my own, in northwestern Arizona, illustrates the situation. I was crossing one of the few large uninhabited tracts in the United States. During four days my Mormon companion and I saw no sign of human habitation except two tents of Indians. One of the Indians attempted to guide us to a spring which we should reach at sunset. After a long, hot, wearisome day, during which we rode bareback because our wagon had broken down, we reached the spring. But there was no spring there, only a damp rock. We searched for water, but there was no Moses to smite the rock, or to dig into it so that water might gush forth. The only thing to do was to go on. So we tramped from six o'clock in the evening till two in the morning, down a close, hot, suffocating rocky valley. Then we came to the Colorado River. To this day I can feel the sliminess of the lukewarm water as we threw ourselves on our stomachs on the sands and eagerly gulped it down. So muddy was the water that in twenty-four hours a pail of it would settle only enough so that there were a couple of inches of clear liquid on top. The rest of the mud would not settle. Perhaps the Nile was something like that when it looked like blood, except that it was intensely foul instead of merely muddy.

Difficulties like these are the ordinary routine in the desert.

Where such conditions exist it may be possible for large bodies of well-equipped troops to cross a desert by rapid marches. It certainly is not possible for nomadic keepers of sheep and camels to wander about for decades in groups of thousands, as the Israelites are reported to have done in the biblical account. But perhaps the Bible comes nearer to the truth than we sometimes think. It says that after the Israelites had been gone from Egypt a little while, Moses' father-in-law, Jethro, who seems to have been a sagacious man of the desert, advised his son-in-law not to carry on all the work of administration himself, but to appoint assistants as "rulers of thousands, rulers of hundreds, rulers of fifties, and rulers of tens." Of course this passage may reflect the organization of the Jews at the time when this section of the book of Exodus was put in final form, hundreds of years after the events which it describes. But may not Jethro really have said to Moses: "Why do you keep so many people together? You will all die unless you split into small bands." And doubtless that is what they did, for otherwise no nomadic people with their flocks and herds could possibly wander through the desert for scores of years.

So we may picture the Israelites of the Exodus as living in little encampments much like those of the Arabs of to-day. Most of their animals were either sheep or goats. Cattle, in the modern sense of the word, and likewise horses, were almost or entirely lacking. Even camels and donkeys were probably scarce. Doubtless the nomads lived in low tents of dark brown goat's hair, supported by many little poles, each pole making a hillock. In our day such tents are rarely more than eight feet high in the centre, and large parts of them are so low that one can only walk in a stooping position.

Inside the tents there were no iron tools, for not until the days of David did iron become common among the Israelites. Doubtless there were stone implements of various shapes and sizes. Presumably spoons and bowls of wood were used for the sour milk which formed the main article of diet. The milk was doubtless kept in leather bags, made like those of to-day from entire skins of goats or sheep turned wrong-side out. And doubt-less then, as now, the hair was only imperfectly scraped from the hide, and floated freely in the milk. Sour cheese was presumably put away in such bags during the months when milk was abundant, just after the lambing season, toward the end of the relatively wet winter. And doubtless the cheese then, as now, was very hard and sour, and full of bits of goats' hair.

The rest of the furniture in the tents, presumably, consisted of a few simple implements used in caring for the animals and in cooking, but most of the cooking was done over open fires. The Israelites may have had a few vessels of copper, silver, or gold, but even copper was a great luxury. Iron vessels were unknown, and earthenware vessels are so breakable that few nomads find it worth while to carry them. The remaining furniture in the tents consisted largely, no doubt, of felts and woollen cloth, for linen was the expensive luxury of the rich, and there was no cotton so far as we know. If we had seen the Israelites in those days they would have seemed ignorant, dirty, and backward, a people who had practically none of the conveniences of life, and who were still utterly barbarous, little better than savages.

Many authors have delighted in describing experiences of their own which run parallel to those of the Israelites. I, too, find this most interesting. For example, "the children of Israel also wept again, and said: Who shall give us flesh to eat? We remember the fish, which we did eat in Egypt for nought; the cucumbers and the melons, and the leeks, and the onions, and the garlic: but now our soul is dried away; there is nothing at all save this manna to look upon." And behold a great flight of quails alighted about the camp. And the people ate until they became sick, and many died. But how could the Israelites be so eager for flesh when they had plenty of sheep and goats?

Such a question shows a complete misunderstanding of the economics of life in the desert. The sheep and the goats represent capital, for the most part. Some of the male animals, to be sure, can be killed for food, but more must be used to buy grain, dates, implements, and clothing from the settled people of the better-watered lands around the desert. In hard times, especially when water and grass are scanty, the young animals die at such a rate that very few grow to maturity. Then the desert people dare not kill the adult animals, for that would destroy their capital and put them permanently face to face with starvation. If their cheese is gone, they must be content with milk, and happy are they if even that is available.

That is doubtless the way the Israelites felt. That they found quail in great abundance I can well believe. In northwestern Persia, for weeks, one winter, we shot desert quail each day, and ate them morning and night. We did not have them long enough to loathe them as did the Israelites, but we were glad to get something else.

Other difficulties beset these wanderers in the desert. A plague followed the abundance of quail, and at two other times the plague is said to have afflicted them. Whether the plague had anything to do with the quail we cannot say, but in Mongolia and Manchuria the outbreak of the fearful pneumonic form of the plague has been definitely proved to be associated with the use of marmots for food. Again "Jehovah sent fiery serpents among the people, and they bit the people, and much people of Israel died." It is not probable that any large percentage were killed by the bites of serpents, but even a few such deaths would make a great impression. Contrary to what is usually supposed, snakes are often abundant in deserts. In Transcaspia, for example, I have seen them in great numbers.

Two more great difficulties afflicted the Israelite wanderers. One was internal dissension. When people are suffering from bad and scanty water, from bad and scanty food, from pestilence and all sorts of other disasters, their tempers naturally are bad. The Israelites were not yet hardened to the real life of the desert. For several generations they had been living in a relatively comfortable land, on the Egyptian border, where they could easily buy grain and vegetables in exchange for their animals, and where they were protected from enemies. It is not strange that internal dissension arose, and that Aaron was persuaded to make a golden calf when Moses was away. It is quite in harmony with the spirit not only of the times but of their precarious situation, that Moses ordered the Levites to slaughter the worshippers of the calf. Korah's rebellion and the disobedience of Dathan and Abiram, for which the penalties are said to have been fire from heaven to consume Korah and his false incense-bearers, and an earthquake whereby the earth opened and swallowed up Dathan and Abiram with all their men and their families, are illustrations of the same thing.

Worse than this, perhaps, were the dangers from the people whom the Israelites met on their devious wanderings. Of course, there cannot be many people in a desert, but the Amalekites and others were there. Moreover, the borders of the desert were full of towns and villages. Like other sensible persons, the agricultural people who lived in the villages resented having bands of marauders camp upon their land, eat up the grass, and spoil the grain-fields by letting sheep and goats stray among them. In central Asia I once came in contact with a body of perhaps a thousand Dungans, or Chinese Mohammedans, who had been trying for a decade or more to settle. Driven from their home by droughts and over-population, they wandered forth much as did the Israelites. In one place, which I visited, they made a settlement beside a great river, where they thought that irrigation was possible. But the water proved too saline, and they had to move on. Another time they passed through a certain area and had a battle with the people of the land. They tried to settle somewhere else, but soon were driven out by the villagers. That is the sort of thing which was happening to the Israelites during this period of wandering.

Again, on the southern and eastern borders of Palestine I have seen the people of the desert trying to press in over the agricultural land. The agriculturists were trying likewise to press out into the desert, for they had planted considerable areas which for some years had not been cultivated. For a season or two they got good crops, and thought they could establish permanent villages beyond the old limits. Then came a bad year. I saw thousands of acres where the wheat had merely sprouted and sent up a few poor, little, spindling shoots. Grain that ought to have been two or three feet high, and thick with heavy heads, was six inches high, and very sparse, with heads too small to be worth reaping. The owners valued even that, if not as grain for themselves, at least as food for their flocks. But the desert people by the hundred came flocking in from their desiccated homes. In one place I saw them gathered in such numbers that thousands of camels dotted the plain. Elsewhere they had turned their sheep and camels into the grain-fields of the settled inhabitants. I was among them when they made raids and drove off the animals, not only of the nomads but of the villagers. Did the villagers submit to such things? Of course not. In spite of being much less warlike than the nomads, they retaliated, and fights were common. A missionary physician in Hebron, who had been practising there for sixteen years, told me that in all the years of his previous experience, he had never treated so many gunshot wounds as that summer. All this illustrates what happened to the wandering Hebrews. They were trying to penetrate lands where they were not wanted; every one, whether nomad or villager, was against them.

It makes no difference for our present purpose whether the wandering was forty years, or more, or less. Nor does it make any difference whether all the Israelites came from Egypt, or whether a part had always been in the desert, as is probable. The point to be emphasized is that the climatic crisis which forced them to leave Egypt also imposed upon them a period of strenuous natural selection. This was one of several times when the Jews passed through a tremendous sifting process, wherein many perished, or else abandoned their companions, and only a chosen remnant endured to the end. These crises appear to have been one of the greatest factors in giving the Jewish race its strongly marked characteristics. During the wanderings in the desert the death-rate, especially among those who left Egypt, must have been extremely high, and only the sturdiest survived. Indeed, the Bible says that in forty years all who left Egypt, save two of the spies, had perished.

The case of the Israelites at this time was closely analogous to that of the Armenians, which I have described in *The Character of Races*. Toward the end of the Great War, 1,000,000 Armenians, more or less, were driven from their home in the Armenian plateau into the Syrian desert, the northern part of the same desert where the Israelites wandered. Later they drifted back, chiefly through Aleppo, but only about a quarter returned. The rest had died. The returning sufferers had been half-starved; they had been almost frozen in the cold of winter, and parched and baked in the heat of summer. They came back in rags, covered with vermin, afflicted with sores, and weak and ill. At first their condition seemed hopeless, but the Red Cross physicians were surprised to find how quickly they responded to treatment. Cleanliness, clothing, good food and rest quickly restored them. When restored they seemed more intelligent and energetic than the average of their race. The reason is obvious. The afflictions of the desert had killed those with either organic or mental weaknesses. Only the strong, the vigorous, the mentally alert could survive. Moreover, many whose courage failed them had given up and "turned Turk," as they say.

This same sort of selection takes place whenever a group of people are suddenly subjected to conditions of great hardship. It is one of the most potent means of obtaining a strong and vigorous race. Thus, when the little clan of genuine Israelites was ready to enter Palestine, its members were presumably a picked remnant. They doubtless had the general qualities of nomads rather than of settled people. Even in Egypt they had been cattle-keepers, and during their later migration those who lacked the desert qualities would be the first to die. The desert qualities include not only physical vigor and power to endure hardship, but the capacity for strenuous exertion, at least for a short period. Another dominant quality is the power of leadership. Agricultural people can exist for centuries without leaders and without much necessity for being led. Nomads, on the other hand, need leaders at frequent intervals. When a sand storm comes up, when wolves stampede the flocks, when enemies make a raid, the prime necessity is some one who says: "You go this way; you others that way, and the rest of you yonder. Meet at the spring of Nebi Musa." Unless some one can do that, disaster, starvation, and death are almost certain.

The desert people must also have the capacity to obey as well as lead. The two things are different, but they go together; one is useless without the other. Then, too, if the desert man is to succeed, he must have considerable power of initiative. Alone in the desert in one of the frequent crises which overtake man or animals, he must be able to act on the spur of the moment. The point of the matter is that such crises, and the necessity for leadership and for submission, are almost daily events in the life of the desert people, whereas they occur infrequently in the lives of farmers, and still less in the lives of laborers in cities. Thus we infer, and the Bible record bears us out, that the Israelites came to the borders of Palestine with the desert vigor, the desert power of leadership and of submission, and the desert power of original and vigorous initiative. And with all this they had not lost the old religious zeal. It may have been dormant during the stay in Egypt, but it was doubtless inherent in the descendants of Abraham and Jacob. It flared up gloriously in Moses. Even though large sections of Genesis and Exodus are of late origin, enough of early date remains to indicate that during the wanderings the religious spirit was intensified, both culturally and biologically. Not only was Moses a supreme law-giver, but those who transgressed the religious ordinances were put to death or driven out from the camp. This, then, was the kind of people that were sifted out by the Exodus to be the future occupants of Palestine, the bearers of the flaming torch of the great religions of the West.

CHAPTER XIV

THE ISOLATION OF JUDEA

THE next step in our study of how geography and biology have modified the history of the Jews depends upon the land which they conquered. Just as biological selection was the great factor in founding the Jewish race, and climate was the great physical control of the desert wandering, so the relief of the earth's surface dominated their actions while conquering Palestine, and for the next few centuries. But first let us see why Palestine was the goal of the Hebrews in the desert. According to the Bible, they went there to reoccupy the home of Abraham, Isaac, and Jacob, but the Bible also repeatedly emphasizes the fact that Palestine was a land "flowing with milk and honey." A rainfall map of Asia shows a vast, lightly tinted area, embracing most of the western and central parts of the continent, but there is one isolated little dark spot on the eastern shores of the Mediterranean. The difference between twelve inches of rain, or less, out in the desert, and twenty or thirty near the seacoast, and probably more in the past, was what made Palestine the Chosen Land of the patriarchs, the goal of the Exodus.

Let us see what kind of land they went into. The division of Palestine into four long, narrow strips, running north and south, is well known. From west to east, as appears in Figure 17, the strips are: (1) the Philistine Plain, or Plain of Sharon along the Mediterranean coast; (2) the four western plateaus, which are by far the most important part historically; (3) the deep, narrow "rift" valley of the Jordan and the Dead Sea, also known as the Ghor and the Arabah, and (4) the eastern plateaus. The Philistine plain has good soil, and is level, easily tilled, and easily traversed. It is the kind of place where people like to live. It corresponds to the good counties in our previous comparisons of good land and poor in the United States. On the north the plain is

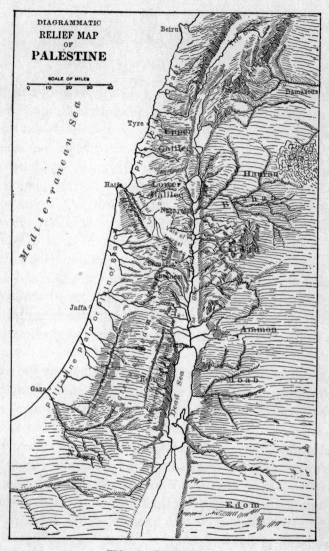

FIG. 17. PALESTINE.

From *Palestine and Its Transformation.* Courtesy of Houghton
Mifflin Co.

broken by the headland of Mount Carmel, then reappears around Haifa, but farther north disappears so that the hills come directly to the sea along most of the Phœnician coast.

East of the coastal plain the western plateaus form a north and south line—Judea in the south, then Samaria, Lower Galilee and Upper Galilee. But between Samaria and Lower Galilee there intervenes a very important feature—the lowland known as the Vale of Jezreel and the plain of Esdraelon. This forms a shallow east-and-west trough running from the Jordan Valley south of the Sea of Galilee to the Mediterranean at Haifa north of Mount Carmel. In the eyes of the geographer the four western plateaus are very different in character. Judea is composed of fairly hard strata, mainly limestone, which have been uplifted to a height of 2,500 or 3,000 feet above sea-level without much bending or folding. These rocks form a flat-topped arch, broken off steeply on the east side by a great geological fault and sloping down less abruptly, although quite steeply, toward the west. When nearly horizontal rocks like those forming the flat part of the arch are raised to high levels and subjected to the erosion of streams and rivers, the normal result is an intricate series of deep valleys with precipitous sides. These are omitted in Figure 17 because they would make the diagram too complex, but the whole Judean plateau is simply cut to pieces by them. If the different layers of rock vary in hardness, as is the case in Judea, the sides of the valleys consist of a series of steps, first a cliff where the rock is hard, next a relatively level bench where the rock is soft, then another cliff, another bench, and so on indefinitely. If the land has been uplifted in relatively recent geological times, as in Judea, the valleys are narrow, with rocky bottoms, and the cliffs on the sides are steep and near together, while the benches are narrow. To climb out from such a valley over a succession of benches and cliffs is often most arduous and sometimes impossible.

On the east, the Judean plateau terminates in a bristling escarpment along the line of a great fault where the rocks on the east side have been dropped out of sight, as it were. They are buried at least 1,300 feet beneath the water of the Dead Sea, and the sea itself lies 4,000 feet below the top of the plateau. Since the faulting the escarpment has been shredded into tatters by streams which have cut hundreds of precipitous canyons. Hence, not only is it almost inaccessible, but movement along its top in the Wilderness of Judea is almost equally difficult. On one of the few trails which lead down to the Dead Sea my horses slid again and again, and once one of them fell ten or fifteen feet, with a terrible clatter of hoofs, and landed on his back.

On the west side of Judea, the hills are not so steep but are hard to traverse and are readily defended. Only on the north and south can the plateau easily be entered. On the north, however, the line of easy entrance is merely a narrow band along the centre of the plateau, for steep-sided valleys have bitten deeply into the rocks on either side. On the south there are many lines of approach, for one merely ascends a long slope with no special obstacles, but even there the invader must climb, which is always difficult; and the desert likewise serves as a protection. In addition to all this, Judea is a poor country, stony and rough, with practically no broad level fields. Whoever would wrest a living from the rocky soil must work hard from morning to night; even then he will get no more than a scanty sustenance. Moreover, aside from the soil, there are practically no resources except sheep and goats; even for cattle most parts of the plateau are too rugged. Thus Judea not only is hard to enter, but offers little to attract an invader. Although the Judean plateau is part of Palestine, it stands by itself—a small, rugged, infertile, inhospitable bit of hill country, with a habitable area no more than forty miles long from north to south, and scarcely twenty miles wide.

The essential part of Samaria is no larger than the Judean plateau, but it is quite different. The rocks not only are for the most part softer than those of Judea, and hence more easily worn into broad open valleys, but they are folded gently into broad hollows and arches. The result is that here the rains and streams have etched broad, easily accessible valleys, and relatively fertile basins. Moreover, Samaria does not stand so high as Judea. In Judea the cultivated lands lie on top of the plateau, and the narrow, inaccessible valleys make it hard to reach them. In Samaria the cultivated lands are largely in the hollows, where travel is easy, while the more or less isolated mountains which stick up here and there can easily be avoided.

The accessibility thus given to Samaria is increased by the northward decline of that plateau. Its northern edge is separated from the smooth transverse plain of Jezreel and Esdraelon only by a low escarpment, easily crossed at many points. Since Mount Carmel interposes a rough barrier close to the coast, practically all the traffic from Egypt and Philistia to Phœnicia, Syria, Damascus, Mesopotamia, Assyria, and Babylonia passes directly through Samaria, along one of the three or four main roads.

Lower Galilee, which extends from the plain of Esdraelon and Jezreel to a latitude just north of the Sea of Galilee, is like Samaria, but still smaller and with lower mountains, broader valleys, and even less protection against invaders. It, too, is traversed this way and that by great highroads, connecting the nations. Its position and its openness compelled it to be Galilee of the *Gentiles*, as it is called in the Bible. Even from as far north as Tyre and Sidon the ancient caravans, bound for Damascus, often swung south to Lower Galilee in order to avoid the rough mountains of Lebanon, Upper Galilee, Hermon, and Anti-Lebanon. Upper Galilee, on the other hand, is somewhat like Judea. It lies more than 2,000 feet above the sea, and has a capping of hard volcanic rock which has prevented it from being worn down into gentle relief like Lower Galilee. It is hard to enter, hard to traverse, relatively unfruitful, and not crossed by easy main lines of traffic, but in none of these respects does it equal Judea. Nevertheless, it possesses enough of the Judean quality so that it formed a place of refuge for the Jews after the final destruction of Jerusalem.

One interesting feature of these four little plateaus of western Palestine, each no larger than a small county, is that the degree to which each was Jewish agrees closely with the degree of physical isolation and of infertility. Lower Galilee, which is the most open and fertile, was never Jewish except for a few brief intervals, such as the time of Christ; Samaria was Jewish, or rather Israelitish, for several centuries after the original conquest of Palestine by the Jews, but the Jewish character began to decline almost as soon as it was acquired; Upper Galilee was not really conquered by the invading Israelites when they first arrived, and does not figure in the Old Testament, but after the time of Christ it was the centre of a fairly vigorous Judaism for centuries; Judea almost from the time of the original conquest until the destruction of Jerusalem, in 70 A. D., was the main centre of Judaism, except during the Babylonian captivity. The form of the land was very potent in producing these differences.

East of the four plateaus the Ghor, the hot, dry trench of the Jordan and the Dead Sea, furnishes a conspicuous example of a valley formed by movements of the earth's crust. The surface of the Dead Sea lies nearly 1,300 feet below sea-level, and even the Sea of Galilee is nearly 700 feet below the Mediterranean. On the western side of the Dead Sea, as appears in Figure 17, huge cliffs rise thousands of feet, so that the ascent to the plateau of Judea, 3,000 or 4,000 feet above, is extremely difficult. On the east, similar cliffs rise with even greater abruptness. Farther north along the Jordan, the cliffs on both sides diminish in steepness, and broad valleys lead out of the Ghor, especially on the west. Thus, although the trench of the Ghor supplies all the western plateaus with protection against invasion from the east, it is far more effective in Judea than elsewhere. In fact, when the Vale of Jezreel is reached the trench almost ceases to be a protection.

The fourth north-and-south strip of Palestine is different from the others in having no sharp eastern boundary. On the west, to be sure, it is bounded by the steep escarpment forming the east side of the Jordan Valley. When approached from the west this seems mountainous because it is so cut up by valleys. On climbing to the head of one of the valleys, however, one sees that he has merely reached the edge of a vast and relatively level plateau, which lies at an altitude of two, three or more thousand feet on the west, and declines gently eastward to the desert. In a few places like Gilead it is quite hilly, and may be said to be really mountainous, but on the whole, as soon as one gets back from the steep-sided valleys of the western border, it is flat and easily traversed.

When the Israelites came out of the desert, it was natural that they should try to conquer this little land of Palestine, with its four north-and-south strips, not only because their ancestors had wandered there, but because winds from the Mediterranean give it a fairly good rainfall. The good rainfall, however, is limited to the winter months, and likewise to the western slopes. In the days of Moses, as now, the summers were doubtless dry in Palestine, because that country lies on the western margin of a continent and in a latitude where subtropical droughts prevail in summer. And then, as now, the dominant winds were from the west, so that the eastern slopes of Judea, and even of Samaria and Galilee, were dry. In Judea the eastern side is so much sheltered from the west winds that it forms a genuine desert, the so-called Wilderness, within five or ten miles of Jerusalem. Beyond Jordan, during the historic period, only a strip from ten to twenty miles wide on the western edge of the eastern plateaus has ever had rainfall enough to be cultivated on a large scale. To-day the best parts are within four or five miles of the crest; beyond that the rainfall diminishes eastward, so that there is a large debatable land between "the desert and the sown." Southward, as well as eastward from Palestine, the rainfall diminishes so that the Negeb or south country is in our day almost desert. In the early days, however, there were cities and towns considerably farther south than now, which is one of the many reasons for believing in historic changes of climate.

When the Israelites tried to get this land of Palestine, which seemed to them especially good because it had enough rain, they attempted first to come in from the south. According to the Bible story, twelve spies were sent out, who climbed the easy southern slope of the plateau in the vicinity of Hebron. They came back with a glowing tale of the richness of the land, and with a huge bunch of grapes to prove their words. But they also told of walled cities and of people strong as giants. So ten out of the twelve advised against any attempt to possess the land. These ten prevailed. The Calebites, to be sure, appear to have entered Palestine from the south, which is, perhaps, the reason why the oldest account speaks only of Caleb as one of the two courageous spies, and omits Joshua. But the bulk of the Israelites wandered away again, swinging southward and eastward across the southern continuation of the Dead Sea valley, and finally approaching Moab and Ammon, which lie on the eastern plateau. Look at the map and see what they did. According to the Bible story, Moses led them as far as Mount Nebo, on the very edge of the eastern plateau, and about in the latitude of the northern end of the Dead Sea. In my boyhood, when I read how Moses viewed the whole land, I looked upon the words as a great exaggeration. But there is nothing exaggerated about them. Standing on the traditional Mount Nebo one looks twenty miles westward across the deep depression of the Ghor and sees the blue, flat-topped range of the western plateaus. Jerusalem is only twenty-five miles away, Hebron forty, and Samaria fifty. Northward the mountains of Gilead are not so far away as Samaria. On a clear day from the highest elevations near the western edge of the plateau in Ammon, if the mountains of Gilead did not intervene, one might even see the glistening snows of Mount Hermon, little more than one hundred miles away. But Hermon is almost as far away as Damascus, and lies beyond the limits of the region that ever was really Jewish. So from some high point a little to the northeast of the Dead Sea, Moses may actually have viewed practically the whole of the land that was to be inherited by his people.

The first step in taking this "promised" land was to occupy the eastern plateau. That was relatively easy, for all parts except Gilead lie open to the invader. If the land was then sparsely populated by reason of an epoch of aridity, as we have inferred, the resistance on the part of the settled inhabitants would be slight. The Israelites would merely have to fight a few times and then settle down, leaving the former inhabitants much as they were. That is what seems to have happened. Of course, the Israelites who settled permanently on the eastern plateau were not welcome, but as the Moabites, Ammonites, and the others could not get rid of them, and they could not get rid of the old inhabitants, both sides made the best of it. So the Israelites gradually mingled with the old inhabitants, which accounts in large measure for the insignificant rôle played by the distinctively Israelite communities east of the Jordan, except in the mountains of Gilead, or Perea, as it was later called. Equally important, however, as a reason why the eastern plateau had little part in the great future of Palestine, was the form of the land and its vegetation. The same gentle slopes and freedom from forests which had made it easy for the Israelites to take possession of the land, made it equally easy for other desert invaders to enter in the same way. During the entire three thousand years since the Exodus they have been doing it. Only in the "Mountains of Gilead," where the land is rough and where the topography favors a more abundant rainfall, which gives rise to wide-spread forests, did the Israelites long persist. There Jephthah's daughter bewailed the fact that she must die to pay her father's rash vow—a human sacrifice, in spite of Abraham's reforms long, long before. And there, in later times, perhaps at the foot of the mountains, Jesus found a Jewish population and blessed their little children.

After the eastern plateau had been occupied, the Israelites went down into the Jordan valley. Just north of the Dead Sea the valley shows a distinct broadening toward the east, and can be entered with relative ease. On the opposite side a little farther north the western plateau breaks down, and several rather easy valleys lead up to the southern part of Samaria. Evidently the Israelites knew the topography well. At first they took Jericho, down in the hot valley near the Jordan, a few miles north of the Dead Sea. There they are said to have marched seven times around the city until the walls fell down at the sound of a great shout. Then they went up the first of the easy valleys to Ai.

Next they hurried westward to the edge of the Philistine plain, then southward along its borders not far from the foot of the Judean plateau, and so clear to the south to the Negeb. Only there did they attempt to penetrate the Judean plateau, climbing the easy slope to Hebron. But perhaps this southern penetration was made by Kenites or Calebites, a portion of the Hebrews who apparently never went to the east of the Dead Sea, but entered along the general lines followed by the spies from Kadesh Barnea. One or another of the groups of invaders made a few raids out toward the sea in the plain of the Philistines, but did not hold that part of the country. The main result of the first onslaught of the Israelites was that they had practically enveloped the Judean plateau and had begun to puncture it on the south. The Philistines, being relatively civilized, were too strong for the invaders; the plateau people, although few and barbarous, were also too strong, presumably because of the inaccessibility of their rough hills. Leaving the Judean plateau unconquered, the invaders next went north up the Jordan Valley, which is easy to traverse. That line of approach, with the open Vale of Jezreel, made it easy to invade Galilee. Then they consolidated their gains, spreading out over the plateau of Samaria with comparative ease from both north and south, and establishing their main centre there, but not conquering Judea completely until the days of David, two hundred years later.

This is the account of the conquest of Palestine as given in the Bible—a rapid, fiery, incomplete invasion at first, followed by a long process of slow infiltration. The latter process was accompanied, on the one hand, by occasional brief and bloody raids on the old inhabitants, and on the other hand, by partial amalgamation with them. Such a course harmonizes with the character of desert nomads, and with the main items of the biblical account. It is quite improbable, however, that the genuine Israelites—the descendants of Abraham, worshippers of Jehovah, and wanderers from Egypt, as they were—formed the only body of invaders from the desert at this time. The Tel el Amarna tablets, or letters, for example, make it clear that small bands of desert people were pressing inward all along the line, from one end of Syria to the other. Some of the most interesting points brought out by the letters, as summarized by Professor H. P. Smith, in his well known *Old Testament History*, are as follows·

Interesting points brought out by the letters are: the comparative feebleness of the separate bands of invaders, and the readiness of the native chiefs to enter into alliance with them. The feebleness is brought out by the requests for help which in all cases assume that only a very few Egyptian soldiers will be necessary. The writers even in their greatest stress seem to think that fifty, forty, even twenty Egyptian soldiers will be able to defend their towns against the enemy. No doubt we here discover a constant feature of the long struggle with the Bedouin. The invaders have no means of compelling walled towns. Siege-works and battering-rams are wholly beyond them. If only the walls are sound and provisions do not give out, the citizens may scoff at the invaders. For the most part the attempt to reduce a fortress by starvation will fail, for the besiegers themselves have no regular commissariat. If they bring their flocks with them they soon graze off the immediate neighborhood and are compelled to move on. . . .

The El Amarna tablets reveal a somewhat extended invasion going on. Whether it be the Hebrew immigration is not yet certainly made out. The *Chabiri* of the tablets cannot be affirmed to be the Hebrews. But Chabiri and Hebrews are a part of the same general stream of migration. We see alliances already forming between the towns and the invaders. The Old Testament testifies that Israel established itself by means of such alliances. Later writers make this, indeed, the basis of a serious charge against Israel.

It is not necessary to dwell on the details of how the Israelites conquered Palestine, nor even to determine how much of the conquest was due to the sudden push described in the book of Joshua, and how much to the more gradual series of little campaigns described in the book of Judges. But two points need emphasis. First, most of Palestine was never really conquered by the Israelites. Everywhere some of the old inhabitants remained. This is the basis of the repeated assertions of the later chroniclers that the Jews failed to obey God by not killing all the old inhabitants. Those old inhabitants remained in greatest numbers, or at least absorbed the Jews most rapidly, in the eastern plateau aside from the mountains of Gilead, and in Lower

Galilee. Upper Galilee and the Philistine plain were never Israelite in any real sense during this period. Look again at the map
and see what a tiny bit remains—the plateau of Judea, forty
miles long, it will be remembered, and not much more than
twenty miles wide in its inhabitable portions; the plateau of
Samaria, of smaller dimensions; and the mountains of Gilead,
even more diminutive. Among these three regions, Judea was
the hardest to conquer, doubtless because it is so rough. But
when once conquered and Judaized it became the most completely Jewish part of Palestine. In other words, the same physical conditions which for centuries kept the Israelites from completely mastering Judea also helped the Judean Israelites to
maintain their independence and develop their own peculiar
civilization long after the rest of the Israelites had disappeared.
The whole story of the conquest of Palestine, as well as of the
persistence of the Judeans, is a remarkable example of the effect
of the form of the land.

The next period in Jewish history is that of the Judges, end-
ing with King Saul. These men were not judges in our sense of
the word, but local sheikhs who combined the functions of military leaders, civil executives, arbiters between their followers,
and avengers of the wrongs of their friends. Even in our own
day the Arab sheikh combines all these functions. It is not our
purpose to describe the wars which fill the biblical books of Judges
and Samuel. We shall merely point out how those wars were influenced by geographical conditions, and how they strengthened
or weakened the peculiar characteristics of the Judeans. One
thing which the stories of the wars bring out is the extreme bar-
barity of the wild Israelitish invaders from the desert. In those
days no one looked askance on a man who got the best of an
enemy by lying to him, and then running him through with a
sword. It was praiseworthy to kill 300 or 400 unarmed people
because they did not worship Jehovah, or talked another language. Even David not only killed his enemies ruthlessly, but
in his old age, perhaps in his dotage, is said to have incited his
son to vengeance, in the face of his own pledges to the contrary.

On his very deathbed he said to Solomon: "Gera, the Benjaminite, cursed me with a grievous curse—but I sware to him by Jehovah, saying, I will not put thee to the sword. Now therefore hold him not guiltless—bring his hoar head down to Sheol with blood." But this sort of thing was not merely characteristic of the Jews; it was characteristic of the times and of the stage of culture.

In the early days of Israel in Palestine there were three kinds of fighting. First, the Ammonites, Moabites, and Edomites east of the Jordan, and the Midianites, or Bedouin, farther east and south, were continually making raids, and the Israelites were continually driving them off and chasing them back. All this was simply part of the day's work. The people living in the desert or on its borders were repeatedly under stress because of drought, or because the population became too dense, or because some other disaster made their food supply short. Moreover, the love of plundering had become part of their racial inheritance, both biologically and socially. They not only plundered each other, but again and again tried to play the same game which the Israelites had played. If they could have taken Palestine for themselves, they doubtless would have done so. Just how far they succeeded is not clear. The result of their raids, however, was that all the country east of the Jordan, except Gilead, where a combination of mountains and forests offered protection, soon was no longer really Israelite. It was inhabited by a mixture of the Israelites and the races around them. This sort of constant incursion from the desert has gone on all through history, except when some strong power like the Romans, or the British, keeps the desert people out.

The second group of people with whom the Israelites fought were the Philistines in the plain on their western border. Bear in mind that if we had been there in those days we should have looked upon the Philistines as far more civilized than the Israelites. They lived in settled towns; they had comparatively cultured manners, although they killed their enemies as freely as did other people; they used horses, chariots, and tools of iron. For a long time after the Jews first acquired iron tools they did

not know how to make them or mend them, and had to go down
to the cultured Philistines to find blacksmiths. As we shall see,
in the sequel, the Israelites did not emerge from the Bronze Age
into that of Iron until the days of David. Naturally, the Philistines seemed to them rich, powerful, and cultured. Accordingly,
they envied them, wanted to rob them, but were afraid of them.
But the desire for plunder was so strong that the Israelites again
and again made raids upon their Philistine neighbors.

Samson furnishes a good example of the manners of the time,
even though his story is legendary. In a peaceful time, from his
home on the western borders of the Israelite plateau, he went
down a few miles to a Philistine village. There he saw a girl who
pleased him, and arrangements for marriage were completed with
the father. Now it happened that on his way to the village Samson had met a lion. Being a mighty man he slew the lion and
left the body lying by the wayside. Incidentally, the lions are
one of many bits of evidence which suggest that temporarily, at
least, the population of Palestine at that time was quite sparse.
Later when Samson went down to be married, he turned from
the path to look at the dead lion. There lay the carcass, and from
it came forth bees. So Samson took a closer look, and found
within the skin a honey-comb. He pulled it out and went on his
way, eating as he walked. Then it occurred to him to have a
little joke with the Philistines of his wife's village. So he bet
with the young men that they could not guess his riddle.

> "Out of the eater came forth something to eat,
> And out of the strong came something sweet." *

The wager was "thirty linen garments and changes of rai-
ment," or thirty suits of clothes, as we would say. Naturally, the
young men could not guess that the answer was a lion with a
honey-comb in it, so they tried to persuade Samson's new wife
to get her husband to tell her the answer. She teased and teased,
and then she wept and wept: "Thou dost but hate me and lovest

---

* Rhymed version by Moore in his *Commentary on Judges*, 1895. The second quotation
is one of the rare examples of a rhymed couplet in Hebrew.

me not." Finally, before the week's rejoicings were over, he told her. The young men laughed scornfully at the simple Israelite whom they had duped. But he was not stupid, for his answer is cleverer than his riddle:

> "If with my heifer you did not plough,
> You had not solved my riddle now."

He was a poor man, and thirty suits of clothes were more than he could muster. Nor was he disposed to pay a bet lost through treachery. So off he went to another village, and with his own hand, unaided, killed thirty men, took their clothes and brought them back to pay the bet.

Even if Samson did not really pay a bet by killing thirty men, the story illustrates the actual kind of relations between the people of the plateau and the plain. Other stories of Samson are equally illuminative. One example is his burning of the fields of the Philistines by tying the tails of foxes together, setting them on fire, and turning the animals loose in the standing grain. Another tale relates how Samson slew a thousand men with a stone-age weapon, the jaw-bone of an ass. Such acts are typical of the fierce raids made by the uplanders upon the Philistines. The Philistines, in turn, retaliated to such an extent that for a long time they ruled the plateau, but never could completely subdue it.

A third kind of fighting was perhaps even worse than the conflict with the desert barbarians, on the one hand, or the civilized Philistines on the other. That was the quarrels among the different branches of the Israelites themselves. The Ephraimites in Samaria, west of Jordan, fought with the Ephraimites and Gileadites east of Jordan. Judah fought against Benjamin. Sometimes the eastern desert raiders burst across the Jordan valley and raided the western plateau. Then the western Israelites, "faint yet pursuing," or perchance "exhausted and famished," as seems to be a truer but less poetic reading, crossed the lands of their eastern brethren. But the eastern Israelites were afraid to help them, for the fear of their desert neighbors was upon them.

"Are the lands of thine enemies now in thy hand, that we should give bread to thine army?" said they to the western Ephraimites. When the westerners answered rudely, war broke out between the two parts of Israel. Life was a rough matter in those old days; Palestine was no place for a weakling, or for the stupid and dull.

Turn to the map of Palestine and see just where this fighting took place. That is important because it helps to explain how the Jewish customs and ideals could persist so marvellously. One line of fighting was the Jordan valley. Again and again the people from the two sides were opposed to each other. An even more important line was the Vale of Jezreel. That was the easiest place at which to get out of the Jordan valley on the west. Moabites, Philistines, Egyptians, Assyrians, Israelites, no matter where they started from, seemed to converge on that one valley for the final fight. Megiddo, in the Vale of Jezreel, stands almost unrivalled as a place where many kinds of people have fought important battles. The reason is simply that there the gentle relief of the land makes it easy to get across from the coastal plains to the valley of the Jordan, and thus reach the eastern plateau.

Another line of fighting was the Shephelah, the line of hills at the western base of the Judean plateau. There and at the corresponding borders of the Samaritan plateau, the men of the plateaus and the men of the plains often met. So constant and pitiless were the raids during the days of the Judges that some of the Danites could no longer stand it. Far to the north, near the source of the Jordan—in other words, 110 miles away—their spies found a place called Laish, where "the people dwelt in security after the manner of the Sidonians, quiet and secure." So they moved from their stormy Samaritan home, stole a priest on the way, together with an ephod, terephim, a graven image, and a molten image, smote the harmless men of Laish with the edge of the sword, and burnt their city with fire. Nobody blamed them. That was the way things were done in those days.

We do almost exactly the same thing, but by a different method. Our immigration problem represents a contest as to who shall inherit the land. Our ancestors from western Europe dispossessed the Indians. Then the dispossessors, in turn, began to be dispossessed by people from eastern and southern Europe, and even from Asia. So we made an immigration law, with quotas and restrictions. We made a gentlemen's agreement with Japan and were not gentlemen enough to keep it, and we shut out Chinese, Hindus, and others. All this is essentially the same thing that the Edomites did when they refused to let Israel pass through their land. It is what the Israelites did when they tried to exterminate the people whom they dispossessed, and what the Philistines did when they fought with Israel. The Europeans who now get themselves bootlegged across the border in defiance of our immigration laws are doing, in their modern way, just what the men of Dan did when they killed the quiet people of Laish.

The last of the areas where fighting was especially common in the days of the judges of Israel was the border zone between Samaria and Judea. This lies only a few miles north of Jerusalem. Ai, Beth Horon, and Mickmash are some of the places where famous struggles took place. South of this zone, invaders from either the east or the west almost invariably found great difficulty in penetrating the Judean plateau: invaders from the north likewise had difficulty in getting south of it: and invaders rarely came directly from the south. The secret of all this lies largely in the relatively level position and young, rugged stage of dissection of the rocks in the Judean plateau, coupled with the alternation of hard and soft layers which gives rise to innumerable cliffs, both large and small, along the steep sides of the narrow, intricate valleys. In other words, the prevalence of fighting along the border zone between Judea and Samaria is merely an evidence of the fact that Judea is difficult of access, and that political and military frontiers tend to be located in accordance with the dictates of physical geography, especially among primitive people.

The prevalence of fighting along this zone is probably the reason why various legends arose as to how the small tribe of Benjamin, whose territory it was, came near to being annihilated. All the women, so we are told, were destroyed. The few men

who remained were allowed by the other Israelites to perpetuate
their tribe by smiting Jabesh-Gilead, which "came not up unto
Jehovah to Mizpah," and thus failed to help the other tribes
in taking vengeance on the evil-doing of the Benjaminites. For
the sake of Benjamin the Israelites slew all the adults of Jabesh-
Gilead, but saved "four hundred young virgins," whom they
gave to the Benjaminites for wives. "And yet so they sufficed
them not. . . . Then the elders of the congregation said, What
shall we do for wives for them that remain, seeing the women
are destroyed out of Benjamin? And they said, There must be
an inheritance for them that are escaped of Benjamin, that a
tribe be not blotted out from Israel. Howbeit, we may not give
them wives of our daughters; for the children of Israel had
sworn, saying, Cursed be he that giveth a wife to Benjamin.
And they said, Behold, there is a feast of Jehovah from year to
year in Shiloh which is on the north of Beth-el, on the east side
of the highway that goeth up from Beth-el to Shechem, and on
the south of Lebonah. And they commanded the children of
Benjamin, saying, Go and lie in wait in the vineyards; and see,
and, behold, if the daughters of Shiloh come out to dance in the
dances, then come ye out of the vineyards, and catch you every
man his wife of the daughters of Shiloh, and go to the land of
Benjamin. And it shall be, when their fathers or their brethren
come to complain unto us, that we will say unto them, Grant
them graciously unto us; because we took not for each man of
them his wife in battle, neither did ye give them unto them;
else would ye now be guilty. And the children of Benjamin did
so, and took them wives, according to their number, of them
that danced, whom they carried off: and they went and returned
unto their inheritance, and built the cities and dwelt in them.
And the children of Israel departed thence at that time, every
man to his tribe and to his family, and they went out from thence
every man to his inheritance. In those days there was no king
in Israel; every man did that which was right in his own eyes."

The history of Israel in the days of the Judges admirably
illustrates the general truth that an unfortunate physical loca-

tion may permit one people, or a type of culture, to decline, while a favorable physical environment preserves and expands another type. In most parts of Palestine the physical features were such that invasions, wars, and internal quarrels destroyed the racial, social, and religious integrity of the Israelites in the first centuries after they came to Palestine. But the history of this period also illustrates how the geographical environment may preserve a race and a culture. The Judeans fought like their brethren, but practically all their fighting took place on their border lands. When David, for instance, fled from Saul, the two factions seem almost never to have come into conflict on the plateau. They met near the Caves of the Shephelah—the foothill belt at the western edge of the Judean plateau—or in the desert tracts near Engedi down toward the Dead Sea on the east, or in the south beyond Hebron, or along the transition zone at the northern end of Judea. Thus, because of Judea's rough topography, and because it was surrounded by the Dead Sea and the Jordan valley on the one side, and by the Shephelah and a difficult line of ascent on the other, its people alone among all those in that part of the world were left more or less to themselves. They went out again and again against others; they must have lost great numbers of their own people; but almost no one penetrated into their midst. Thus there remained a centre where the old Jewish type of character, the type perhaps which flowed by direct descent from Abraham, Isaac, and Jacob, was preserved almost intact.

CHAPTER XV

THE BIOLOGICAL ANTECEDENTS OF JESUS

AFTER the pioneer period when the Judges tried to bring unity among the barbarous Israelites who then inhabited Palestine, a really great leader named Samuel came to the front. Under his guidance Saul became king of Israel and almost succeeded in bringing all Palestine under a single rule. The territory that he tried to master was, to be sure, no larger than the State of Connecticut, and he by no means succeeded in ruling all of it. Nevertheless, he struck a severe blow at the relatively civilized Philistines of the coastal plain who had been oppressing the Israelites, and whom the Israelites, in turn, had loved to plunder. When Saul failed, Samuel turned to David, another really great man. After many exciting adventures, this son of the tribe of Judah succeeded in establishing a kingdom, which expanded until it was larger than New Hampshire or Maryland, and more than a quarter as large as Pennsylvania. Under David and his son, Solomon, the Israelites, for the only time in all the three or four thousand years of their history, unless it be in the days of the Maccabees, possessed a sovereign state having genuine political importance. From the view-point of the ordinary historical recital this fact stands out pre-eminently. And so it does from our present view-point. But here we are especially interested in the cause of this sudden expansion of Israel, and in its effect on the biological future of the Jewish race.

How did it happen that the tribes of Judah and Benjamin were able to conquer the rest of the Israelites, and that the barbarous Israelites, in turn, were able to subdue the civilized Philistines and other relatively advanced peoples who lived on the borders of Palestine as far as Damascus? The answer lies partly in the fact that none of the great kingdoms which surrounded Palestine was especially strong at that time, about a thousand years before Christ, and partly in the fact that Israel produced some truly great leaders in the persons of Samuel, David, and perhaps Saul. These are the causes usually assigned, but two others may be equally important. One is the type of character inherited by the Israelites from their desert ancestors, and preserved in special purity in the Judean plateau. The other is the introduction of iron.

We have already seen how small is the Judean plateau and how isolated its people. How was it possible for this little plateau not only to dominate all the rest of Palestine, but to become for a while a real political power in the days of David and Solomon? The answer seems to lie partly in the fact that the Judean environment preserved to an unusual degree the hardy, active qualities of the desert. Where life was so strenuous the weaker types of people either died off or migrated. Moreover, the presence of vigorous parents, together with the necessities of the physical environment, presumably made it essential that the education of the children should be especially directed toward the hardier, more active kinds of virtues. Life in the desert, as we have seen, puts a premium on the strong, wiry physique, on the power of quick, decisive action, the capacity for leadership, and the temperament that makes men loyal followers of their chief. David is a fine example. On the Judean plateau, more than anywhere else in Palestine, this type was probably preserved among the Israelites during the two centuries of the Judges, for there the isolation largely prevented the Judeans from mingling with other people. Moreover, the hardships of life in the plateau probably weeded out the weaklings to an unusual degree. Some of the plateau people were attracted to the pleasant land of the Philistines in the plain on the west. Samson, with his love affairs with two Philistine women, is a good example. But the intense racial feeling which had already become highly developed among the Israelites, helped to keep the stronger-minded people apart by themselves in their rugged plateau.

In spite of all this, the Philistines of the plain, with their iron tools, chariots, and horses, were far superior to the Jews in culture. They were relatively civilized in their art, architecture, dress, and manners. Among the Israelites in their mountain fastnesses, on the contrary, even as late as the days of Saul, there was, as we have seen, "no smith found throughout all of Israel; for the Philistines said, Lest the Hebrews make them swords or spears: but all the Israelites went down to the Philistines, to sharpen every man his share, and his coulter, and his axe, and his mattock; yet they had a file for the mattocks, and for the coulters, and for the forks, and for the axes, and to set the goads. So it came to pass in the day of battle, that there was neither sword nor spear found in the hand of any of the people that were with Saul and Jonathan: but with Saul and with Jonathan his son was there found."

The critics are almost unanimous in holding that the foregoing passage from the thirteenth chapter of Judges has been tampered with by the later priestly editors of the Bible. But its main fact is abundantly witnessed by other evidence. That fact is that in the days of the Judges the Israelites had practically no iron tools. For example, only a little before the days of Saul, the Israelites are said to have fought with the Canaanitish prince, Sisera, who apparently lived in the lowlands of southern Galilee. Sisera had "nine hundred chariots of iron," but "was there a shield or spear among forty thousand in Israel?" The writer of the Song of Deborah, one of the oldest and most authentic parts of the Bible, gives here no hint of disarmament of the Israelites by the Canaanites, but he is well aware that none of the highlanders then possessed iron weapons. Samson's use of the jawbone of an ass quite surely means that even so bellicose a hero had no iron knife, sword, or dirk. David, with his sling, is introduced to us as a user of weapons of stone. Moreover, the archæological evidence in the Jordan valley indicates that only at this time was iron beginning to be introduced in the most advanced communities.

Why then do biblical students so universally assert that among the Israelites "the fighting men were disarmed," as H. P. Smith puts it, by Sisera's Canaanites, and again by the Philistines? The answer seems to be that the students have been led astray by some late writer who could not understand why there was "no smith found throughout all of Israel." It probably never occurred to him that there was a time when men used stone instead of iron. Therefore he added what seemed to him the most probable explanation, "for the Philistines said, 'lest the Hebrews make them swords and spears.'" That the Philistines, the Canaanites, or any one else at that time, could take away all the weapons from the whole highland population is utterly improbable. But what they could easily do was refuse to sell weapons to the highlanders. Perhaps they sold agricultural implements, at a good stiff price, but even as to this we have no certainty that the phrases as to the share, coulter, ax, and mattock quoted above belong to an old account or a later addition.

The fact of the matter appears to be that between 1100 and 1000 B. C., iron tools were a relatively new thing, just as automobiles and airplanes are to-day. You and I may have automobiles, but the chances are about one in ten thousand against our owning airplanes. We in the United States have plenty of automobiles, but in China only an insignificant handful of the most wealthy Chinese in the large cities own them. That is the way it was with iron weapons in the days of Saul. They were common among the advanced people, but were only beginning to spread among those who were more backward.

The steam-engine, telegraph, telephone, automobile, and all the other mechanical inventions of the last century and a half have made a huge change in our civilization, but practically none in that of the people of western China. The introduction of iron tools had a similar and perhaps even more revolutionary effect. For a time it made the civilized Philistines and Canaanites almost immeasurably superior to the barbarous Israelites of the mountains. But about the time of Saul the use of iron, and perhaps also of horses, seems to have spread so rapidly that the rough Israelites of the plateau were soon as well armed as their Philistine oppressors, or as their enemies farther north in Syria. The transformation in them was like that which the introduction of

European methods produced in Japan between 1850 and 1900. Just as Japan changed from a negligible factor in world politics to one of the great powers, so Israel suddenly found itself a kingdom which was almost as great for its day as Japan is for ours. Being suddenly placed on an equality with its more civilized neighbors so far as arms and tools were concerned, the native vigor of the Israelites, their sense of racial unity, and their combined powers of leadership and loyalty enabled them to throw off the yoke of the Philistines and sweep into power. Thus we see that the sudden rise of Israel to genuine political importance is explained not only by the political causes which figure so prominently in the ordinary historical records, but also by physical environment, by the biological inheritance which determines the quality of the leaders as well as of the common people, and by cultural inventions such as the discovery of iron, which may revolutionize the relations of one people to another.

If the power of the Israelite kingdom had not been shattered by internal dissensions, their kingdom might have had a glorious career for hundreds of years. Suppose, for a moment, that it had rivalled Egypt, Assyria, and Babylonia, as one of the world's great and enduring monarchies. Would that have increased the contribution of the Jewish race to the world's store of ideas? I doubt it. In fact, such a course might have been fatal. Under such circumstances it is very doubtful whether Israel would have been the world's great source of religious inspiration.

In order to explain this last statement let us turn back for a moment to a seemingly minor event which took place in earlier times. According to the biblical story the sacred shrine known as the ark was brought by the Israelites from the desert. During the stormy days of the Judges it had no permanent abiding-place. In the days of Eli when Samuel was a boy, to be sure, it was lodged at Shiloh after having been at Bethel. Then at a time when Saul was engaged in a losing fight with the Philistines, it was brought out to help the Israelites. At first the Philistines were frightened when they heard the triumphant shouts of the Israelites as the famous old ark came out before them. But the

Philistines regained their courage, routed the Israelites, captured the ark and carried it off to Ashdod. There, according to the story, it overthrew the image of the god Dagon, and caused an outbreak of plague. The frightened Philistines moved it from city to city, but disaster came in its wake. Finally they placed it on a creaking cart and let the lowing oxen carry it where they would. Thus it came up the hills to Beth-shemesh, spreading death as it went.

Back among its own people the ark still moved from place to place, always on the border line where the rough plateau of Judea merges into the gentler hills and valleys of Samaria. Until Israel had a real capital the ark likewise was without a permanent abiding-place until the days of David. Then David captured Jerusalem, made it his capital, and finally brought thither the ark with much rejoicing. He wanted to build a temple for it. But that work was left to the more magnificent reign of Solomon. From the point of view of racial development it is hard to find any single incident more important than the triumphant procession in which David danced before the Lord so violently that his garment flew up like those of a ballet dancer, and one of his wives, the embittered daughter of Saul, reproached him sourly for his indecency. But the ark had found a permanent home, Israel had at length acquired a definite religious centre, and that centre was in Judea. Attempts were, indeed, made to establish other religious centres, but they never had much success.

Now let us see how this moving of the ark joined with other things to produce what seems to be a distinct effect upon the racial temperament of the Jews. After the glorious days of Solomon, the Jewish kingdom fell to pieces. The people of the Judean plateau and those of the rest of Israel had never gotten on very well together. Rehoboam, the son of Solomon, in the pride of his young heart, made matters infinitely worse. Did he not say: "My little finger is thicker than my father's loins. And now whereas my father chastised you with whips, I will chastise you with scorpions"?

So the old jealousies flared up. Jeroboam founded a rival

kingdom and led off ten tribes. We shall not trace the vicissitudes of the bloody wars between Judea and Israel, and between
these two and their neighbors. The whole record is intensely
barbarous when stripped of the religious significance which the
Bible everywhere reads into it. What we are concerned with is
the way the split between Israel and Judah affected religion.
According to the book of Kings (I, 12, 26–28), when Jeroboam of
Samaria took the ten tribes away from Rehoboam of Jerusalem,
he did not have the sympathy of all his people. So the king
"said in his heart, 'Now will the kingdom return to the house of
David: if this people go up to offer sacrifices in the house of
Jehovah at Jerusalem, then will the heart of this people turn
again unto their lord, even unto Rehoboam, king of Judah.' . . .
Whereupon the king made two calves of gold . . . and this thing
became a sin, for the people went to worship before each of them.
. . . And he made priests from among all the people that were
not of the sons of Levi."

The Chronicler, as the writer of Chronicles, Ezra, and part
of Nehemiah is called, says that what Jeroboam feared actually
happened. "The priests and the Levites that were in all Israel
resorted to Rehoboam out of all their border. For the Levites
left their suburbs and their possessions and came to Judah and
Jerusalem, for Jeroboam and his sons cast them off that they
should not execute the priest's office unto Jehovah. And he appointed other priests for the high places, and for the he-goats,
and for the calves which he had made. And after them out of all
the tribes of Israel such as set their hearts to seek Jehovah, the
God of Israel, came to Jerusalem to sacrifice unto Jehovah, the
God of their fathers. So they strengthened the kingdom of
Judah."

Biblical experts tell us that the Chronicler wrote for the ex-
press purpose of glorifying the kingdom of Judah and its religion.
Accordingly some of the more extreme biblical critics imply that
no such migration of religiously minded people from Israel to
Judah ever occurred. They assert, correctly, no doubt, that
Jeroboam had a religious motive in setting up the two golden

calves, or little bulls, as they doubtless really were. They assert
with equal accuracy that Jerusalem was only one of many sanc-
tuaries, not only in northern Israel but in Judea. But it is hard
to see how the truth of these facts proves that the statements
in Kings and Chronicles as to the Levites and other religiously
minded people are untrue. The fact is that for more than two
generations the Ark of the Covenant, the supreme symbol of
the Hebrew religion, had been at Jerusalem, for a generation it
had been sheltered within a temple there, which appears to have
been the most magnificent structure ever built by the Jews.
Moreover, for about seventy years all Israel had looked to Jerusalem as the great centre of national life, both politically and religiously. Even after the exile, nearly four hundred years from
the time we are discussing, Jeremiah tells of people who came
from Ephraim—from the heart of the former kingdom of Israel,
to make their offerings at the ruined sanctuary of Jerusalem.
In addition to all this no one seems to doubt that Jeroboam
ousted the former religious officials of his new kingdom—those
who had looked to Jerusalem as their centre—and installed new
priests of his own choosing. Under such circumstances, only the
most submissive kind of priests, Levites and other persons closely
identified with the old form of worship, would stay in northern
Israel. Even if the Bible did not explicitly say so, we could be
morally certain that the more strong-minded of the ousted priests
and Levites, and perhaps some of their sympathizers, would
move to Jerusalem. There they were undoubtedly welcome, and
could certainly get a living far more easily than in Israel, where
they had been forcibly expelled from their positions. Of course,
some religious people remained in Israel, for Elisha and some of
the other great prophets arose there in later days. Nevertheless,
there can be little doubt that there occurred a migration of priests,
Levites, and other religiously minded people from Israel into
Judea.

In our own day, as we have already seen in another chapter,
people of the religious temperament are especially prone to migrate. Among people so religious and so zealous as the Jews this

certainly must have been the case. If the Mormons would abandon all things and migrate a thousand miles into the wilderness at the dictates of their faith, would not religiously minded Israelites migrate a few score miles for the same reason, even if there were no question of daily bread? Even a few hundred such men, if they were of strong calibre, would greatly alter the religious balance between the region that they left and the one to which they went. The truth of this last statement becomes still more evident when we recall that the territory which remained loyal to the house of David quickly shrank to a habitable area of scarcely more than 1,000 square miles, and probably had a population of less than 100,000 people, for it is very rough and infertile. As the years went on, the power of Jerusalem to attract a few of the most deeply religious souls from Israel must have been intensified by the fact that the kingdom of Israel turned more and more to the worship of Baal and other gods of the neighboring people. The Bible is full of stories like that of Ahab and his wife, Jezebel, who made Israel to sin by introducing heathen practices. This was only natural, for Samaria, where was the centre of the Israelite kingdom, lies open to all sorts of foreign influences. People who have not travelled by caravan in oriental lands can scarcely appreciate how the presence of a great highway brings the people in constant touch with foreigners. The average caravan travels only about fifteen miles a day. Each night it stops, and the caravan men fraternize with the townspeople or villagers. Often it rests several days. If it wishes to recuperate it may move some miles away from the main track and stay for a week or two. Foreigners not only pass through the land, but settle in it. The natives inevitably intermarry with the foreigners. Thus a great road destroys the isolation of a race. That was what happened to Samaria, for that part of Palestine is an open land, easy to traverse, whereas the plateau of Judea, by its physical harshness and isolation, keeps people out, and thus long remained relatively free from foreign influences. Thus it happened that for several hundred years the part of Palestine outside Judea became less and less truly Jewish, and less and less a place where the old religion of Jehovah persisted. But all through these centuries there must have been a steady trickle of religious migrants out of Israel into Judah. On the other hand, there must have been a counter-stream of Judeans who did not like the intolerant strictness which was gradually increasing in Judea. Or, perchance, there were outward migrants who left Judea because they wanted wealth, culture, and opportunities for self-expression. Judah became more and more religious. Some of its late kings, like Hezekiah and Josiah, introduced great and sweeping reforms. Thus the historical result of carrying the ark to Jerusalem, and of all which it implies, was that after three or four centuries the percentage of religious people had become high in Judah and low in the rest of Israel.

What happened next? At first sight the next event appears to nullify the effect of all that had happened before. That event was the exile. First Israel was wiped out as a kingdom, but Judah, in its mountain fastnesses, held on for another century. At last it too fell a victim to the Assyrian armies. Jerusalem was besieged and captured in 597 B. C. Then happened something which, at the time, seemed the worst of all calamities. Not only was Jerusalem sacked, but the cream of its population was carried away captive to Babylonia. As the book of Kings puts it, Nebuchadnezzar "carried away all Jerusalem, and all the princes, and all the mighty men of valor, even ten thousand captives, and all the craftsmen save the poorest sort of the people of the land. And he carried away Jehoiachin to Babylon; and the king's mother, and the king's wives, and his officers, and the chief men of the land, carried he into captivity from Jerusalem to Babylon. And all the men of might, even seven thousand, and the craftsmen and the smiths a thousand, all of them strong and apt for war, even them the king of Babylon brought captive to Babylon." But that was not the end. Nebuchadnezzar set up the old king's brother in his stead to rule the land as a vassal. For some reason the suzerain changed his vassal's name, perhaps as a sign of the might of the conqueror. But this new king, Zedekiah, rebelled against the king of Babylon. So Nebuchadnezzar was forced to invade Palestine again. Once more the Chaldeans overwhelmed the city, then chased the Judean army to the plains of Jericho, and burned Jerusalem. The book of Kings adds that "the residue of the people that were left in the city, and those that fell away, that fell to the king of Babylon, and the residue of the multitude, did Nebuzaradan, the captain of the guard, carry away captive. But the captain of the guard left of the poorest of the land to be vinedressers and husbandmen."

Thus again what cream was left was skimmed from Judea and carried away to Babylonia. But "those who were left were not always of the lowest class of the people [as] is made evident by the book of Jeremiah and the history of Gedaliah there given" (H. P. Smith). According to Jeremiah still a third group were later carried into captivity. He says that Nebuchadnezzar carried away 3,023 Jews in the seventh year of his reign, 832 in the eighteenth year, and 745 in the twenty-third. Probably these numbers refer to men alone, but even if they include women and children, the captives constituted a substantial portion of the leading people, for all Judea probably contained no more people than one of our cities such as Wilmington. Nevertheless, after the first skimming, and doubtless also after the second, as Jeremiah puts it, "the poorest of the land" were reinforced by others. "When all the Jews that were in Moab, and among the children of Ammon, and in Edom, and that were in all the countries, heard that the king of Babylon had left a remnant of Judah, and that he had set over them Gedaliah, the son of Ahikam, the son of Shaphan; then all the Jews returned out of all places whither they were driven, and came to the land of Judah, to Gedaliah, unto Mizpah, and gathered wine and summer fruits very much." What kind of people were these who returned? Some may have been cowards who fled at the first hint of danger; some may have been brave people who escaped after fierce fighting; but all alike almost certainly included an unusually large percentage in whom love of country, of race, and of the religion of Jehovah burned most strongly—in other words, a selected type in whom selection worked along the same general lines as in previous cases.

Finally, as Jeremiah vividly portrays, the Jews who still dwelt in Judea rebelled once more, and the Chaldeans came to smite them. So "all the people, both great and small, and the captains of the forces arose and came to Egypt, for they were afraid of the Chaldeans." That is how the book of Kings dismisses the matter. But Jeremiah gives far deeper significance to the story. After the rebels had slain Gedaliah, whom the king of Babylon had made governor over them, "all the captains of the forces, and . . . all the people from the least even unto the greatest, came near and said unto Jeremiah the prophet, Let, we pray thee, our supplication be presented before thee, and pray for us unto Jehovah thy God, even for all this remnant (for we are left but a few of many, as thine eyes do behold us), that Jehovah thy God may show us the way wherein we should walk, and the thing that we should do." And Jeremiah answered, "If ye will abide in this land, then will I build you and not pluck you down . . . but if ye indeed set your faces to enter into Egypt, . . . then shall my wrath, saith Jehovah, be poured forth upon you, and ye shall be an execration, and an astonishment, and a curse, and a reproach; . . . ye shall die by the sword, by the famine, and by the pestilence in the place whither ye desire to go to sojourn there . . . and ye shall see this place no more. . . . And it came to pass that all the people obeyed not the voice of Jehovah, and came into the land of Egypt" (about 587 B. C.). Jeremiah, old now, but still vigorous in upholding the cause of righteousness, was forced to go with them, but a remnant still remained in Palestine. That remnant, small as it doubtless was, must have contained a relatively large proportion of people who heeded Jeremiah's denunciations and his plea that they keep faith with Jehovah. Hard indeed was the lot of this last highly selected remnant. Here is the way they are described in H. P. Smith's *Old Testament History:*

For them barbarism was the first danger. They had all they could do to wring a living out of the reluctant soil. The Bedawin from the east and from the south overran the country. Edom was crowded upon by the Nabateans, and pushed up into Judah. A half-century later almost the whole of Judah's territory belonged to these invaders, and the bitter hatred of the Edomites, which finds expression in later times, dates from this period of encroachment. The people of the land seem, indeed, to have kept alive the religion of their ancestors. We read how men came with offerings to the site of the Temple, after the sacred building had been destroyed. They came in the garb of mourners, so that we cannot suppose them ignorant of the calamity which had fallen. Evidently the sacredness of the site could not be erased by the destruction of the edifice. At the place which Yahweh had once chosen, men might still hope to approach him. This was the feeling of these poor people. And we may suppose that during the years that followed the sacredness of the site was, in some way, kept in mind—perhaps marked by the crude offerings which a peasant or pastoral people brings to its God.

But our main interest is now with the little community in Babylonia, which had followed with the keenest sympathy the fortunes of their native country, and whose grief at its conquest was not the less poignant that they were so far away.

The fearful catastrophe gave them two alternatives. Either they must give up their faith in him and hold him to be a God too weak to protect his own, or else they must believe in what his prophets had said. No doubt many—like the fugitives to Egypt just spoken of—chose the former alternative. These became worshippers of other gods, loosened the ties of kindred, and became absorbed in the surrounding heathenism. But some there were who chose the other alternative, held on to their faith in Yahweh, and began to value more justly the words of the prophets. It is this fraction of the people—a sect, a church, no longer a nation—which has influenced the history of the world. And it is with these that we must now concern ourselves.

Here, then, was the situation about 550 years before Christ —in Judea a handful of oppressed Jews, part of whom were there because they were the poorest of the land, but many of whom had stayed because of their loyalty to home, to race, and to Jehovah: in Babylonia another and much abler remnant, which had likewise been tried by fire, so that few remained in the Jewish community save those who held most strongly to their faith in Jehovah.

The next step in the building up of the Jewish type which made the supreme contribution to the world's religious thought was the return from the exile. That is a very interesting story. About sixty years after the exile the Babylonians suffered defeat at the hands of the Persians. Now Cyrus, the Persian, was a broadminded man. He adopted the modern British principle of letting each race follow its own religion, so far as that did not interfere with the political integrity of the central government. In fact, he even encouraged the rebuilding and improvement of the temples of the various native peoples. So it happened that the Jews shared his kindness. Thus far we are on well-established historic ground. Now comes the application of this to the Jews. The only record of this preserved to us is in the book of Ezra, written, as many suppose, by the Chronicler. A great controversy has arisen over this book. At one extreme men like Meyer (*Enstehung des Judentums*) believe that the whole story is genuine; at the other extreme men like Torrey (*Composition and Historical Value of Ezra-Nehemiah*) hold that practically the whole of the book of Ezra is a romance, founded indeed on fact, but greatly exaggerating what actually occurred.

The truth doubtless lies between these two views. Let us tell the story briefly, following the book of Ezra but greatly toning it down. Here is the Chronicler's transcript of a proclamation said to have been issued by Darius in the first year of his reign. It is undoubtedly greatly garbled to give it a religious and Judaistic tone, but probably expresses the general purpose of Cyrus.

All the kingdoms of the earth hath Jehovah, the God of heaven, given me; and he hath charged me to build him a house in Jerusalem, which is in Judah. Whosoever there is among you of all his people, his God be with him, and let him go up to Jerusalem, which is in Judah, and build the house of Jehovah, the God of Israel which is in Jerusalem. And whosoever is left, in any place where he sojourneth, let the men of this place help him with silver, and with gold, and with goods, and with beasts, besides the freewill-offering for the house of God which is in Jerusalem.

Some of the exiles are said to have jumped at the chance thus offered.

Then rose up the heads of fathers' houses of Judah and Benjamin, and the priests, and the Levites, even all whose spirit God had stirred to go up to build the house of Jehovah which is in Jerusalem. And all they that were round about them strengthened their hands with vessels of silver, with gold, with goods, and with beasts, and with precious things, besides all that was willingly offered. Also Cyrus the king brought forth the vessels of the house of Jehovah, which Nebuchadnezzar had brought forth out of Jerusalem, and had put in the house of his gods; even those did Cyrus, king of Persia, bring forth by the hand of Mithredath the treasurer, and numbered them unto Sheshbazzar, the prince of Judah.

According to the Chronicler over 40,000 people thus returned. The chances are that this number really represents the entire Jewish population of Jerusalem and of the region tributary to it. Remember what was said above as to the small size of Judea, only 800 or 1,000 square miles, all told, and a large part of that too rugged and rocky for cultivation. A population of a hundred per square mile in times of peace and prosperity would be decidedly dense, even if we include the towns. But we are talking now of a time of adversity and distress. Moreover, as we saw above, a large part of Judea was occupied by hostile Edomites from the south, who continued to be a thorn in the flesh of Judah for centuries. Thus to a geographer it seems eminently reasonable to believe that the Chronicler used a fairly complete census of the Jews of his day—which may have been almost as late as 300 B. C., and stated that all of the families in his list came back from exile a century and a half or even two centuries earlier. But if this were the population then, it is probable that it was even less in the dark days before any exiles returned. Even if no such great body of people returned across the desert from Babylonia, the critics all seem to agree that a certain number took advantage of the liberality of Cyrus. Zerubbabel, the governor of Jerusalem, whose name appears to mean "born in Babylon," was a grandson of Jehoiachin, the last king. Joshua, their high priest, was doubtless of the ancient priestly line. These men directed the work of restoring the temple. How many Jews from Babylon actually joined them, no one can tell, but even if only two or three thousand came in the course of a score of years, their presence among a population so small as we have inferred would go far toward determining the character of the people. The significant fact concerning them is that they represent still another vigorous selection. Remember that the cream of Judah was carried to Babylon. Remember that the Judeans as a whole, through a long process of natural selection and training, had become a very religiously minded people. Remember, too, that during the seventy years of the captivity there must have been much apostasy among the exiles who were not of a strong minded and religious temperament. Now from this intensely religious remnant there was selected a relatively small number "whose spirit God had stirred to go up to build the house of Jehovah which is in Jerusalem."

Such selective migrations occurred not once, but several times, as appears from the story of Nehemiah, a justly famous man, who returned to Jerusalem about 445 B. C., if he lived in the days of Artaxerxes I; or more probably about 375 B. C., if he lived in the days of Artaxerxes II. In the one case ninety years, and in the other case a century and a half had elapsed since the first exiles came back in the days of Cyrus. His story, fortunately, is preserved in his own words, and is universally regarded as authentic. It shows that the Jews who returned in earlier days had not met with much success in restoring Jerusalem. Here are his words:

It came to pass, as I was in Shushan the palace, that Hanani one of my brethren came with certain men out of Judah, and I asked them concerning the Jews that had escaped, and that were left of the captivity, and concerning Jerusalem. And they said unto me the remnant that are left of the captivity there in the province are in great affliction and reproach. The wall of Jerusalem also is broken down and the gates thereof are burned with fire. And it came to pass that when I heard these words I sat down and wept, and mourned certain days and I fasted and prayed before the God of heaven. And it came to pass when wine was before king Artaxerxes that I took up the wine, and gave it unto the king, for I was his cup-bearer. Now I had not been beforetime sad in his presence, and the king said unto me, Why is thy countenance sad, seeing thou art not sick? This is nothing else but sorrow of heart. Then I was very sore afraid. And I said unto the king, Let the king live for ever: why should not my countenance be sad, when the city, the place of my fathers' sepulchres, lieth waste and the gates thereof are consumed with fire? Then the king said unto me, For what dost thou make request? So I prayed to the God of heaven. And I said unto the king, If it please the king, and if thy servant have found favor in thy sight, that thou wouldest send me unto Judah, unto the city of my fathers' sepulchres, that I may build it. And the king said unto me (the queen also sitting by him) For how long shall thy journey be? and when wilt thou return? So it pleased the king to send me; and I set him a time. Moreover I said unto the king, If it please the king, let letters be given me to the governors beyond the River, that they may let me pass through till I come unto Judah: and a letter unto Asaph the keeper of the king's forest, that he may give me timber to make beams for the gates of the castle which appertaineth to the house, and for the wall of the city, and for the house that I shall enter into. And the king granted me, according to the good hand of my God upon me.

Thus Jerusalem, together with the little neighboring area which was all that the Jews possessed in Judea, was once more reinforced by very highly selected people. This does not mean that the richest, most influential, or most able among the Jews went back to their old homes. In most cases such people had established themselves and preferred to stay where they were. Only those in whom religious and racial fervor burned very strongly found sufficient incentive to make the long journey back across the desert where they were in fear of their lives from desert raiders. Nor was there much to attract them at the end of the journey, for there, as Nehemiah vividly relates, the neighboring people of the land raised all sorts of difficulties, trying to prevent the rebuilding of Jerusalem, and trying to make the Persian kings believe that the returned Jews were plotting revolt. Remember, too, that more than two centuries had probably elapsed since the ancestors of these migrants had been carried away to Babylonia. If England were in a state of poverty like that of Judea four hundred years before Christ, how many Americans whose ancestors came to this country before 1750 would think of going back there under any circumstances? Only those in whom the fire of religious zeal and love of race and of tradition burned with extraordinary fervor, or those to whom the love of adventure appealed most strongly, would find much incentive to go back to the old home. Thus this selection was, perhaps, the most drastic of all through which the Jews passed in their long history. They had been sifted and sifted until only a grain of one particular size was left, and that size represented a temperament which was extraordinarily religious, and extraordinarily imbued with the feeling of the mission of its race. Even a few hundred or a thousand such people would be a potent factor in revivifying the old spirit and the old inheritance among people descended in part from earlier returning exiles, and from people who had clung to their Judean home through faith in the teachings of Jeremiah and devotion to the land of Jehovah.

Now for the last step in this great eugenic problem of the Jews. "The period which began with Nehemiah's visit was the formative period for the Judaism which we find dominant in New Testament times." * The books of Ezra and Nehemiah both end with the same climax. As soon as Jerusalem had been rebuilt there cropped out an old trouble. The daughters of the land were fair: the Jews were a small minority in the midst of people who were akin to them in blood and language, but remote in religious ideals. So far as the exiles from Babylon who had come back with Nehemiah are concerned, the number of men was doubtless much larger than of women. Naturally, such men took to themselves wives of the people of the land, thus temporarily exaggerating a tendency which always aroused the keen antagonism of the ultra-Jewish party. Such men as Ezra and Nehemiah, intensely Jewish, intensely religious, intensely bigoted, if you will, raised a storm of protest against the foreign marriages, and they had their way. So drastic was the policy that every foreign wife and child was expelled. If the men would not put away their wives, they, too, must leave. Thus during these years of trial there became intrenched in the Jewish social system one of the strictest rules that has ever prohibited intermarriage with other races.

At first sight it seems that the more fully we accept the biblical narratives the stronger becomes the argument that we have just presented. But if we turn to the other extreme and examine the writings of men who go so far as to regard the book of Ezra as a romance, the result is the same. Here is how Professor H. P. Smith puts it:

As has been pointed out by others, Ezra is unknown, not only to Nehemiah, but to Jesus ben Sira, who wrote in the early part of the second cen-

* H. P. Smith, *Old Testament History.*

tury B. C. In his catalogue of heroes of Israel he has a place for Nehemiah, but none for Ezra. In II Maccabees also it is Nehemiah, rather than Ezra, who collects the sacred books in a library. It is impossible to suppose that either of these writers would have passed over Ezra had he been known to them.

What then is the historical fact which the story of Ezra represents? It is this: During the century after Nehemiah the community in Judah was becoming more rigid in its exclusiveness and in its devotion to the ritual. Ezra is the impersonation of both tendencies. Whether there was a scribe named Ezra is not a matter of great importance. Very likely there was such a scribe to whose name tradition attached itself. First it transferred the favor of Artaxerxes to him from Nehemiah. Then it made him the hero of the introduction of the Law. And finally it attributed to him the abrogation of the mixed marriages. It is not unlikely that Nehemiah, after building the wall, induced the people to take upon themselves obligations such as are recounted in the history. The things emphasized there are such as the Babylonian Jews had most at heart—purity of blood, observance of the Sabbath, and care of the Temple service. The signing of such a covenant would put the scribes in a position of advantage. To do them justice, these men were fully possessed by an idea—the idea that if the Law of God could be perfectly obeyed, Israel's future would be glorious. The Law which was to be obeyed was in their hands, and they were its authoritative expounders. If only the Great King would give them power to enforce it, what might they not do for Israel's benefit! . . .

The ideal of holiness—that is, of complete separation from all that is not consecrated to Yahweh—is most plainly, we might say brutally, set before us in the account of the divorce of foreign wives. The seed of Israel must be kept pure from intermixture; this wholly physical precaution is the Chronicler's interpretation of the injunction to be holy. In his zeal for purity of blood he puts the people of the land (most of them Israelite in blood) in the place of the Canaanites and Amorites of which history told him. This is no doubt the idea of Babylonian Judaism carried over into Palestine. It was natural for those who, in the time of Nehemiah and after, returned to the old home, to affiliate themselves with the stricter party there. This party would readily count their opponents to be heathen. The separation became wider with time, and culminated in the Samaritan schism. It was pictured in the Chronicler's mind as a divorce between faithful Jews and their Gentile wives. The cruelty of turning wife and child out of doors would be no reason why the Law should not be observed. But the logic of the scribe would certainly have failed to carry through a measure of the kind had the test been actually made. What the narrative means to do is to emphasise the prohibition of intermarriage; and since to refuse to take a Gentile wife is a very different thing from divorcing one who has acquired rights in the home, the prohibition prevailed, at least, among the stricter Jews. . . .

The Chronicler affirms that the rigid law, directed primarily against the

Moabite and Ammonite, was extended so as to cover every case where mixed blood was suspected. . . .

It is possible that we have here a confused account of the Samaritan schism. Concerning this we have Josephus's narrative as follows: One Sanballat was appointed satrap of Samaria by Darius, the last king of Persia. He gave his daughter in marriage to Manasseh, brother of the Jewish high-priest. The elders of the Jews, however, were indignant at the marriage of one of priestly blood with a foreigner, and demanded that Manasseh should divorce her. He, supposing himself to be next in succession to the high-priesthood (the highest dignity in Judea), told his father-in-law that though he loved his wife he was not willing on her account to be shut out from the high-priesthood. On this representation Sanballat promised Manasseh that he would make him high-priest and governor in Samaria, and would build him a temple on Mount Gerizim. Manasseh agreed to this, and on migrating to Samaria was joined by many priests and Levites, who left Jerusalem because of the proscription of mixed marriages. So far Josephus.

The Sanballat of this account is doubtless the Horonite who gave Nehemiah so much trouble. It is not improbable that the quarrels between Nehemiah and the country party led to a definite separation. In that case Josephus's date is not accurate. But what is quite certain is that the stringency of the Jews in Jerusalem in the matter of foreign alliances led to the formation of the Samaritan community. Each party was sure that it was the true Israel and the people of Yahweh. When the Temple at Jerusalem was closed to all who could not prove their genealogy, or who would not subscribe to the new regulations, those who were shut out were obliged to organize about another centre. Mount Gerizim naturally suggested itself. It was an ancient sanctuary, as is evident from the way it is treated in the book of Deuteronomy. As a sanctuary of Yahweh it could claim greater antiquity than the one at Jerusalem. There was no reason why this might not be a second Jerusalem with a Temple rivalling the other. So the schism became fixed and incurable, and the hatred of one sect for the other was as bitter as the hatred of brothers estranged usually is. But it must be remembered that the Samaritans were Jews to all intents and purposes. They even adopted the Law in the form in which it is recorded in the Pentateuch and observed its precepts, though rejecting the later Rabbinical refinements.

What has been said about Ezra shows that the account given of the introduction of the Law by him belongs in the category of legend rather than fact. But the great historical fact remains that in this period the codification of ancient customs and regulations reached its conclusion.

It seems to me that this Samaritan schism and the rigid codification of Jewish law represent the last great step which paved the way for Christianity and made it possible for the Jews to be the originators not only of Judaism, but of Mohammedanism and

Christianity. Because foreign marriages were so strictly prohibited, and because the laws were so strict, so exact, and so
well known, the religiously minded, exclusive, legalistic and self-
absorbed community formed by the union of Jews who came
back from exile and Jews who clung tenaciously to Judea when
their brethren fled to Egypt, was able to maintain its racial inheritance almost unimpaired down to the time of Christ. Three
or four centuries is not a long time for a race to preserve the
same characteristics. If a stock is kept pure, and if those who
depart from the accepted standards are lopped off unsparingly,
as happened with the Jews, the same characteristics may exist
indefinitely. Well-known historical cases of this kind are found
among the Parsees of India, and the people of Iceland. Among
biologists the extraordinary force of heredity is universally recognized. Certain types of lower animals have remained practically
unchanged for hundreds of millions of years. They are likely to
remain thus for other hundreds of millions, provided their environment remains constant, mutations are exterminated, and
there is no disturbing selection.

Here, then, is the upshot of the whole matter. We see in the
Jews an unparalleled example of natural selection and migration,
aimed more or less consciously at the segregation of the religious
temperament. We see that thus there was produced a race
which is rightly called "peculiar," for it is peculiar not only in
the sense of being unique, but of being greatly honored. That
race, as might be expected, gave birth to Jesus, the greatest of
religious teachers. He is the natural culmination of such a type
of racial evolution. But Jesus did not stand alone. One of the
most remarkable features of New Testament times is the strong
group of men whom he was able to gather about him, or to influence through his teachings. John, Peter, and Paul were great
men in their own right. The authors of the Gospels were men of
real power. The great religious leader can make his doctrines
effective only if he finds among his contemporaries a group of
people whose minds go along with his. There must be similarity
of temperament. Moreover, the great leader is almost sure to

fail unless he is surrounded by other men who also possess at least a certain degree of greatness. Jesus was thus surrounded, 1900 years ago. A long eugenic process, which began with the patriarchs and culminated in Jesus, had made the Jews the most religious of all nations.

CHAPTER XVI

THE DISPERSAL OF THE JEWS

CAN a race change its character? Of course it can adopt new habits, but can its innate mentality be altered? One of the most remarkable facts about the Jews is that a decided change of temperament appears to have taken place between Bible days and the present. Ask any group of Gentiles whether the Jews were warlike in the days of David. You will get a chorus of assent. Ask that same group whether the Jews are warlike *to-day*, and the chorus will chant "no." The Israelites were among the most warlike of peoples when the Judges ruled Palestine, when Samson and David raided the Philistines, and when the kings of Israel and Judah led forth their hosts year in and year out. The greatest heroes were those who slew the most of "Jehovah's" enemies. "Saul hath slain his thousands, and David his ten thousands," sang the maidens as the victor returned from the slaughter. To-day, on the contrary, the Jews seem to be peculiarly prone to avoid war. Even the relatively unwarlike character of our age can scarcely explain their tendency to shrink from forms of conflict that involve physical danger. Of course, they are not the only people among whom this is the case, nor is it so with all of them. Yet there seems to be much truth in the general opinion that the average Jew avoids physical conflict to an unusual degree.

When and how did this change take place? Was it due to the lessons of the captivity, five or six centuries before Christ? That is doubtful, for when their enemies tried to prevent the rebuilding of Jerusalem, the returned exiles built with one hand and wielded the sword with the other. A century or two later the Jews were still so warlike that they enlisted in Alexander's army in considerable numbers, and served as mercenaries for later rulers, both in Syria and Egypt. In the period of the Maccabees, in the middle of the second century before Christ, the Jewish feats of daring rival anything in the whole range of history. At one time (165 B. C.) Judas Maccabæus, with 6,000 men, was faced by an army of overwhelming strength, 40,000 footmen and 7,000 horse, so it is said. The contest must have appeared almost hopeless. Yet according to the old Hebrew law, Judas issued a proclamation that all who had married wives within a year, built houses and not lived in them, or planted vineyards and not eaten of the fruit thereof, and all who were fearful, should return home. His force dwindled to 3,000 ill-armed men, but this little army won a great victory, killing 3,000 of the enemy on the first day of fighting, and many more later.

The fighting spirit of the Jews burst forth again with extraordinary fury at the time of the destruction of Jerusalem in 70 A. D. For four or five years before that time Palestine, and especially Judea, suffered untold agonies from the bloodiest kind of warfare. The Jews were ostensibly fighting to free themselves from the yoke of Rome, but the worst fighting was between Jew and Jew. The zealots wanted to get rid of everything foreign, root and branch. The moderates wanted to compromise. Rival leaders arose; at one time three factions held different parts of Jerusalem, each hating the other with almost unbelievable intensity. They fought like cats and dogs. Meanwhile a Roman army besieged the city, ready to crowd in upon it at any moment. But Titus had no desire to massacre his men. Why should he waste good Roman soldiers in killing the Jews, when the Jews were killing one another as fast as they could? So he let them fight it out for two heartrending years. Almost up to the end recruits kept dribbling in from other Jewish communities, just as in the days of the Maccabees, and in other great crises. The recruits knew that they had to fight; they must have realized that most of them would die; but still they came. Zeal for race and religion was doubtless their main motive, but the fighting spirit was surely there in full force. Only when famine and disease, as well as cruel fighting, had brought the Jews to the verge of destruction, did Titus press the siege. Then, too late, the rival factions united, and fought to the bitter end with indomitable courage.

According to Josephus, more than 1,350,000 people were killed in the battles which he lists, and there were many minor engagements. His account and those of others make it appear that something like 900,000 of the people of Palestine were taken captive, and either forced to fight in the arena, or sold as slaves all over the world. In addition to this, great numbers died of massacre, famine, and disease in almost every district. Moreover, many Jews had previously migrated from Palestine voluntarily to escape the terrible disorder of the war. The numbers given by Josephus and others are evidently much exaggerated. Nevertheless, the loss of life and the exodus of emigrants and captives reached huge proportions, and four or five centuries of comparative peace, save in the Maccabean days, had allowed the number of Jews to increase enormously. The sufferings of the Belgians during the World War were mild compared with those of the Jews in the days of Vespasian and Titus; the bravery of the Belgians was surely no greater than that of the Jews; their losses were far less. After the sack of Jerusalem the province of Judea was well nigh a desert.

Did all this discourage the Jews or destroy their warlike spirit? It seems as if it ought to have done so. But only forty-six years later, in 116 A. D., the Jews rose violently against the dominant race in each of the main Jewish centres. As Grætz puts it, in his history of the Jews, they spread anarchy through a great portion of the Roman Empire. In Egypt they are said to have put to death some 220,000 of their neighbors at Alexandria and elsewhere. In Cyrenaica and Cyprus equally huge figures are given, while Babylonia and Palestine saw similar carnage. The Jews in those days were certainly fighters of the fiercest sort. When the authorities recovered from the shock of this fiery outbreak, great armies were launched against the Jews. For every Gentile's life the life of at least one Jew seems to have been the rule. Moreover, hosts of captives were deported, while many of the more peaceful Jews had already moved away from the scenes of violence. In Cyprus all Jews were killed or deported. Thereafter none might set foot on the island; shipwreck there meant death for any Jew. In Palestine the disturbances ended only with the defeat of the fierce Bar-Cochba, a pseudo-Messiah, and with the final destruction of Jerusalem (135 A. D.), a destruction even more complete than that of 70 A. D.

This time the Jews seem to have received so terrible a setback that the military spirit was finally crushed. In the eighteen centuries that have since elapsed there is no record of any great military leaders such as David, the Maccabees and Bar-Cochba. Here and there, to be sure, the Jews have occasionally indulged in small local revolts. A few Jewish military officers have risen to fairly important positions under Gentile rulers; a few bodies of Jewish troops have distinguished themselves for daring, as did some of the East-side Jews of New York in the World War. But compared with their record in other lines, the Jews have done practically nothing in a military way for eighteen long centuries. As merchants, physicians, artists, musicians, religious interpreters, scientists, and statesmen, they have distinguished themselves conspicuously, but not as warriors. A great transformation apparently occurred between 50 and 150 A. D.

Historians almost universally recognize the magnitude and importance of this change. Gibbon, who is none too friendly to the Jews, says that: "Gentle treatment insensibly assuaged the stern temper of the Jews. Awakened from their dream of prophecy and conquest, they assumed the behavior of peaceable and industrious subjects. Their irreconcilable hatred of mankind, instead of flowing out into acts of blood and violence, evaporated in less dangerous gratifications. They embraced every opportunity of overreaching idolaters in trade." The historian Just, in a more friendly tone, traces the growth of the love of wealth which he regards as the natural result of the commercial spirit. Still others say that the Jews simply evolved faster than other people. The world is on the way to pacifism; the Jews got there nearly eighteen centuries ago.

But why did the Jews make such a sudden jump from war-likeness to pacifism? Three main causes are commonly given. The first is the absence of any political centre. After the great uprising from 116 to 135 A. D., the plough was dragged over Jerusalem, a new Roman settlement was established outside the old city, and a swine's head was placed over the entrance to the ruins. For a long time Jews were rigidly excluded; they could not even come by stealth to mourn over their departed glory. Doubtless the loss of Jerusalem was an important factor in diminishing the warlike tendencies of the Jews. But a strong Jewish centre arose thereafter in Galilee and flourished for centuries. The Jews of Babylonia persisted as a compact group for a thousand years, and much of the time were ruled by the princes of the captivity, supposedly lineal descendants of King David. Moreover, the great insurrection of 116 A. D. broke out in Egypt, Cyrenaica, Cyprus, and Babylonia, where the Jews had no political unity, before it did in Palestine. If the Jews had been warlike in the old way, they might have revolted again, even when they no longer possessed a centre in Jerusalem.

This leads to the second reason why the Jews ceased to be a military people. They had tried to throw off the oppression of the Gentiles on three main occasions and several minor ones. Each time they had ultimately failed, and each time their punishment had been worse. Being a canny people, so the argument runs, they at last concluded that rebellion does not pay. Thereafter submission to authority was inculcated in each succeeding generation. "Render unto Cæsar the things that are Cæsar's" were the words of Jesus, but if they mean mere submission to authority, they are more Jewish than Christian. In the last eighteen centuries Christians have revolted against their established rulers time and again. They have risen in small groups and large, in hopeless causes as well as in those where success was assured. In spite of their peaceful religion, Christians have been the world's great fighters for fifteen hundred years. They have not followed Jesus: the Jews have done that. Has this been because the Jews teach their children that "all they that take the sword shall perish with the sword"? Even though the children are born with a warlike spirit, do they learn to submit to oppression?

But a third factor enters into the matter. The Jews, through bitter experience, are supposed to have learned that violence is only one way of getting even with an oppressor. A better, safer way, they say, is to get your enemy into debt and let the law squeeze him. Or wheedle him into giving you peace. Buy him off, pretend to submit, and secretly undo him! Appear to conform to his unrighteous and oppressive demands, but secretly follow your own customs and grow rich! Accomplish your purposes indirectly! Bow low before the strong wind, but rise again when it is past! This, we are told, has become the Jewish attitude, and is inculcated in the children from earliest infancy.

Although the absence of a political centre, the terrific penalties of violence, and the effectiveness of the indirect method seem to most students to explain the great contrast between the warlike Jews of the past and the peaceful Jews of the present, a fourth condition may join with these in affording a complete explanation. We have already referred to the terrible carnage, the slavery, and the migrations which accompanied each Jewish uprising, but we have not taken account of the kind of people who suffered one fate or another. Recall what happened in Palestine after the last great Jewish uprisings. The historian Grætz says that when Bar-Cochba proclaimed himself as the Messiah who would redeem Israel (about 131 A. D.): "Jewish warriors from all countries poured forth to aid the Messianic king. . . . Even the Samaritans joined their former enemies. . . . The heathens made common cause with the Jews. . . . It seemed as if the whole Roman Empire were about to receive a heavy blow, by which the various members of its gigantic body were to be rent asunder. From these facts the number of warriors cannot be considered as exaggerated if the Jewish sources put them down as 400,000, while the pagan historian, Dio Cassius, rates them at 580,000."

When the Emperor Hadrian, after three years of victory on the part of Bar-Cochba, finally conquered the great Jewish soldier, "one can scarcely credit the numbers said to have been slain, and yet they are confirmed both by Jewish and Greek historians. The authentic historian, Dio Cassius, says that beside whose who died of hunger and fire there fell half a million Jews. . . . Hadrian established three military stations to capture the fugitives. . . . Whoever escaped the one garrison was captured by the other. Thus all the warriors were destroyed, all towns and villages laid waste, and the land was literally converted into a desert. The prisoners, mostly women and children, were dragged by thousands to the slave markets of Hebron and Gaza, where they were sold. There were, however, some fugitives who lived in caves in order to escape the enemy. But even this miserable existence was not permitted to them. Heralds announced that to those who voluntarily yielded themselves up, mercy would be granted. Many listened to the temptation, but were carried off to the plain of Rimmon, and the victors were commanded to massacre their prisoners before Hadrian tasted food. Many fugitives, however, fled to Arabia."

Slaughter and massacre do not form the whole story of this final expulsion from Palestine. During many previous centuries there had been a steady seepage of Jews to other countries. During the wars the seepage swelled to a strong stream. Of what kind of people did it consist? The answer is written in the clearest letters in every history of the Jews. Those who migrated while there was merely a seepage were mainly merchants, or traders, with some artisans. When the seepage swelled to a stream, the migrants whose aim was commercial were joined by great numbers to whom peace was more to be desired than anything else. On the other hand, during the wars the more zealous and warlike types of Jews from all parts of the world flocked to Jerusalem to aid their embattled countrymen. Thus now, as in the days of the kingdoms of Israel and Judah, two streams flowed in opposite directions. This time the peacefully inclined, commercially minded, and submissive type went outward from Jerusalem; the zealous, warlike, bigoted type came inward. The people who streamed outward may have been as religious as those who streamed inward. Many of their descendants have certainly stuck to their race and religion with marvellous tenacity. But their way of showing attachment to their faith has been commercial, not military. For many centuries each Jew in foreign lands paid a yearly tax to the Temple. In fact, the Temple became one of the world's greatest treasuries. So huge were the accumulations of wealth that after the sack of Jerusalem, in 70 A. D., the buying power of gold in Syria is said to have sunk to one-half its former level. How exact this statement is we do not know, but there is no doubt as to the vastness of the sums sent to Jerusalem by pious Jews, not only as taxes, but as free-will gifts. The commercially minded outward migration of Jews paid its debts to its God and its church with gold; the inward migration paid with lives.

This last point can scarcely be emphasized too strongly. In proportion to the total number of Jews the deaths through war, famine, disease, and hardship during the Maccabean period, a century and a half before Christ, and especially during the final period, from 65 to 140 A. D., were enormous. Among the Jews who thus perished there tended to be a strong majority of the warlike type which prefers death rather than surrender—a splendid type, but futile for the upbuilding of future generations. The wives and children of this type largely died of famine and hardship, or were taken captive and sold as slaves. Most of the slaves were so separated from Jewish influences that they, or at least their children, became heathen. Thousands upon thousands of women and girls were taken into Gentile homes and became the mothers of Gentile children. Occasionally, to be sure, as at Worms and Mayence, near the Rhine, women of this kind were abandoned by their soldier husbands in such numbers that their half-Jewish children were brought up in the way of the Law, and became the nucleus of a Jewish community. Some Jewish captives were doubtless bought and set free by rich merchants of their own race. But cases of both these kinds account for only a small fraction of the captives. The vast majority appear to have been lost to the Jews, even if they did not perish.

In addition to those who were slain or taken captive, some of the warlike Jews escaped when their cause was finally lost. After the destruction of Jerusalem, in 70 A. D., a considerable body of such people took refuge in Egypt, while others reached Cyrenaica, crossed the sea to Cyprus, or went eastward to Babylonia. There they started new uprisings. At Alexandria they stirred up part of the large Jewish colony to a serious revolt, but the commercially minded leaders, who had most to lose, not only squelched them but handed over 600 to Lupus, the governor, who executed them on the spot. Others fled to Thebes, but were pursued, seized, and tortured to death. Elsewhere, as in Cyrenaica, almost identically the same thing occurred, the number there delivered over to be slain being over 3,000. When these disturbances had subsided, the newcomers settled down as part of the Jewish communities. But many of them must have been poor and discontented. They were not the kind who make the best merchants or artisans. In the main they came from the agricultural sections of the Jewish people. Or if they were from the cities, they were of the Zealot type, the kind who thrust their Jewish idiosyncrasies down the throats of all around them. After the more hot-headed had been delivered to the Romans by their co-religionists, the others probably remained relatively quiet for a while. Their sufferings, their poverty, and their lack of organization would tend to keep them so. But the next generations were presumably less handicapped, and probably were not much influenced by the sufferings of their fathers and grandfathers. The presence of the children and grandchildren of the Zealots who fled from Jerusalem may have been one of the chief reasons why the Jews of Egypt, Cyrenaica, Cyprus, and Babylonia all were on the point of revolt less than fifty years after the destruction of Jerusalem. In the great final débâcle the troublemakers, as we have seen, were killed by the hundred thousand, while such of them as survived were largely enslaved and scattered abroad.

All this appears to have produced a genuine biological change in the Jews. To use an old illustration, suppose the horses of a country are of all colors from white to black. Let large numbers of people acquire an antipathy to dark horses, so that at frequent intervals they kill every dark beast they can find. Before many decades the horses would be much whiter than formerly. Animals of every shade might still be found, but where the average herd had given a dark impression originally, it would now give a light impression.

This illustrates what seems to have happenea to the Jews. In generation after generation Greeks, Romans, Syrians, and others killed the warlike, fiery kind of Jew unsparingly, and by the hundred thousand. The peaceful, submissive type, which accomplishes its purposes by quiet, indirect methods, escaped. Naturally that kind of temperament now gives color to the Jews as a whole, in spite of many individuals of the more warlike type. The persecutions of later days have accentuated this condition. The Jew who resists by violence has been the first to be killed by his kind Christian neighbors. The irony of it all lies in the fact that those neighbors have done their evil deeds in the name of a Jew. The Jews, in this respect at least, have approached the Christlike ideal, and the Christians have been a main agent in forcing them to do so.

But enough of this. Our main conclusion is that a real change in the temperamental inheritance of the Jews is one of the chief reasons for the contrast between the warlike Jews of the Bible and the peaceful Jews of to-day. Because the peaceful temperament prevails, the absence of a political centre has a peculiarly strong effect in checking military aspirations. For the same reason the lessons of past persecutions sink deeply into the minds of the young; and the advantages of the indirect way of attaining one's ends are accentuated. Thus here, as in many other cases, the biological inheritance of a race works hand in hand with its social institutions and other cultural conditions to produce and perpetuate a vital historical change.

One other perplexing feature of the modern Jew seems to be at least partially explained by the principles of racial selection. The Jews of to-day by no means form a pure race. They are sharply divided into two main types, the Shephardim, or Spanish Jews, and the Ashkenazim, or Russian Jews. Physically these two are as different as Anglo-Saxons and Bulgarians. The Shephardim are long-headed, black-haired people with finely chiselled features. They are typical Semites, much resembling the Arabs, and not greatly different from the Mediterranean race among whom they live. The Ashkenazim are broad-headed people, with large, coarse features. Often, although by no means always, they have what we mistakenly call the Jewish type of nose. Generally they are black-haired, but ruddy or sandy hair is common, and blue eyes are not unknown. According to the common methods of distinguishing races the two types have no right to be classed together. Yet both claim descent from the same Jewish ancestors.

In addition to the divisions of the Jews into two major branches, there is great diversity within each branch. Anthropologists have constantly been astonished at the closeness with which the physical type of the Jews who have long been settled in a region agrees with that of the surrounding Gentiles. The agreement seems greater than would arise from the amount of intermarriage which is commonly supposed to take place.

In spite of this great physical diversity the Jewish race appears to possess a marked uniformity of character. The Shephardim, to be sure, are generally considered more cultured than the Ashkenazim, and have contributed a larger proportion of great men. Nevertheless, both branches of the race display the same submissive, indirect, and unwarlike qualities. Both tend to be merchants, or at least artisans, rather than farmers. Both are pre-eminently city people. In addition to this the religious element is very strong in both groups, as is the tendency toward loyalty to their race. Of course many Jews are free-thinkers, and have little respect for religious forms and theological formulæ, but even such men tend more strongly than do corresponding Gentiles to be loyal to their church and race. In other words, we seem to have a curious anomaly. The Jews are a highly diverse race physically, they are relatively homogeneous mentally.

The explanation of the physical diversity of the Jews lies

largely in three factors, slavery, intermarriage, and proselytism. In the days of the Bible, in Roman times, and even in the Christian era, slavery was almost universal. The Jews of the dispersion, being relatively rich and prosperous, owned many slaves. Their regular practice was to circumcise the slaves and make "Jews" of them. It made no difference to the owner whether his slave was Greek, Scythian, Arab, Jew, or Goth, provided he was properly inducted into Judaism. Being thus inducted he could intermarry with other Jews, or at least his children could. Thus the more a Jewish community prospered, the more rapidly it ceased to be really Jewish. So common was the practice of converting Gentile slaves into "Jews" that many of the earliest limitations placed upon the Jews by the Roman emperors had to do with this matter.

Intermarriage between Jews and Gentiles has been much more common than is usually supposed. Previous to the spread of Christianity, Jews had made their way into many regions remote from Palestine. Where the Jewish community was large, a prejudice against it soon arose, mainly because the Jews kept themselves apart, practised special rites, and looked upon their heathen neighbors with contempt. Where the Jews were few, as in Spain and France, such prejudice scarcely existed. Intermarriage was not frowned upon, and was practised freely. In Spain stringent laws against it were passed only in the third century A. D., and were largely disregarded for generations. Even in later times there has been much intermarriage, not only in Spain but elsewhere. This has been especially the case during periods when persecution and racial rancor have died down, as has frequently occurred for generations. It is commonly supposed, among Gentiles at least, that when a Jew marries a Gentile the Jew is likely to leave the Jewish community and the children are brought up as Gentiles. But this is by no means universal. Moreover, in practically every period Jewish women and girls, by reason of the contempt in which their race has been held, have been basely violated, and there has been no redress. In times of persecution such women have often been kept in

Christian homes for months or years. We have already seen how the children of Jewish mothers by Roman fathers formed the nucleus of a Jewish community in Gaul. In many other cases the strong faith of the Jewish mother sweeps the children away from the faith of their father and makes Jews of them. On the other hand there have been, and still are, many instances where Gentile women become the wives of Jewish men, and the children are brought up as Jews in the Jewish community.

This brings up the important question of proselytes. Judaism is not a missionary religion in the same sense as Christianity. Nevertheless, it has made a vast number of converts. Some of the earliest and most detailed of the laws in the Bible deal with this matter. In the Roman Empire edict after edict was issued to limit the steady flow of converts to Judaism. Some of these converts were Christians. The Jews of that time, as well as Jewish historians to-day, exult over cases like that of a well-known monk who renounced Christianity for Judaism. Strangely enough, or rather naturally enough, the flow of proselytes to Judaism has often been stimulated by persecution. This was pre-eminently the case with early Christianity, and why should it not also be true of Judaism? The high moral code, and the principles of duty to God and man are as noble in Judaism as in the Christianity which borrowed them. The person whose temperament leads him to become a Christian in the face of persecution, might equally well become a Jew.

In addition to the slow infiltration of other elements which thus modified the racial inheritance of the Jews, there were certain cases where large bodies of people adopted Judaism. The largest and best known of these helped to produce the Ashkenazim type of Jew. The Khazars were a broad-headed, large-featured race who lived in southern Russia north of the Caucasus. In the eighth and ninth centuries they were converted to Judaism in large numbers. So numerous were they that their racial type greatly modified the appearance of the Jews of that part of the world, and has since spread widely, thus producing the Ashkenazin.

Now for the last element in the physical diversity and mental unity of the Jewish race of to-day. From beginning to end two processes have gone on side by side. Sometimes the Jews have gained recruits, either rapidly as when the Khazars were converted, or more often slowly. Sometimes the Jews have lost part of their people, either rapidly under the stress of persecution, as when hundreds of thousands were "Christianized" in Spain and Portugal, about 1492, or slowly, as when Heine, Börne, Gans, Neander, and Felix Mendelssohn adopted Christianity. This movement to and from the Jewish fold has been, perhaps, the greatest element in giving the Jews their present homogeneity. In this respect their case is almost identical with that of the sects of Christianity. The Roman Catholic Church is continually losing some of its members and gaining others. Those who are lost are generally of an inquiring, independent type of mind: they cannot accept certain doctrines which do not agree with their personal methods of reasoning, and they are not willing to accept limitations on their thinking. Those who join the Roman Church are likely to be of an emotional and submissive type, persons who love beautiful forms and ceremonies, and who desire to escape from the torment of doubt by a single great act of faith. Compare the Salvation Army and the Unitarians. Temperamentally they are as far apart as the poles. To one the main element in religion, and in life, is the emotions; to the other the intellect. The Salvation Army listens to the exhortations and imprecations of a popular evangelist with the greatest delight; the thoughtful Unitarian finds the same man repulsive, or else interesting merely as a study in psychology. If a person with the Salvation Army temperament happens to be born in a Unitarian family, which does not often happen, the chances are that while he is still young he will leave the Unitarians. If he is too intellectual to join the "Army," he may become an Episcopalian, or join some other cultured denomination that displays warmth and fervor. And if a child with a thoughtful, unemotional temperament happens to be born of Salvation Army parents, is he not likely to become a Presbyterian or Congregationalist?

In the same way, all through the ages, the Jews have made their proselytes largely among people of their own temperament; they have lost to other faiths not only those who were weak in the peculiarly Jewish traits of religious and racial tenacity, or who departed widely from the accepted Jewish standards, but also those whose temperaments were especially similar to that of the Gentiles around them. This process is going on to-day. Just at present the Jews are rapidly losing, but if the Christians should begin to persecute them, who knows what might happen? The shape of a man's nose, or the width of his head, seems to make relatively little difference in his aptitudes and abilities, or in his choice of a religion. The mental attitude is what counts. Thus through the generations, by keeping slaves, by intermarrying with the heathen, and by making proselytes, the Jews have become highly diverse in racial composition and physical appearance. Yet at the same time, by shedding the people who did not conform to the dominant type of mentality, and by attracting others who conform, they have preserved a high degree of temperamental unity.

CHAPTER XVII

THE INTERPRETATION OF HISTORY

THE preceding discussion of the history of Palestine lays special emphasis on geography, race, natural selection, and migration. It pays relatively little attention to the great body of facts summed up in such words as society, inventions, and institutions. This has been done advisedly. We are breaking new ground and cannot finish our task if we must create a perfect garden at once. It would be a mistake, however, to leave the reader with the impression that the historical method illustrated in this book ignores the supreme importance of social, political, and other cultural conditions, or of great personalities, and the ideas, inventions, usages, and institutions which they originate. Hence this chapter is devoted to a brief résumé of Jewish history in which we shall try to bring out the interaction between some of these cultural conditions and the geographical and racial conditions previously discussed.

The history of the Jews may be divided into five great eras. Each begins with a crisis during which migration and natural selection play a prominent part. Each is characterized by a special form of government and a special phase of religious development. The five introductory crises are (1) the migration of Abraham, which may have taken place anywhere from 2100 to 1500 B. C.; (2) the Exodus and the wandering in the wilderness, beginning about 1230 B. C.; (3) the separation of the kingdoms of Israel and Judah, 930 B. C.; (4) the Exile to Assyria and Babylonia, culminating in 586 B. C.; (5) the destruction of Jerusalem, 70 A. D.

The first great crisis is marked by the peaceful migration of a single family. For reasons already discussed we assume that Abraham was a genuine historical character whose life followed the general course indicated in Genesis, but whether he was a real person or merely a type makes little difference for our present purpose. No special economic or political difficulties appear to have led to his migration. He and his relatives are pictured as wealthy and influential. The only clue to the reasons why they left home and country—and that a very slight one—is the statement of late Jewish authors that Abraham was actuated by religious motives. Whether this particular statement is true or not, it represents a principle of the utmost importance. Religious convictions are one of the great causes of migration. They may actuate people of all grades of society, and may be effective under almost any kind of political or economic conditions. As a rule, they are especially potent among people who possess relatively little of this world's goods, and at times of political distress.

Two main religious innovations appear to have been dominant in the mind of Abraham. One was the first glimmerings of monotheism—the conviction that for him and his family there was only one god. Other people might have many gods, but he owed allegiance to Jehovah alone. Of course we do not know how far this idea actually originated with Abraham, but he at least represents its crystallization for the Hebrews. His second innovation was the idea that human sacrifices are not pleasing to God; or at least to his Jehovah. Here the evidence of Abraham's actual deeds seems relatively strong, for the story of the sacrifice of Isaac reads like truth, with only a little veneer of later adornment and interpretation.

Religious migrations are especially important because of their strong tendency to keep the migrants separate from the people around them. It would be difficult, if not impossible, to name any other motive which so effectually limits or even prevents intermarriage, and thereby promotes racial purity. Thus, whether the Hebrew patriarchs were real people or not, they stand as an admirable illustration of the way in which a few people may long maintain their racial and cultural identity in the midst of aliens, provided they are imbued with deep-seated religious convictions, and are fortified therein by special rites and usages.

The expiring remnants of another social custom, wide-spread

in its time, made it much easier for the Hebrews to preserve their biological aloofness. That custom was the matriarchate, that is, the habit of counting inheritance through the mother. Doubtless, it had already gone far toward being broken down, but it was still strong enough so that in Egypt the throne went to the pharaoh's daughter, and not his son. Among the Jews an only daughter inherited the whole of her father's property. The laws of inheritance were utterly different from those of the modern Turkish sultanate, for example, where the heir to the throne is always a man, perhaps the son of the former ruler, but often his brother, nephew, or other relative. Among people who possess much property an almost necessary corollary of the matriarchate is endogamous marriage, or marriage within the tribe. In practice that generally means the marriage of close kin, perhaps brother and sister, uncle and niece, or at any rate first cousins. In no other way can the property be kept in the family. Among the early Hebrews the matriarchal rules of inheritance were still strong enough so that they powerfully seconded the influence of religious peculiarities in preventing the descendants of Abraham from being swamped among their less religious neighbors.

The early Hebrews were patriarchal as well as matriarchal. The combination of these two opposed tendencies is most interesting. The Hebrews were patriarchal largely because among wandering nomads who depend upon cattle for a living, that form of organization is almost essential. Among a hunting people there is rarely any need of concerted action. A woman in her cave can easily be the head of the family. Among agricultural people much the same is true. But among pastoral nomads concerted action is essential, because of the constantly recurring crises brought on by raids, storms, wild animals, and the necessity for frequent migrations. Such crises can be met only by persons of decisive character and active physique. The kind who can endure long hardship and strenuous exertion, and who are able both to obey and to command. Women rarely possess all these qualities in sufficient degree to make them the heads of nomadic families.

The religious migration of Abraham culminated in Moses, the Lawgiver. His outstanding importance is due to the way in which he drew together the threads of old customs and new aspirations. Incipient monotheism, aversion to human sacrifices, traces of matriarchal inheritance, endogamous marriages, pastoral nomadism, and the patriarchal form of government were all present in the practices of the Hebrews from Abraham onward. Moses appears to have molded them into a definite code of laws which, after many centuries, was finally remodelled into the elaborate code of the Bible. He imparted a new and deeper significance and a new authority to the animal sacrifices which gradually replaced human sacrifices after the days of Abraham. Perhaps he believed that by constructing a movable ark as the symbol of Jehovah's presence he had freed the Hebrews from the idea that their god was limited to any one place. But later events proved that to the people at large he had merely constructed something which Jehovah followed, so that where it rested, he also rested.

Note how completely Moses sums up the racial, environmental and cultural elements of his time, place, and people. The matriarchal aspect of the man is evident in the fact that his mother was own aunt to his father. How much of the blood of Abraham, Isaac, and Jacob actually ran in his veins we shall never know. The endogamous system of marriage may have made that share very large, especially if he belonged to only the seventh generation from Abraham. At any rate, he displayed to a remarkable degree the very qualities in which Abraham and Jacob excelled. He combined the good points of both to such a degree that he probably stands second only to Jesus in the long line of great Jewish teachers of religion. But doubtless he would have failed to stand so high had he not possessed a broad cultural background, derived not only from his ancestors, but from Babylonia, on the one hand, and Egypt on the other.

The patriarchal aspect of Moses appears in his prompt assumption of authority over the tribe as soon as a crisis developed. Throughout his career he displays the qualities which are most noteworthy among people who have been trained in the school of desert nomadism, or at least whose forebears have been selected in that school. This is evident in his quick, decisive action, his readiness to strike and slay when an Egyptian wrongs his countrymen, his fearlessness before kings, his democracy among his own people even when still known as the son of the Egyptian princess. It also appears in his power to command implicit obedience, even in the greatest crises of hunger, thirst, and attack by enemies. Moses, to an extraordinary degree, was an epitome of the racial, geographical, and cultural conditions which had prevailed among his ancestors for the past few hundred years.

Now for the next great crisis, the Exodus. In discussing the first crisis we had little to say about geographical environment aside from the effect of the desert. Nor did we have anything to say about the material aspects of human culture. Our attention was focused on two main lines, first the extraordinary power of religious ideals and laws, and second the potency of selective and limited marriage in preserving and accentuating human characteristics. With the second crisis the case is quite different. Geographical environment and a material advance in human culture seem to be the dominating themes. The way for the crisis was doubtless prepared by political events in Egypt and elsewhere, but the actual occurrence which precipitated it appears to have been purely geographical according to our interpretation. That occurrence, it will be remembered, was an extreme drought. Moreover, there is considerable evidence that a prolonged period of increasing aridity had much to do with causing the disturbed political conditions which prepared the way for the Exodus.

After the Israelites had left Egypt they were exposed to the fullest effect of a desert which, at that time, may possibly have been more habitable than at present, but which for a while, at least, was presumably much less habitable than it had been when previously traversed by the earlier Israelites. Moreover, the Israelites were intruders into a land where every man's hand is against his neighbor and where the people were probably in distress from drought. Thus everything seems to have combined to subject them to the sifting processes of the desert with unusual vigor. By the time the wanderers made their final attempt to enter Palestine the climate had perhaps begun an amelioration which may have continued intermittently for two centuries, but this presumably came too late to tempt them back into the desert.

No sooner had the Israelites escaped from the stress of the desert than they were confronted by another geographical difficulty. This new difficulty lay in the rough and impassable quality of the land where they now made their homes, especially Judea. The energy and courage of the desert Israelites enabled them to take possession of the land, but not till the days of David, two centuries later, were they able to appropriate the strongest fortresses such as Jerusalem. Indeed, although they conquered and exterminated many of the former inhabitants, their conquest was in considerable measure a mere filling up of the empty spaces round about the towns where the old inhabitants held out. That such should be the case is easily understandable if we are correct in our supposition of a pronounced amelioration of climate between 1200 and 1000 B. C. In that case the dryness at the earlier epoch must have forced the partial or perhaps complete abandonment of many sites in Palestine. But when the rainfall became more abundant, old sites again became habitable, the population could easily increase, and there was room for the invaders.

Before the impetus of the Israelite irruption into Palestine had spent itself, a totally new factor came upon the stage. This was iron, the use of which was rapidly spreading over the earth at this period. We need not repeat what we have said as to how its adoption placed the Israelites on a par with their more cultured Philistine neighbors. It is enough to point out that such an advance in material culture may work in much the same way as a new religion, a new custom as to marriage and inheritance, a period of great drought, or various other factors. Different as these factors may be, they are alike in their ability to swing the course of history away from its old path and lead it along lines which no man has expected. Each is a potent cause of the pulsations which form the framework of history.

David represents the culmination of the period ushered in by the crisis of the Exodus. He exemplifies a new type of political organization, the kingship, which was destined to play a profound part in producing or accelerating still other historical pulsations. He likewise exemplifies the new culture that came in with iron. Quite unconsciously, but with telling reiteration, the Hebrew authors love to dwell on David's sword, and spear and shield. He was the man of war, the sword of the Lord, who hewed his enemies in pieces. As a boy he represents the stone age, for with his sling and stone he slew Goliath. But at that very moment the age of iron dawned for him. Did he not draw Goliath's huge sword and therewith smite off the giant's head? Perhaps it was Elhanan, the son of Dodo, David's fellow villager and henchman, who actually did the slaying, as an old fragment of II Samuel seems to indicate. But that makes no difference so far as our present use of the story is concerned. But in spite of his iron tools, David was still, in many respects, the nomad of the desert. Who was more skilled than he in making a quick foray and plundering his enemies? Who had more fully the power to obey, which made him submit for a long time to Saul's indignities? He also possessed in the highest degree the power to command, which endeared his men to him so that they gloried in risking their lives to get him water from the clear spring, where he had drunk as a boy of the stone age. And lastly, David still bore in his veins the blood of Abraham. Was this the reason why he had such full measure of the deep religious spirit which animated Abraham, Jacob, and Moses? He brought the ark to its final resting-place in Jerusalem, he danced before the Lord, he was grieved that he himself dwelt in a palace, while Jehovah still dwelt in tents. Although he did not write all the Psalms, he doubtless wrote some of them. Thus in him we see all the old qualities of his race, but moulded anew by the land where he was born, by the permanent villages in which his people now dwelt, by the fields that they tilled, by the iron weapons which gave new opportunities for prowess, and by the new custom of kingship. Solomon, even more than David, exemplifies the changes that had taken place since the crisis in the days of Moses.

Hard on the heels of the climax of this era follows the next great crisis. This time the political element looms large as the main precipitant, for the split between Judah and Israel was primarily a political quarrel. But back of the political facts lies the geographic contrast in the topography of Samaria and Judea, and the presence of the great highways in Samaria. If we look deeply into almost any great crisis in human affairs we find this same combination of many types of causes. In the present case the racial element enters because the Israelities, far more than the Judeans, had intermixed with the people of the land. The commercial element enters because commerce was the main agent which covered the Samaritan roads with foreign travellers and filled the villages with talk of Baal, Ashtoreth, and other abominations of the Gentiles.

Religion and migration both seem at first sight to have played little part in this third crisis, but they were there as usual. The break between Judah and Israel ultimately threw the whole burden of maintaining the Hebrew religion upon Judah. That happened because of the way in which the rocks lie and the roads run, but it also happened because David brought the ark to Jerusalem and Solomon made a magnificent temple for it. And of course it happened because many other conditions prevailed, for every human result is due to the combined effect of many diverse causes. This time the migration was so slow and inconspicuous that some authorities doubt its existence, but it seems to have been real and to have been highly selective. How many Levites, priests, and such as set their hearts to seek Jehovah came out of Israel to Judah, and how many of the opposite type migrated the other way, we can only guess. But it is clear that at the end of the period the kingdom of Israel had fallen away from its old religious faith, while Judah had been through a genuine reformation. The Book of the Law had been found, read, and interpreted, and many of the people, as well as the king and the priests, made sincere attempt to follow it.

This time it is a prophet, the first Isaiah, who stands forth as the greatest man of his time, the epitome of the spirit of his age. In Isaiah we see a man of high birth, wealth, and culture, a frequenter of the court, and a familiar friend who dares rebuke the king. Gone are the old desert characteristics, or at least they do not come to the surface. But moral courage of the highest type, and a religious fervor perhaps surpassing that of any of his predecessors still remain. The prophet has replaced the patriarch, the law-giver, and the king. And the prophet speaks with a depth, sincerity, and beauty which stand almost unrivalled. Aside from the sayings of Jesus, few sentences have brought such comfort to burdened souls as have the words of Isaiah: "Come now, and let us reason together saith Jehovah; though your sins be as scarlet, they shall be as white as snow; though they be red like crimson, they shall be as wool. . . ." They are wingéd words, as old Homer would put it—words that sing themselves in the great choruses of Handel's *Messiah*, and in the hearts of the people who mourn. Even if these words should be translated otherwise, as some critics believe, the greatness of Isaiah is no less.

The next main Jewish crisis is likewise of political origin. The captivity was the direct result of the rivalries of two great nations, Assyria and Egypt, and of the attempts of a little nation to play politics with first one and then the other. But events framed themselves as they did not merely because of human ambitions, but because Palestine happens to lie on the route which those two nations perforce must traverse if they would tear each other's throats. Our concern, however, is not primarily with politics or geography this time, but with migration. The exile of the Jews, with its threefold skimming of the best of the population and the flight of all but a tenacious few of the others to Egypt, is one of the most extraordinary examples of natural selection. One curious fact about it is that by selecting the best citizens, the Assyrians unconsciously took one of the most effective means of preserving an alien remnant in their own midst. But they likewise gave Judaism a superb opportunity to take a long step toward acquiring a universal character. Those Jews who went perforce to Babylonia were familiar with the lofty thoughts and beautiful pleadings of Isaiah. They had been framing a more and more noble idea of God. But all the time they had thought of their God as Jahweh who lived in the Temple at Jerusalem. Now the temple was in ruins, Jahweh had no home. Yet still they prayed to him. And praying thus they slowly framed the idea that God is everywhere, that walls and sacrifices are of small moment, that the spirit of worship and obedience is what counts, and that a man can commune with his God through prayer anywhere and any time. The captivity was needed to give the Jews a religion that could stand the terrible strain of later centuries when its adherents were scattered all over the world and had no home of their own.

The captivity was needed even more, perhaps, to sift the Jews and concentrate in Jerusalem a little remnant in whom there flamed most brightly the old religious fervor of Abraham, Moses, David, and Isaiah. The more one compares the history of the Jews with that of other people, the more clear it becomes that they experienced an almost unique selection, whereby the nation was turned back to its old course and given a new lease of its pristine spirit time and again. No, such selection is not unique, for any group which inhabits an especially severe environment experiences it. The desert most unmercifully weeds out those who cannot endure its rigors, and carry on its business of keeping the animals safe, or of raiding other people to provide food for the wives and children when nature refuses to yield her rains. The Eskimos are subjected to a process of selection which with merciless insistence eliminates all who cannot endure cold and hunger. The people who cannot endure the constant blowing of the fierce "roaring forties" on the west coast of the tip of South America are bound to die among the lowly Alikulaf. Thus examples of rigid selection are well known so far as physical environment is concerned, but are almost unknown, as yet, when the

selective factor is some high quality like the religious temperament.

From this selective migration we swing back once more to a
social and religious custom, a custom without which the whole
selective process might have been in vain. That custom was
merely a revision of the old matriarchal custom of endogamous
marriages. Among the Jews after the Exile it took the form of
the strictest prohibition of marriages outside the Jewish fold.
But such a prohibition, in turn, would have been in vain without
a strong political system to back it up. The kingship had gone
the way of the rule of the patriarchs and of the intermediate
stage when the so-called judges were leaders of the people. In
its place the Jews had evolved one of the less common forms of
political organization, yet one that has often been attempted,
and which reached its zenith in the temporal power of the Popes
in the Middle Ages. Among the Jews after the Exile the rule of
the priests, the hagiocracy, or hierarchate, as it is called, reached
an almost unrivalled perfection. The perfection lay in the fact
that it minutely regulated almost every act during every hour
of the day. A man could not eat, walk, sleep, work, or enjoy
the society of his neighbors without being in danger of trans-
gressing the Law and coming in conflict with the priestly authority. This made it possible to enforce the laws against foreign
marriages to an unusual degree, and thus largely preserved the
racial and religious unity of the Jews for many centuries.

The priestly rule had another effect which can scarcely be
overestimated. Because it dealt so minutely with every detail
of life, the books in which the Law was recorded acquired great
and growing sanctity, and the rabbis who interpreted those books
also increased in importance. The rabbis were the natural suc-
cessors of another and more original set of religious leaders, the
prophets who exercised a growing influence from the days of
Samuel to those of Jeremiah and the second Isaiah. Both rabbis
and prophets owed at least part of their extraordinary sway to
the wide dissemination of the religious temperament. Although
the rabbis were not great enough to be prophets on their own

account, they were great enough to preserve the writings of the prophets, the books of the Law, and the histories of their ances- tors. The older the document, the more carefully it was pre- served and followed. Thus the Old Testament was framed, and Judaism became the first great religion of a book. The tremen- dous influence of the written word upon the thought of later times can scarcely be appreciated until one studies religions which have no holy book. All great religions, to be sure, have some type of written documents, but a religion like Hinduism does not get its sanctions from the Word to any great extent. If it degenerates as time goes on, there is relatively little chance that a revival will arise merely because earnest souls study the old books, and are thereby led to start a reformation.

The rule of the priests, the enthronement of the Book, and the preservation of Jewish racial integrity find their culmination in Jesus. Although he was pre-eminently a reformer who started new ideas, he nevertheless sums up the development of his age and people quite as perfectly as did his predecessors from the days of Abraham, through Moses and David to Isaiah. Gone now was the old desert fury, at least so far as Jesus himself was con- cerned. He was a man of marvellous steadiness, not quick and impulsive like Jacob, Moses, and David. He approached more nearly to the agricultural type that succeeds best through steady labor, day after day, and month after month. But he was pri- marily a villager, of the type that tended to be preserved in Pal- estine as the commercially minded people migrated elsewhere, and the warlike type was exterminated. According to modern nomenclature he was a reformer, an idealist, and almost an in- tellectual highbrow. Strange as it may seem, in view of their re- jection of him, Jesus belonged to the intellectual and tempera- mental type which the Jews themselves to-day recognize as their own best product. He resembled the higher type of modern non- commercial Jew, the type which produces philanthropists, scien- tists, and philosophers—men of thought rather than action. Such a type is very far removed from the original fiery desert type, where action is everything. Both biological and social evolution had long been weeding out the desert type because it is not adapted to life in peaceful towns, amid a dense population. But, the old fiery temperament flared up in Peter when he suddenly drew his sword to protect Jesus from arrest, and cut off the ear of the high priest's servant. It flared up terrifically a generation later when Jerusalem was destroyed. Most of Jesus' disciples and most prominent followers, however, were of the same reflective, philosophical, philanthropic type as Jesus himself. The writer of the book of John is the embodiment of the reflective, mystical temperament, while Paul is one of the world's outstanding philosophers. Few features of the time of Jesus are more noticeable than the facility with which the great leader found highly competent disciples who shared his spirit. But according to our interpretation that is natural, for a great man usually represents merely the peak of a pyramid, not an isolated star floating detached in space. He is the culmination of a long biological and cultural process, and is practically certain to be surrounded by lesser geniuses of a similar type.

The truth of the matter seems to be that while a thousand years of biological and social evolution had made the fiery desert type of character more and more out of place in the peaceful village life of Palestine and in the city life of the larger communities, it had made no appreciable change in the religious fervor of the Jews. It scarcely could do so, for from first to last one selective process after another had tended to restore and purify that type, and each advance in social and political organization had made that type more central and vital to Judaism. It would be wonderfully interesting to trace the consequences when the religious spirit is united with the warlike spirit, as in David; with the legal spirit, as in Moses; with poetic genius, as in Isaiah; with commercial aptitude as in certain modern philanthropists; with the philosophical spirit as in Paul; and with a supremely well-balanced altruistic temperament, as in Jesus. Wherever it is found the religious temperament—the attitude of reverence, the recognition that man is probably far from the most lofty of all beings—seems to add something which vivifies and enriches life most wonderfully.

To return to our historical recital, it is interesting to note how quickly a crisis follows the rise of each of the greatest exponents of the main eras of the Jews. The crash of civilization —as it doubtless seemed to the early Israelites—and the migration into the wilderness from Egypt occurred while Moses was still active. Only the reign of Solomon intervened between David and the collapse of the kingdom which he had so vigorously built up. Even while Isaiah was preaching, the Assyrians were carrying away the people of Israel, although Judah persisted another century. And Jesus was separated from the main act in the final collapse of Judaism by only a generation.

That final collapse, like the exile to Babylon, can be interpreted as a purely political event. But crop failures due to declining rainfall, economic distress due to undue density of population, racial antipathies, religious intolerance, and the independent spirit fostered not only by racial and religious zeal but by the relative inaccessibility of Judea are among the other factors which also played a part. This time the decision as to what Jews should survive or perish had little to do with religion. The choice lay between the old fiery desert temperament, which flares into action at the slightest provocation, and the city temperament which makes men love the market-place and step aside instead of knocking a man to the ground when he treads on their toes. The desert temperament was almost exterminated, the city temperament survived.

From that time onward the city temperament has become more and more accentuated among the Jews. All sorts of processes, both biological and social, have tended in this direction. For example, all through the Middle Ages the Jews were a great asset to the rulers of western and middle Europe because they excelled all others as merchants, money-lenders, and capitalists. Their wealth exposed them to oppression and even exile and death. But if a Christian ruler depended upon a group of influential Jews, as was often the case, he protected them. Usually, however, he was unwilling to do this for Jews who showed an independent spirit; in many cases only those who were willing to endure contumely even at the hands of their benefactors, or who were willing and able to buy protection by repeated uncomplaining contributions of money, had the assurance of survival. Again, if Jews attempted to practise agriculture, their isolation not only rendered it easy to kill them, or drive them out in times of persecution, but deprived them of close contact with their fellow Jews and with the rites of their religion. Thus they were likely to intermarry with their Christian neighbors, or in some other way be lost to Judaism.

The ghettos of the larger cities were the places where the Jews could best resist the tendency toward extermination and apostasy. There the Jews were crowded together in greatest numbers, and there city life was most intense. The Jews who did not possess a high degree of the city spirit and the herd instinct tended to migrate away from those same ghettos. Those who thus migrated were the most likely to mingle with non-Jews and to apostasize.

Thus down to our own day there has been a steady tendency for the surviving Jews to become city people. This implies that they tend not only to be merchants, but to go into such trades as tailoring. The tailor does not require a strong physique, but he does need to be able to resist bad air, lack of sunshine, crowded quarters, and the other well-known evils of the city environment. Among the Jews, by reason of two thousand years of city life, the types which cannot stand such conditions have been largely weeded out. Moreover, city people of whatever type rarely possess such strong physiques as do rural people. But the rural people swarm into every city, and tend to fill the occupations which require manual strength. The Jewish traits, as Kautsky puts it in *Are the Jews a Race?*, "are an exaggerated form of urban traits in general. . . . The Jew has become the city dweller par excellence. The uniformity of the artificial environment has imparted to the Jews everywhere a uniform mental type, in spite of all the variations in their natural environment, and all the differences in the inherited race elements."

Kautsky is right except that the uniformity of the artificial environment does not merely impart to the Jews a uniform mental type, but actually weeds out those who do not inherently conform to that type. Moreover, it attracts those who do conform. Thus environment and natural selection work together toward the same end. In similar fashion they work together to cause engineers, as a rule, to possess certain traits which can easily be recognized. If the children of engineers intermarried only with one another and lived apart by themselves, and if those who did not like engineering moved away in every generation, a race of engineers might soon develop with mental traits as pronounced as those of the Jews. Those traits would be partly hereditary and partly due to social environment. The same is true of many other occupations. Almost every one recognizes that ministers, professors, lawyers, doctors, business men, farmers, sailors, dock laborers, and many other types possess characteristics almost as distinct as those of the Jews. The only difference is that among the progressive nations these others do not live in segregated ghettos, they marry outside their occupational group, and their children pursue other occupations. In India, however, each occupation remains by itself, and the system of caste prevails. The Jews, in a way, are merely a caste which specializes in a few main occupations and resides in cities.

Here we must leave this interpretation of the Jews. We have only sketched the high-lights; we have completely omitted many disputed points; and we have merely opened others for discussion. Such treatment is inevitable when a new point of view is first presented. The one thing at which we have aimed has been to give an example of how geography, migrations, and racial selection combine with genius, sociology, politics, religion, and other phases of human culture in explaining human history. Only by combining all these factors with even-handed impartiality can we understand the true philosophy of history.

CHAPTER XVIII

THE SUICIDE OF RUSSIA

THE processes which we have discussed in relation to Jewish history are still at work. Geographical environment and racial selection co-operate as actively as ever with political, social, and other cultural agencies in determining the fate of nations. Russia affords a good example. The future of that country seems to be inextricably connected with three great facts which pertain to our present point of view. The first fact is that Russia is the seat of a great and original experiment. The second is that the success of this experiment appears to be jeopardized by the unfavorable biological selection which has taken place since 1914. The third is that its success is likewise jeopardized because the geographical environment of Russia is relatively unfavorable to progress.

It is not necessary here to explain the social and political system which has prevailed in Russia since the Great War. One of its most fundamental features is its denial of the right of the individual to own property or to enjoy the fruits of his own labors without first sharing them in due measure with others. A second feature is the substitution of occupations instead of geographical districts as the basis on which political representatives are elected. Whether these two principles are right or wrong can scarcely be determined as yet. Neither is original in Russia, and both are in operation to a certain extent elsewhere. One of the most characteristic and successful features of Australia, for example, is the minimum-wage laws. The basic principle of the Australian system, as of the Russian, is that every man is entitled not only to a living wage, but to a wage which enables him to support a family in health, and to give his family an ordinary education. The essence of the whole thing is that in each case the stronger members of the community are not allowed to retain for themselves all that they can possibly grasp. On the contrary, they are compelled to share with the weaker, at least up to the point where the weaker have enough so that they can live according to a reasonably high standard. Of course, the Russians carry the matter much farther in theory, but in practice they do not distribute the good things of life much more equally than do the Australians. The strong are forced to concede to the weak something of what they might retain under some other system, but the strong retain much more than they permit the weak to have; or than they themselves really need in order to accomplish their more exacting tasks.

In Australia such action is legitimate; in Russia it is illegitimate. To most Americans the Australian system seems progressive, while the Russian system seems either reactionary or ultra-radical. In both cases, however, the principle is the same. Moreover, almost all progressive countries now act on this principle when they impose graduated income taxes or utilize other devices so that the gains of the strong are taxed more heavily than those of the weak, and are then used for public purposes such as education or health, which benefit the weak more than the strong.

Australia, as I have said in *West of the Pacific*, has been constantly progressing toward a condition in which the state not only insists on, but almost guarantees, high standards of living for people of all classes. Thus Australia has evolved a social and political system which is pre-eminent as one of the important recent contributions to human progress. The reasonableness, stability, and effectiveness of this system stand in marked contrast to the seeming unreasonableness, instability, and ineffectiveness of the system whereby the Bolsheviki have ostensibly sought the same results. In the one case we have an example of what happens when two divergent and somewhat opposed groups, composed of persons of more than average ability, join hands in an attempt to frame a system which shall inure to the ultimate advantage of all concerned. In the other, the most competent members of all classes from peasant to royalty have been largely exterminated or driven away, while a small minority impose their will on a huge majority who represent the almost helpless residue after most of the able leaders have been culled out.

So far as I can see, the main trouble with the Australian social organization to-day seems to be that having accepted the great principle of minimum wages, the country has not adopted the obvious and inevitable corollary of that principle. Here is the corollary: If the standard of living is high, the standard of production must also be high. Much must be produced if much is to be enjoyed. Hence, if it is right and wise to say that a man's wages must never have less than a certain purchasing power, it is equally right to say that a minimum amount of work shall be required of each worker. But this the Australians do not yet realize. The Russians are even farther from realizing it, and therein lies, perhaps, the greatest immediate reason for scepticism as to the future of the Russian system of denying that the individual has a right to control the products of his own labor.

So far as the other fundamental feature of the Russian system is concerned, every progressive country practises it constantly. We do not, to be sure, elect our government officials on the basis of occupations rather than geographical districts. But we continually appoint all sorts of commissions and committees on that basis. We regard it as a matter of course that a coal commission, for instance, should contain representatives of the operators, the miners, and the public. A similar commission containing also representatives of manufacturers, railroads, household consumers, and retail dealers would seem sensible. Yet such commissions really carry out the soviet system in its underlying principle. Thus it appears that there is nothing very dangerous in experiments along the lines attempted by Russia. The crux of the matter lies not in the *system*, but in the good sense with which the system is put into operation, and the degree to which the new methods come as the result of healthy evolution instead of feverish revolution.

This brings us back to the problem of racial or national character. In a certain way the character of the Russian people seems to have suffered a change during and after the Great War. How deep and how permanent this change may be cannot yet be determined. But let me explain how it has taken place. Some of my own experiences illustrate the matter.

Years ago, in 1903, I was dining with some Russians in old Merv, a famous oasis of Transcaspia, where the Pumpelly expedition of the Carnegie Institution of Washington was making excavations. Although nearly a quarter of a century has passed I can still hear the fervent voice of our hostess, a Russian baroness, the wife of a high official. "Impossible," she said; "I am willing to do anything and everything for the peasants. I am ready to work my fingers to the bone in taking care of them when they are sick. I am glad to feed them and clothe them when they are in trouble. I would cheerfully spend my nights as well as my days advising them and helping them. But they shall never have the same laws as we. They are of different clay."

During our conversation after dinner some one had incidentally stated that the laws governing Russian peasants, in those days before the war, were different from those governing the upper classes, the intelligentsia. I had protested against such discrimination. The baroness had replied with an earnestness which, for the first time, made me really understand the old doctrine of "the divine right of kings." She was absolutely convinced that certain rights, and likewise certain duties, are the inherent, God-given, and inalienable endowment of kings and aristocrats. According to her, they are a biological inheritance, and no human system of laws or social customs can change them. To an enthusiastic young believer in America's great mission to spread democracy, her conviction seemed pitiful and archaic. Yet to-day I am not so sure. Was she half-right? At least she was not wholly wrong.

In the days before the war the educated Russians, the intelligentsia, especially those who had behind them a background of culture, were among the most delightful people in the world. I have travelled in many countries, but nowhere have I found people more cordial, more friendly, more "sympathetic" as they love to say, than those Russians of the upper classes in the days

when they ruled Russia and were governed by laws different
from those of the peasants. Their fate in these later years has
been as sad as that of any people on the whole round earth.
Large numbers of them are now gone, at least from Russia. The
question which concerns us is how far they have carried with
them the hope of that country for the future. How far does their
loss nullify the gain. if such there be, which comes from the new
social system?

During the war I was in the Military Intelligence Division
of the American Army and was stationed at Washington. My
work was to gather information as to foreign countries, especially
Siberia and Russia. During the summer of 1918 and after the
armistice until the following July, when I left the army, there
came to my office a stream of Russians. Some had been sent
out of the country on official missions before the Soviet came into
power. Others had fled for their lives. Almost all were seeking
some means of breaking the power of the Soviet, and restoring
to Russia a régime resembling that of England or France, such
as was planned by Kerensky. As I look back to those days, the
fact which stands out most strongly is not the political aspirations of these exiles, but their pathetic appeals for something to
do. Here is a captain in the Russian navy, a man of wide intelligence and most assiduous industry, who worked in the army
offices overtime for weeks, trying to give us exact information.
He was hunting for work as an engineer, and nearly starved for
a year or more till he found it. Here is another, a professor in a
Russian university, a brilliant man with a phenomenal capacity
for looking up facts and amassing information. For years he
struggled to find the proper niche in America, and at last went
back to Poland, but dared not go to Russia. Practically all the
Russians who came to us were well educated and of genuine
ability, but a great many did not know how to turn their hands
to the practical affairs of life.

Here is a concrete illustration of the type of Russian that has
recently come to America. Bryn Mawr College has for several
years conducted a summer session for working girls. These girls

are carefully selected because of their ability and promise. Some of the regular college girls remain during the summer as assistants in administration. One of these assistants, Miss Katherine Symonds, described her experiences in a speech at College Vespers. Here is part of her speech as given in the *Bryn Mawr Alumnæ Bulletin* for May, 1926:

> The Russian girls were, as a rule, the most interesting people there, much more alert and vehement than the others. There were twenty-three of them this year—more than any other nationality except American, and, together with some Hungarian and Polish girls, they formed more or less the leaven of the school. Many of them came over after the Russian revolution, and several of them had ghastly experiences during the fighting there.
>
> They always made me frightfully ashamed of how little I knew. Practically all the Russians knew Tolstoi and Ibsen backward and forward. And they go to concerts all the time, and manage to see most of the good plays. It really means something to do that after you've been working eight or ten hours a day. They were, as a rule, more radical than the other girls.

America is by no means the only country to which Russians of this kind fled in large numbers. I was walking in the streets of Kobe, in Japan, one day in 1923, and wanted to inquire the way. I looked for some one who might, perhaps, speak English. Soon I saw a fair-haired, pretty girl of about sixteen, with two small European children. I spoke to her in English. She answered in that language, speaking correctly except for an accent. She was a Russian who had lost her parents and was acting as nurse in an English family until she could save money to come to America. I know nothing more about her, but a brief talk while she walked with me two or three blocks was enough to show that she had more than the average ability. In Constantinople my brother and sister tell of a Russian general who served as a gardener, a countess who was a dressmaker, and others of high positions at home who were doing all sorts of menial tasks until they could find something better. I have received from Constantinople letters typed by Russian ladies who wanted to act as stenographers until they could perfect their English. I might go on to give many other instances of high-grade Russian emigrants such as the charming Russian lady who taught French to my small boy. All over the world they are in evidence—these Russians who thought that by some divine right they should be subject to laws different from those of the peasants.

The straits to which the Russian emigrants were put after the war led some of them into lives of crime. In Paris Russian criminals are said to have given the police no end of trouble. Various estimates are made of the number of Russians domiciled in Paris after the war. A police inspector is reported as putting the number at 100,000 in 1924, but others who ought to know call that a decidedly short count. According to a newspaper report: "Only the upper classes of Russians are resourceful in crime. The average lowbrow Russian is an exceedingly dumb individual, and his wrongdoing chiefly is snatching some article of food from a stand and running with it." But the upper classes of Russians in Paris and other foreign cities are relatively numerous, compared with the lower classes. It is mainly the intelligentsia who have been crowded out of Russia and forced to make a living by their wits.

Not all the Russians of the upper classes have migrated. Many have died. Here are some statistics from the *London Times* of September 1, 1922. A dispatch from Riga stated that, according to official Bolshevist figures, the tribunal known as the Cheka executed 1,766,118 persons before being renamed the Supreme Political Administration, in February, 1922. All those people were done to death in a period of less than five years. Many more have been executed since. The total, as printed in the *Times*, includes 6,675 professors and teachers, 8,800 doctors, 355,250 other intellectuals. Beside this there were 1,243 priests, 54,650 officers, and 12,950 landowners. This makes something like 440,000 persons, all of whom belonged to the upper classes. A large part of these, by right of birth or ability, had made themselves influential leaders. The rest of those executed comprised 59,000 policemen, 192,350 workmen, 260,000 soldiers, and 815,100 peasants. The policemen, workmen, soldiers, and peasants can scarcely have been the most stupid and ignorant of their respective classes. On the contrary, it is safe to say that they were among the most intelligent, for they had the strength of mind and character to stand up for what they believed to be the right in the face of the overwhelming strength of the Soviet régime. Thus since the revolution, through executions alone, Russia has lost nearly 2,000,000 people of more than ordinary ability.

The 2,000,000 who were executed by no means measure Russia's full loss of competent citizens. Those who fled from Russia are probably as numerous, perhaps more so, than those who were executed. Part found refuge in Siberia, but hundreds of thousands, perhaps millions, sought foreign countries. Many went through terrible experiences whose marks will never be effaced. Here are two stories told by an American woman who herself fled from Russia. During the dead of winter, after hairbreadth adventures, she escaped into Finland. While she was resting in a peasant's house safely beyond the border, some other fugitives were brought in. One was a woman, of evident refinement and culture. Food was set before her, a dish of porridge, for she had long been hungry. She took from the table three bowls and served porridge in each. "There," she said, "is your dish, Ivan; there is yours, Katrinka; and here is mine." There were no children there. They had perished, but her mind was gone, and she thought her children were there.

Near the Rumanian border at that same time a young wife and her husband were separated. She was finally smuggled across the border, but kept seeking her husband. He was found and brought to her. A year later her poor distraught mind was still seeking him, although they had been together all the time. Such tales not only mean that great numbers of the better classes of Russians have migrated, but that many, especially the children, have perished. Moreover, because of the hardships and wanderings of the adults, the birth-rate among the upper classes of Russia, both at home and abroad, has inevitably been greatly reduced. Thus to-day, among the children who are growing up in Russia the proportion who inherit the qualities which give leadership, and who belong in homes where they receive training in leadership, is far smaller than formerly.

This adverse selection is one of the most discouraging aspects of Russia's present situation. In one brief decade that country has apparently done to itself what Spain did in many generations. In Spain, during the Middle Ages, and well on toward modern times, vast numbers of the most thoughtful, competent, and strong-willed people were killed, imprisoned, or driven into exile by religious persecution. Many others of the same kind were reduced to such straits of poverty that they and their children languished and perished. Another great group of the most virile, energetic, adventurous, and alert Spaniards went forth across the seas to the new lands of America. Most of them married commonplace Indian women, so that their children had no great share of either the biological or social inheritance of Spain. Probably no other country of Europe ever saw any such wholesale exodus or destruction of its ablest people until the Russian collapse in our own day. That seems to be one great reason for the sad contrast between the Spain of to-day and of four or five centuries ago.

Selective social upheavals and migrations such as those of Russia and Spain seem to be so common that we may almost speak of racial character as plastic. In China, for example, as I have related in *The Character of Races*, certain especially poverty-stricken villages have, for centuries, been subject to a constant, though slow, loss of their more able people through migration. So incompetent are these villagers, and so scanty their land, that even in good seasons they cannot raise food enough to support themselves through the year. For a few months almost every winter they wander among the neighboring villages, begging, stealing, raiding, and occasionally working. Only rarely can they find work, for jobs are very scarce, and abler people snap them up at once. A score of men seem to be on hand for every little bit of work, no matter how trivial. People are far too numerous. But even if there were not such density of population, the villagers whom we are now discussing might have much difficulty.

The process of weeding out the more able people among them seems to have gone so far that during the famines of 1922 the American relief workers concluded that, as a whole, the villagers were almost subnormal mentally. Apparently they have not brains enough to better their condition. Therefore, they live on and on for generations in growing misery. Yet strange to say, from that same general region, though not necessarily from those particular villages, there has been selected a group of Chinese who are actually European in their energy and ability. They have migrated by successive stages to the far north of Manchuria, and are said to be one of the most able groups of Chinese anywhere in the world. The contrast between these competent people and the incompetent ones who remain in the poorest Chinese villages seems to be of the same kind as the contrast between the people who have been eliminated from Russia and those who remain, although fortunately the Russian contrast is less extreme.

Another case of this kind is the Parsees. Long ago, at the end of the sixth century of the Christian era, the Zoroastrians of Persia had been through a period of great distress and commotion. In 651 A. D., on the fall and death of the king of Yazdagird, a number of these people, as the ancient chronicle puts it, "abandoned their houses and gardens and palaces for the sake of their religion, and lived in Kohistan for one hundred years." There, too, they suffered, for in those days the Mohammedan Arabs had come into the land. So the Zoroastrians, to quote the chronicle again, "became anxious for their religion," and went to the city of Hormuz on the shore of the Indian Ocean, in A. D. 751. There they lived for fifteen years, but being harassed by the Arabs, they set sail for India. Perhaps there was only a single boatload of them. At any rate the number of migrants was small. They landed at Div, on the shores of Kathiawar, just east of the mouth of the Indus. Apparently they were not welcome there, for after staying nineteen years they sailed eastward to Gujarat and reached Sanjan in 785. There they were allowed to form a permanent colony, with liberty to follow their own religion, provided they adopted the language and customs of the country. Later they migrated to Bombay, where most of them now live.

Two facts about the Parsees are especially remarkable. The first is the rigor of the processes by which they were first differentiated from the rest of the Persians. They were selected partly by their strong religious convictions, partly by their tenacity of purpose which made them prefer hardship and migration rather than apostasy to their religion. They were presumably chosen also because of their courage and physical vigor, for without these qualities they could scarcely have faced the difficulties and privations of migration after migration in the face of hostile neighbors. Moreover, they were not selected from among the peasants or common people, but from among the upper classes—from among those having houses, gardens, and palaces, and from those who either practised various handicrafts, or were leaders in the life of the community.

The second remarkable fact about the Parsees is that to-day, in proportion to their numbers, they are generally recognized as the most competent people in all India, aside from the British. The Parsees of our day number only about 100,000. They are largely merchants, but are keenly interested in preserving and purifying their old religion. Theirs, indeed, is almost the only religion in India, aside from Christianity, which actually inculcates and insists upon a high moral code as well as upon charity and altruism. In spite of their small number the Parsees have many leaders in literature, philanthropy, and politics. Two such leaders are the only natives of India ever elected to the British House of Commons. Another, who had migrated to China, founded the University of Hongkong. Their women are freer and more respected than those of any other set of people in India except the British; their girls as well as their boys are better educated than those of any other native caste or race of India.

Why do the Parsees thus excel? Partly, perhaps, because they not only started with a highly selected inheritance, but because they have kept themselves unmixed, although completely surrounded by Hindus. The caste system of India has helped in this, and the strict rules of the Parsees have done likewise. Although their women are freer than any other women in India in one sense, yet they are very carefully protected, and marriage either by Parsee men or women with other castes is prohibited. Not even if other people wish to become Parsees is it allowed. When a Parsee married a French lady who was ready to adopt the religion of her husband, the Parsee officials, after long argument, decided that although the creed of Zoroaster theoretically admits proselytes, their admission is not consistent with the practice of the present day in India. Any one who marries outside the faith ceases to be an integral part of the Parsee community.

The point of all this is that processes of selection, such as we have lately seen in Russia, seem to be competent to cause different stocks or races to differ unmistakably in innate ability. If that is so, what bearing does it have on the future of Russia? Russia to-day has suffered a most serious loss of leaders. The peasants, on the contrary, tend to be a rather dull, inert set of people, although kindly and pleasant. The majority are like faithful Mikhail, who served me on a long journey in Persia. "What do you think about as you ride along on horseback day after day?" I asked. "Oh," he answered, "sometimes I think of the people at home, and wonder whether the hay is harvested, and whether the cows are well, but mostly I think of nothing." Such people may till the ground, but can they build up a great nation unless well supplied with leaders of unusual ability? Can they adopt a new social and political system and really make it work? Or will their experiment fail, and merely serve as a lesson whereby nations with stronger leaders will be able to sort out the wheat and leave the chaff? Of course, Russia is not wholly leaderless. The socialistic type of leader has actually been attracted from other countries. Moreover, some leaders of other types still remain in Russia. Some, too, are growing up, although their number is doubtless small compared with what it might have been. Others will come from Siberia, for many intelligent Russians have taken refuge there. Still others will, in due time, return from foreign countries, but the prospects in this respect

grow less as time goes on. The most competent of the emigrants
have become established in foreign lands and are losing their desire to return. Thus relatively few of the exiled Russian leaders
will probably return, and the proportion of their children who
go back to Russia will presumably be almost negligible. But the
peasants still remain. Their total number has been diminished
relatively little, and their number *in proportion to the number of
leaders* has greatly increased. Russia to-day, far more than ever
before, is a nation of peasants.

The peasants in all parts of the world are peculiarly subject
to the influence of physical environment. The two outstanding
features of the Russian environment are the vast plains with
their endless monotony, and the climate with its long, severe
winters. The plains may be dismissed briefly. They help to
make communication and transportation relatively easy, but
they tend to cause all parts of a vast area to be very much alike.
Therefore the average Russian, even if he travels hundreds of
miles from home, which the peasants rarely do, sees little that
is new. He finds the same scenery, the same crops, the same
animals, the same kinds of houses, the same ways of work, the
same kind of people, and the same ideas and aspirations. He
rarely brings back any new inspiration, or ambition, unless he
goes to the city. And if the city inspires him, the result is apt
to be merely discontent rather than a determination to use new
methods which he has observed in the course of his travels. The
monotony of the plain seems to be a real curse in Russia.

The climate is no better than the plain. Turn to Figures 3,
4. and 13, opposite pages 102 and 112. Notice how rapidly
climatic energy, health, and civilization decline from central
Europe eastward in Russia. Notice too that Finland, the Baltic
States, and Poland, where the climate is relatively stimulating,
where the people enjoy good health, and where civilization made
most progress in the days before the war, are the very parts
which have rejected the soviet form of government and have set
up independent republics. Thus Russia to-day suffers not only
from the handicap of having killed or exiled a great many lead-

ers, but from having repelled the most progressive parts of what was formerly the Russian Empire.

As to the climate itself, the chief handicap is the long, monotonous winters. Any one who has studied the seasonal distribution of health knows that even in a climate no more severe than that of the northern United States the death-rate rises to its highest level toward the end of the winter. As a rule the maximum comes in either February or March. Moreover, during those months great numbers of people in the northern United States are conscious of a nervous, tired feeling, accompanied by a great longing for the end of winter. We are aware that the long winter has frayed us out, so to speak. And the more nervous we are, the more likely we are to become sick. Now in large parts of Russia the winters are far longer, colder, and more trying than in the regions inhabited by most of the people of the United States. The effect on health is even worse than here, not only because the cold season is longer, but because the houses are even more stuffy and hot than ours, and the general care of health less intelligent. Although we have no exact data, it is possible that the long winters cause a differential death-rate, so that the nervous types of people, who are also likely to be the ones who become leaders, tend to die out more rapidly than those who are more phlegmatic. The death-rate is certainly high, the nervous types of people certainly find the winter especially hard to endure, and the Russian peasants are notably phlegmatic.

Still another condition tends almost inevitably to make the Russian peasant inefficient. That condition is the enforced idleness which prevails for months each winter. Of course, the animals must be fed and milked, wood must be cut in the forest, and a few other tasks must be attended to. Nevertheless, for five months or so each winter, the Russian peasants, the men at least, do not have enough work to keep them busy. A few hours a day is enough in many cases. The rest of the time they loaf. Even if they do all the work they can possibly find, their high latitude makes the working day very short in winter. The net result is that for many months a large proportion of the Russian peasants practise idleness. When the spring comes, it stands to reason that a man who has been unwholesomely idle much of the winter will not work so hard or so enthusiastically as one who has been healthfully active. The idle man suffers in both body and mind, and he suffers as much from enforced idleness as from that which is voluntary. This, perhaps, is one reason why the Russian peasants are so notoriously phlegmatic and submissive, and why they give rise to so few leaders.

The upshot of the matter is that during the present century many circumstances have combined to make it difficult for the people who live in what is now Russia to swing their new political and social system. Perhaps they will be able to do it. I make no prophecy. It is enough to point out that the selection exercised by persecution and migration on the one hand, and the forces of geographical environment as represented by the climate and the relief of the land, on the other hand, co-operate with the political dismemberment of the old Russian Empire in producing an extraordinarily difficult combination of circumstances. Leaders who can cope with such a situation may indeed arise, but thus far the tendency seems to be for Russia to slip slowly back into a condition where it fails to profit by the social and political system which it has been foremost in introducing.

Many possibilities suggest themselves. A land as rich as Russia and Siberia holds out a beckoning hand to all the nations of the earth. Again and again our papers are full of the importance of Russian trade. Who will go in and capture that trade? Perhaps the most probable answer is: "A few English, a few French, a few Americans, a few others, and a great many Germans." Germany, to be sure, suffered in the World War like all the combatants. But in Germany there was no such tremendous weeding out of leaders as in Russia. In fact, the German upper classes, on the whole, perhaps suffered less than the lower classes. And Germany is still overpopulated. Her people are still energetic and capable. They still have the power of leadership in business, in science, and in politics. With all this they are nearer to Russia than is any other great and powerful nation. What is more natural than that they, with their power of achievement, should gradually supply leadership to Russia? In the past this has happened to such an extent that many of the old Russian families bore German names. This was especially true in the Baltic provinces, but far away in Central Asia I have more than once been entertained by leading citizens who called themselves Russians, but bore German names. If this could happen in the days when the Russian intelligentsia were still numerous and able, and when Russia had a good supply of leaders of her own, how much more likely is it to happen on a vast scale in the future? Here we must leave the problem. From the biological point of view, the Soviet régime seems to have skimmed from Russia a large percentage of her leaders. Has this doomed Russia to generations of stagnation and backwardness, unless leaders pour in from Germany or elsewhere?

CHAPTER XIX

THE CENTRES OF POWER

THE power of the world is concentrated in two chief centres —western Europe on one side of the Atlantic, and the United States and Canada on the other. Japan forms a third real centre, although less powerful than the other two, while Australia and New Zealand form a small fourth, by reason of their activity and progress. Relatively speaking, these centres have been the main seats of power for only a short time. Can they continue to hold their own? Will they be supplanted by tropical countries, as General Gorgas predicts? Will the centres of influence move northward into Canada, Russia, Siberia, and Scandinavia, as others feel confident?

The answer to these questions seems to depend on climate and natural selection quite as much as upon the more commonly recognized social, industrial, and political factors. If New York City should be swathed in ice, as was the case perhaps twenty-five thousand years ago, it could scarcely compete with Havana, or Singapore for the world's financial supremacy. A swing in the other direction, to conditions such as have frequently prevailed in geological times, might place Finland and Alaska among the world's best regions for agriculture, manufacturing, and commerce. A far smaller change, such as might occur within a few decades, would produce far-reaching results. During the fourteenth century, it will be remembered, England almost starved because of its cold, rainy summers, and the Baltic Sea was sometimes frozen from Germany to Sweden. (See Figure 16, page 122.) Corresponding conditions in America for a century or two would mean that New York harbor would frequently be closed by ice for two or three months, and snow might accumulate in the city to a depth of four or five feet. The milk supply would often be interrupted, suburban trains, surface trolley-cars and motorcars would be delayed and put out of commission, and great congestion of traffic would ensue. The almost inevitable result would be that hundreds of steamships would find it advisable to make their winter calls at relatively southern ports, such as Norfolk, Virginia. Many steamship lines would presumably shift their headquarters to the southern ports rather than maintain two sets of terminals. Railroad transportation would correspondingly be adjusted to New York's loss and Norfolk's gain. Many warehouses, wholesale markets, and factories would follow suit. Hence vast numbers of people, perhaps millions, would move permanently to cities farther south. In spite of its wonderful harbor and magnificent line of communication with the interior, New York might lose its supremacy and become scarcely more important than Boston or Montreal.

Suppose a change in the opposite direction should bring mild conditions, and the St. Lawrence River should contain so little ice that the channel could be kept open at all seasons. This would presumably be accompanied by correspondingly increased productivity in the wonderful wheat regions of Manitoba, Saskatchewan, and Alberta. At the same time the southern and western parts of the great plain in the United States would probably become drier and less productive than now. Thus the centre of power would shift northward and the Great Lakes would become more than ever the focus of one of the most productive areas in the whole world. Then Montreal, freed from its handicap of winter ice and stimulated by the increased productivity of its hinterland, would have a location excelling that of New York. Even if New York did not suffer from a climate more enervating than at present, it might have to accept its northern neighbor as a rival, and Canada's power might equal that of the United States.

All this is simply another way of restating our previous conclusion that the distribution of civilization is closely dependent upon climate, and that climate is subject to fluctuations. From this point of view no country has any assurance of permanent supremacy. The chief practical importance of what has just been said lies in its emphasis upon the value of discovering the causes of climatic changes. If the cause is once known, we are well on the way toward learning how to predict the future. If we knew that a mild climate was impending during the next half-century, and would cause New York to wane and Montreal to wax great, it would make a vast difference in where people would build factories, invest money, and establish institutions of learning.

But suppose the climate of the earth remains unchanged for several centuries. Will the centres of power remain where they now are, or is General Gorgas right in saying that tropical regions will become the great centres of civilization because they are the regions whose potential productivity is greatest? How about Stefansson's predictions as to the development of cultural centres in northern Canada, and other people's enthusiasm over Siberia as the next seat of human dominance? And what of China and India, with their vast swarms of people eager to work for a living? Are any of these destined to be the future centres of power, or will the palm still remain with the great areas of Nordic culture and with Japan? What chance is there that good government, a purified and lofty religion, a good educational system, and the best modern methods of business and science will in due time raise the backward parts of the world to the same cultural level as the most advanced parts? Can culture and human skill fully neutralize the effects of physical environment?

The experience of the past does not afford a very hopeful prospect in this last respect. Four centuries of intimate contact with the white man have not brought the Indians of central America any nearer to the most advanced civilization than they were before. They have learned to use iron tools; they have seen railroads and automobiles; they know of the telegraph and radio, but aside from a few simple tools and a few other luxuries such as woven cloth, the life of the Indians is not appreciably touched by any of these new devices. Their culture has not changed nearly so much as has that of the people of England, for example. In the same way, a thousand years of intimate contact with Swedes and Norwegians has done little or nothing to change the mode of life or the degree of civilization among the Lapps, who migrate with their reindeer as they have done from time immemorial.

On the other hand, the cultural level of the most advanced nations is constantly rising. The innate capacities of the people of the United States, England, France, and Germany may be no greater than those of the ancient Mesopotamians, Egyptians, Greeks, or Romans, but their attainments in industry, commerce, politics, and science—and their social heritage in general—are obviously far greater than those of any ancient nation, and are growing by leaps and bounds.

The contrast between the highest and tne lowest types of human culture grows constantly greater before our very eyes. The airplane is one of the latest illustrations. It is not likely to have much effect on the daily life of laborers on tropical plantations for hundreds of years, but among up-to-date business men in the largest and most progressive cities it is fast becoming a factor of great importance. In countries like China, which stand at an intermediate level of civilization, the same principles apply. New methods are adopted more rapidly than among the savages of New Guinea, but not nearly so rapidly as among people like the Swiss. In spite of very appreciable advances, the people of China, India, and similar countries still retain their median position, and seem likely to do so for a long time to come.

But how about the advanced races themselves? May tney not build up great centres of power in tropical regions, or in cool regions like Siberia and Alaska? The answer to this, as I see it, depends upon climate, migration, and natural selection more than upon any other factors. So far as climate is concerned, the main point is this: Man's increasing command over nature has undoubtedly enabled him to advance from warmer to cooler regions. This has happened regardless of changes of climate. Its effect has been to make it more and more possible for people to spend all their time under atmospheric conditions which closely approach the optimum. In other words, early man was able to live only in places where he could keep warm in winter. Consequently he suffered the unmitigated debilitating effects of long, hot summers, which must have greatly diminished his vigor, just as they diminish the vigor of modern people, even where the winter months are almost ideal. Civilized man, on the contrary, can now live anywhere, for he has learned to overcome low temperature by means of clothing, houses, and artificial heat, and can endure high temperature by means of relative inactivity quite as well as could his primitive ancestors. Nevertheless, modern man, as we have seen, is most healthy and active, and most competent to dominate the world, when he lives where the *warmer* rather than the colder months approach the ideal, but he is better off when the cooler months depart from this ideal as little as possible.

Every departure from the ideal temperature, humidity, and storminess, as we have seen again and again, means a loss in health and energy. Perhaps, some day, mankind may devise a method whereby *within doors* he can create an absolutely ideal climate, although I doubt it. But even so, it will still be necessary to go out-of-doors. Thus there is every prospect that, other things being equal, people will always enjoy the best health and have the greatest energy in places where the climate approaches most closely to the ideal. The location of such places does not depend upon man's volition, but upon his physiological structure. Therefore, it seems to me that only a change of climate, or a change in man's physiological constitution can permanently deprive the present centres of power of their supremacy. The racial composition of the inhabitants of these centres may change, and so may the type of culture, but that is a different matter.

One of the chief reasons for believing that the most healthful and stimulating regions will long remain the centres of power is the fact that they attract and retain competent people because they are the best places in which to work. We may well use Arctic and Tropical regions to illustrate this point. Such regions can scarcely be developed unless people from other climates go there. But what kind of people will go? How many will stay? How high a civilization will they be able to maintain? Would *you* like to go to an Arctic region and raise reindeer meat, Gentle

Reader? Most of you say "No," very emphatically, but a few who are young, vigorous, and enterprising, and who are filled with the love of adventure and the spirit of curiosity and conquest, say "Yes." You who say "Yes" are a splendid type, just the sort to build up a new country and to carry the torch of civilization a step farther north. Some of you may actually go to the Far North and make fortunes. But how long will you stay, and how many of you will bring up families in the North?

An illustration will make the matter clear. Suppose that I am ready to take up some new work. I look up various books and articles and find that my good friend Stefansson points out the advantages of the Friendly Arctic; my good friend Spinden does the same for the Friendly Tropics; my good friend East gives reasons for staying where I am in a flourishing centre of Nordic culture. What shall I do? I should hugely enjoy a year or two of herding ovibos—I suppose one would ride the biggest reindeer. I have always dreamed of a time when I could enjoy the wonders of tropical scenery without fear of mosquitoes, ticks, or internal parasites. The enthusiasts over preventive tropical medicine raise hopes that such a time is fast approaching. Nevertheless it is like pulling teeth to leave home. But the Arctic and the Tropics both offer such splendid opportunities that perhaps I ought to pack up my trunk and "go into" reindeer meat or quinine. It would doubtless pay much better than writing books.

But are my wife, my children, and myself well fitted for life, in the Arctic or the Tropics? If we went to the one place or the other, would we retain our health? If we retained our health, would we find that we had the right temperaments for the new environment? And if both health and temperament were right and we made a great success, how long would we and our descendants remain in the new home?

This may sound facetious, but it strikes at the root of the whole problem. The *kind* of settlers who remain in a country is what counts. The combination of Arctic regions, reindeer, ovibos, and human skill will doubtless produce a vast amount of meat; but will it provide the basis for any important centres of civilization? The lands near the equator are capable of furnishing enormous quantities of food and raw materials, but will they attract a high type of permanent white settler or play much part in feeding the world for many centuries to come?

According to the somewhat optimistic estimates of Mr. Stefansson in *The Northward Course of Empire*, the vast grazing area of the great North will support an average of 20 or 25 head of reindeer per square mile, together with five or six times as many ovibos. Bad seasons, not to mention other difficulties, may greatly reduce this estimate, but let it go at 25 reindeer and 125 ovibos per square mile. Mr. Stefansson also tells us that among the Lapps many families get along with less than a hundred reindeer, but in Siberia a man is not considered well-to-do unless he owns several hundred. But the standard of living of the indigenous Siberian as well as the Lapps is desperately low. It is scarcely probable that people of the main European races would be content with a standard of living requiring less than 1,500 reindeer and ovibos per family. Even under the best circumstances that means only one family to ten square miles of grazing land, or about eighteen people per standard township six miles on a side. What about schools, physicians, hospitals, the movies, automobile roads, railroads, airplane service, bridge parties, and Sunday-school picnics? Some of us might enjoy getting along without these things for a few years, but how many of the more competent people would bring up their families there?

It is not necessary to press the argument, nor to point out that in spite of the alleged healthfulness of far northern regions the death-rate in Norway, Sweden, Finland, and Russia rises rapidly toward the north. In view of all these facts and many others, it seems fair to conclude that some day the empty spaces of the Far North will be fully occupied but, except in mining centres, the population will doubtless be very sparse, for it will have almost no occupation except raising meat. It will consist partly of competent people who go north for a few years to superintend the packing-plants, and so forth, but come home to get married. The permanent part of the population will consist mainly of less competent people—the left-overs who are willing to let their children grow up in ignorance. I doubt whether they will raise such huge amounts of surplus food as is sometimes implied. In the first place, the meat which they furnish must be balanced against vegetable food grown farther south, and eaten not only by the herdsmen but by every one connected with the packing and transportation of the meat. In the second place, the population which in due time becomes native to the Far North will probably be less efficient and hence less productive per person than is the population in more favorable climates. That is the case in northern Sweden to-day. Thus, while the waste lands of the North will doubtless show an interesting development, the permanent population—after the first rush of energetic pioneers has spent itself—will presumably be of the marginal type, sparse, ignorant, subject to a high death-rate, constantly drained of its brighter elements by migration to pleasanter lands, and hence not nearly so productive as the same number of people would be in a region like southern Canada. The conditions will be like those of the Kentucky mountains, but far more extreme. Surplus production is the thing that makes commerce and supplies food for industrial populations. Surplus energy and ability among the people are what make centres of power. But the geographical facts make it improbable that there will be any such huge surplus of either kind *except in the pioneer period*.

Is the prospect within the Tropics any brighter than in the Arctic? Will the centre of civilization move toward the equator? Will those warm lands supply food for the rest of us? It is not safe to be too positive, but the facts thus far available suggest negative answers. Of course, all sorts of new discoveries are possible, but the only safe rule of conduct is for the present generation to rely on present knowledge and not count on hypothetical discoveries that may never come to pass.

The problem of whether European races can live and thrive within the tropics is past the stage when mere opinions count for much. Too many facts are available. Here, in a nutshell, are the facts concerning health and efficiency. First, it is practically certain that modern medical and sanitary discoveries have made it possible to eliminate practically all of the more dangerous tropical diseases. That is one of the greatest of human achievements. But its greatness must not blind us to the limitations imposed by a second great fact: even if specific diseases like malaria, yellow fever, hookworm, and sleeping sickness should all be eliminated, it is practically certain that the health and vigor of tropical people will not equal those of people in more bracing climates. A large number of tests made by many people in many different ways show beyond question that at high temperatures there is a marked decline in the resistance of people of European blood to fatigue and disease, and in their inclination to work. The exact temperature where this decline begins varies according to the humidity and movement of the air, but in practically all parts of the tropics the temperature is too high most of the year. Thus even if people are well, they do not feel so much like work as in cooler climates, and they are less resistant to practically every kind of disease.

The chief objection to the conclusion stated in the last paragraph is that it is based on tests made in temperate climates where any given set of weather conditions does not prevail for more than a few weeks at a time. If people live permanently in a tropical climate, so the objectors say, they *may* become accustomed to it, and be as efficient as anywhere else, provided they are kept free from specific diseases. But no one, so far as I am aware, has ever claimed to demonstrate this statistically or experimentally. Panama and tropical Australia are two of the stock examples used by persons who believe that the tropics are well adapted to the white race. In reality both of those regions bear out our conclusions as to the impossibility of the white race being as efficient in an unduly warm climate as in a cooler climate. Of course, people are rendered inefficient not only by a climate that is too warm, but by one that is too cold, as happens to most of us in winter. But we have at least learned in good measure to obviate the effects of cold, while as yet we have made scarcely a beginning toward obviating the effects of heat. When that is done the story may be quite different, but that is not likely to happen for a long time. The trouble is that people enjoy being too warm much better than they enjoy being too cold. Moreover, when they are too warm the easiest way to make themselves comfortable is to do as little work as possible, whereas when one is too cold the easiest way to be comfortable is to be active.

To return to Panama, it is quite true that the death-rate there among white people is remarkably low, one of the lowest in the world. But that proves little except that it is possible to create any death-rate that one desires. If every one who shows any sign of weakness is sent away from a place, the death-rate, aside from accidents, will be zero. If every one whom the physicians believe to be sure to die is sent to a place, and every one else is registered as living somewhere else, the death-rate will be 1,000. At Panama all the white employees of the Canal Company are subjected to physical examinations before going to Panama, and while they are there. Those who show signs of succumbing to the climate are sent away. The records are full of data on this point. Among the white people at Panama who are not employees of the Canal similar conditions prevail, for as a rule only those with good physiques and energetic temperaments go to tropical countries. Moreover, great numbers who find that the climate does not agree with them leave the country when they begin to feel run down. Such a method is bound to give a low death-rate anywhere and everywhere. The size of the death-rate depends mainly on the ability of the people to move away and on the vigilance of the physicians in warning them. At Panama both of these factors rank high. Of course the death-rate is low, but that is no proof that the white race could stand the climate if men, women, and children of every age, temperament, and physique were all dumped in there together, as they are in a normal population.

Australia shows the same thing even more clearly. I have discussed the whole matter in *Civilization and Climate* and in *West of the Pacific*, but a little repetition will do no harm. Northern

Australia is the one place within the tropics where the experiment of genuine white colonization is being tried on a large scale. There, and there only, are large numbers of white people living by themselves and doing all the work of life with their own hands for generation after generation, without going back to cooler lands to recuperate or to educate their children.

How well is the experiment succeeding? Perfectly, some people tell us; doubtfully, according to the exact statistics of the Australian government. Here are the facts. The tropical inhabitants of Australia enjoy one of the lowest death-rates in the world, the number of children is remarkably large in proportion to the number of women of child-bearing age, the women themselves have a remarkably low death-rate in spite of the fact that housekeeping is terribly hard in their villainously hot, unscreened kitchens, where the flies swarm as in the plague which Moses brought upon Egypt. Moreover, the men of tropical Australia show no sign of inferiority according to the measurements made on soldiers in the World War. The sole fly in the ointment is that the men have an unusually high death-rate; but that, we are told, is because so many of them live out in the Never-never on ranches where they take no proper care of themselves.

Does not all this, together with the many sturdy children who are born within the tropics, look as if the experiment were succeeding? It certainly does, but what about selection? The people who live in tropical Australia were not born there, for the most part. They are not average specimens of their race. They have been rigidly selected—not by the government, but by themselves. Tropical Australia has a bad name in England and in the pleasant parts of southern Australia, but fortunes can be reaped there. Who goes to such a place? The weak? The invalids? The persons of timid temperament? Not a bit of it. Almost nowhere in the world can one find people who are dowered by inheritance with better health, greater optimism, and more of the spirit of adventure than those of northern Australia. Of course such people are healthy. Moreover, if they do not like the climate, they move away to southern Australia. Time and again while travelling there I was given evidence to that effect. Even the Australian government admits that the low death-rate in tropical Australia is largely due to the same cause as in Panama, namely to the fact that the population is highly selected, so that the weak are there only in small numbers.

Other evidence from Australia is still more conclusive. Among the people who were *born* in Queensland, the northern province of Australia, as distinguished from the people who *live* there but were born elsewhere, the death-rate is regularly higher than among similar people who were born in the other Australian provinces or in Great Britain. Moreover, the birth-rate is smaller than among similar people born elsewhere. In other words, rigid selection gives the people who go to tropical Australia such vigor that they have a very low death-rate and high birth-rate. But the children born in Queensland to these same sturdy migrants are unusually weak, as shown by both their high death-rate and low birth-rate. Thus the one great and conclusive experiment of white colonization in the tropics does not support the idea that the white race can flourish in equatorial lands as well as in those that are cooler. And this experiment, be it noted, is being tried in a region which is scarcely more than semitropical, and which has the further great advantage of being practically free from tropical natives on the one hand and from the ordinary tropical diseases, such as malaria, on the other hand. White people can indeed live there happily and comfortably, but they apparently cannot, or at least they do not, retain their full vigor. That is the gist of the whole matter.

More sinister than this from the point of view of the development of centres of power is the fact that northern Australia tends to lose its abler and more energetic inhabitants. As long as a man is striving to make a fortune on a sugar plantation, on a cattle or sheep station, or in the mines, he is content to remain within the tropics. But let him succeed and he is very likely to move southward to some place that is cooler and pleasanter. Even if he does not migrate himself, he is almost sure to want his children to live in the pleasanter, more healthful regions where opportunities of every kind are greater. Among professional people the tendency to move away from the tropical parts of Australia is even stronger than among business people. The vast majority of doctors, lawyers, ministers, teachers, and engineers cherish the ambition to get away from the tropics as soon as possible. Not only do they want to move to places where the professional opportunities are greater, but conditions of health and the general discomforts of life act very strongly. Among the railroad men I was told that there are innumerable requests for transfers to cooler regions, even at a sacrifice of salary. In many cases the reason is that the wife does not like the climate and is not well. The greater the success of either an individual or a community in a tropical region, the greater the likelihood that the more able people, or at least their children, will move away. Success means mobility; civilization means the same thing; and mobility means that the processes of natural selection are able to sort out the most able people and install them in the environments that are most attractive. An environment that is attractive for play will attract some people, but one that is attractive for work will draw vastly more.

Even if the most competent people of the white race are not willing to settle permanently in most parts of the tropics and cannot, perhaps, maintain their full ability, is it not safe for white people to go temporarily to tropical regions and superintend the work of other races? Yes, indeed, modern hygiene and medicine certainly permit this, and in due time will make it still more feasible than at present. But it is highly doubtful whether this will ever give rise to great centres of power, or will even enable tropical regions to raise much food to feed the rest of the world. At least, nothing of this sort has happened yet. No one can predict what may happen in the future, but if ever the tropics feed the temperate zones, it will be a complete reversal of what happens to-day. When the white man stays out of the tropics, the people there feed themselves, or else die. When the white man goes to the tropics, he raises some luxuries for himself, but no grain or meat or vegetables worth mentioning. In return for the luxuries, he feeds part of the tropical people with good food grown in his own temperate regions.

This statement runs counter to the commonly received opinion. But look at the figures. Hawaii is a marvellous region. It produces more sugar per acre than any other part of the world, and sends great quantities to the continental United States. But it does not feed itself. Each year, for each inhabitant, its imports of food from the United States amount, roughly, to something over two hundred pounds of rice, nearly as much of other bread grains, four to six dozen eggs, forty or fifty pounds of fish, three dollars' worth of fruit and nuts, eight dollars' worth of meat and dairy products, three or four dollars' worth of confectionery and the like, and another three or four dollars' worth of vegetables. In other words, each family in those rich and highly developed little islands on the edge of the tropics calls upon the United States for anywhere from two hundred to two hundred and fifty dollars' worth of food in addition to what comes from elsewhere. If we should leave the Hawaiian Islands alone, we might have to reduce our consumption of sugar one-twentieth, and cut out about six cans of pineapple for each family every year, but we should have food enough for somewhere near 200,000 more people.

Cuba ranks as another of the most highly developed tropical regions. As a result of its development it is no longer self-supporting, as in the old days, but is almost as dependent as a queen bee. In 1923, for example, Cuba imported staple foodstuffs to the extent of about $30 per person, or about $150 per family. Her demands in this line are increasing. We talk a great deal about England's dependence on other countries for food, but Cuba's dependence is almost equally great. Where Great Britain imported staple foods, aside from such things as coffee and tea, to a value of about $220 per family of five persons, in 1923, Cuba imported two-thirds as much. But inasmuch as Cuban standards of living are lower than those of England, the dependence of our warm, sugar-producing neighbor upon northern countries is relatively about the same as that of Great Britain.

So it goes all down the line. Under Spanish rule Porto Rico

long fed itself. Now it imports about the same amount of food per inhabitant as does Cuba, and most of it comes from us. On the other side of the world Java is, perhaps, the most marvellous of all cases where the white man has developed the vast potential riches of the tropics. And what is the result? Instead of being a self-supporting island with perhaps 5,000,000 people, as it was a century or more ago, Java is to-day well nigh the most densely packed of all lands, a place the size of Iowa, but with over 35,000,000 brown human beings. These 35,000,000 do not provide the rest of the world with any more meat, grain, vegetables, and other staple foods aside from sugar than did one-seventh as many a century ago. On the contrary, to-day the average Javanese farmer actually produces crops and animals worth only about one-sixteenth as much as those produced by the New Zealand farmer, provided the products of both be reckoned according to the same scale of prices. The proportion of farmers in Java is uncommonly large, yet Java does not feed itself. Nearly a billion pounds of rice—about 150 for every family—have to be imported in order to permit the Dutch and the rest of us to have enough sugar, rubber, copra, tobacco, tea, coffee, tapioca, pepper, and quinine.

The Philippines are headed in the same direction. Rice, wheat flour, and dairy products—good staple foods—stand on the import side of their list, and sugar, hemp, copra, cocoanuts, tobacco, and maguey fibre on the other. Japan and England succeed no better than the United States and the Netherlands. Japan feeds Formosa with rice and beans, and British ships have to bring flour and fish to Jamaica in exchange for the products of plantations.

Perhaps all this may be completely reversed one of these days, but thus far there is no hint that tropical countries will ever supply any large quantity of staple food products, that is, grain, meat, and vegetables, to the lands in more bracing climates. Of course, these articles can be produced within the tropics in vast quantities, but that is not the point. The essential fact is that, without exception, so far as I am aware, the tendency of European or American domination is to cause the tropical population to increase rapidly, so that it presses hard upon the food supply, and there is no place for any Europeans except as managers and sojourners. But at the same time the production of staple foods may actually suffer a serious diminution *in proportion to the population and to its standards of living.* This happens because the white man not only diverts many natives from raising staple foods to raising luxuries, but also creates certain new desires among the natives. The final result is to cause the tropical regions to depend on the cooler regions for food as well as leadership.

This is quite different from what happens where the white man actually settles in considerable numbers and the natives die out or are insignificant in numbers. But the evidence strongly indicates that since the white man cannot permanently retain his full efficiency in tropical lands, he will not settle there, if he has to compete with natives. If there were no natives, he might indeed people the tropics. But even if that were done, the brighter and more energetic individuals, and especially those whose temperament leads them to intellectual pursuits, would tend strongly to migrate to other lands, just as the white people of the Bahamas and Hawaii do at present. Hawaii is probably the most attractive of all tropical regions as a place of residence for the white man, but in 1920 there lived in Hawaii only 15,323 native-born Caucasians, other than Portuguese, Porto Ricans, and Spanish. Most of these were persons of British extraction whose ancestors came from the United States, although the ancestors of a few came directly from other European countries. That same year there lived in the United States no less than 9,351 white people born in Hawaii. Some of these may have been Spanish, Portuguese, or Porto Ricans, but the great majority were ordinary "Americans," and belong to the group called "other Caucasians." This means that at least a third of the Americans born in Hawaii migrate to the United States, chiefly to California. If that happens in so pleasant and healthful a place as Hawaii, it is not surprising that in Porto Rico the number of persons born in the

United States declined from 2,303 in 1910, to 1,617 in 1920. Yet Porto Rico is more attractive to the white man than are most parts of the tropics.

The general principle which we have been illustrating by the remote Arctic and Tropical regions applies with no less truth to the most progressive parts of the world. Massachusetts, for example, has so strong a hold on the life of America that it attracts a higher grade of people than it sends out. This appears in the following figures, which show the number of persons in *Who's Who* for each thousand of the native white population who were born in other parts of the United States, but live in Massachusetts (A), and who were born in Massachusetts, but live in other States (B):

	Birthplace of Migrants to Massachusetts or Place of Residence of Migrants Out of Massachusetts				
	Ohio	Ind.	Ill.	Iowa and Minn.	Ky., Tenn., Ga., Miss., Ark.
A. Migrants into Massachusetts...	9.3	8.1	7.1	9.8	4.7
B. Migrants out of Massachusetts..	3.2	3.4	5.3	3.4	3.1

Iowa and Minnesota, and likewise the five Southern States, have been combined in order to obtain groups where the migrants number at least 5,000 in each case. Notice how systematically the native white Americans who migrate into Massachusetts supply a larger percentage of persons for *Who's Who* than do those who migrate out of Massachusetts. It is true that Massachusetts sends out about 75 per cent more native whites than she receives, for in 1920 about 42,000 of her native-born sons and daughters lived in the other States mentioned above, while only 24,600 who were born in these States had taken up their residence in Massachusetts. Yet in spite of this Massachusetts actually received 189 eminent citizens of the *Who's Who* type from these States, while she sent them only 170. Thus the Old Bay State profits in spite of her donations to other States. One reason why Massachusetts shows a relative decline in certain statistical inquiries, in spite of the fact that she still generally ranks near the top, is the large number of foreign immigrants received during the past two generations more or less. That illustrates one of the greatest dangers inherent in being highly favored. The less competent as well as the more competent are attracted, and under special circumstances, such as prevailed so long as the vast, undeveloped stretches of western America were calling the sons of Massachusetts, the less desirable type may increase faster than the highly desirable type.

In Illinois the drawing power of Chicago is so great that conditions similar to those of Massachusetts prevail, as appears in the following figures:

	BIRTHPLACE OF MIGRANTS TO ILLINOIS, OR PLACE OF RESIDENCE OF MIGRANTS FROM ILLINOIS								
	Ohio	Ind.	Iowa	Minn.	Ky.	Tenn.	Ga.	Miss.	Ark.
Migrants to Illinois...	1.4	0.5	1.1	1.0	0.3	0.8	1.3	1.1	0.4
Migrants from Illinois	0.8	0.2	0.2	0.6	0.5	0.6	1.1	0.5	0.1

In 1920 the number of native white citizens who were born in other States and resided in Illinois was about 10 per cent greater than the number of persons born in Illinois who had moved to the other States in question. Illinois received from those States 464 persons who are included in *Who's Who*, and sent them only 192. Thus the gain of that State was very great—greater than that of any other State in our list except Massachusetts. Nevertheless, if we eliminate the effect of the growth of population by reason of the unoccupied western lands, it appears that the interchange of population has benefited Massachusetts even more than Illinois. The upshot of the whole matter is that people go where they find the best opportunities. Those opportunities may arise because of unoccupied land and undeveloped resources, or because the decay or backwardness of the population in certain regions affords great openings for more advanced people. The attractiveness of other regions is due to discoveries which make it possible to utilize resources which were formerly of little value. Yet in the long run the greatest agency in determining the location of areas which attract competent people appears to be a healthful and stimulating climate. Regions with such climates are attractive because they almost invariably become centres of culture and power. This becomes especially evident if we extend our view beyond the present exceptional circumstances arising from the eras of discovery which began about 1492, and of manufacturing which began three centuries later. The power of the best regions to attract people from elsewhere is greatly increased by the extreme mobility which is characteristic of the most highly civilized people.

Extreme mobility, such as has just been illustrated, is one of the most characteristic qualities of our time, and is one upon which we often pride ourselves, but it is not necessarily good. It may do harm even to a highly favored region, and it seems to work almost irreparable harm to less favored regions. Here is an example of one of the ways in which this modern mobility is probably doing great harm to America. The United States has recently put up the immigration bars quite tightly. When people are once inside the border, however, we leave them practically free to do what they like, no matter whether they came in legally or illegally. Our deportation laws are almost a farce so far as criminals are concerned. In addition to this, it is notorious all over the world that our criminal courts are slow and lenient, and that a good lawyer can set almost any one free. Moreover, it is equally well known that the pickings of crime of every sort are extremely high. Thus we have created almost ideal conditions for attracting to our land a great number of the more able type of criminals, men who are willing to be bootlegged across the border, and who are equally willing to act as bootleggers of liquor or to engage in any other sort of lawbreaking that promises profit.

At one time or another in our history we have attracted many different types of people, and as a rule we have obtained persons in whom the special characteristics that led to migration were strongly developed. Thus we have attracted the religious type, the socially discontented, the adventurous, the money-loving, the seekers for political freedom, the pushing and self-assertive type, and the type that is oppressed economically at home. Now we are offering a special attraction to the type which is willing and eager to break the laws. Is it any wonder that as a nation we are zealous, brilliant, energetic, progressive, money-loving, erratic, and wicked? Ye shall reap as ye have sown.

Fortunately the evil effects of the system of selection which we are unconsciously carrying out are at least partially offset by certain good effects. Step by step in one crisis after another we have succeeded in attracting an unusual percentage of persons of more than ordinary ability and strength of character. That occurred among other times when the Puritans came to these shores, when the Huguenots and Quakers followed them, when German seekers for political freedom arrived in the middle of the last century, and after the World War when we received a large proportion of able immigrants, not only from Russia but from other countries. There are probably few ways in which the United States could strengthen itself and insure its future more effectively than by the most strenuous efforts, not merely to check the tide of incompetent and lawless immigration, but to strengthen the tide of immigrants of the very highest types. Suppose the United States were to spend $100,000,000 a year for the express purpose not only of increasing the present cultural strength of the country, but of adding as much as possible to our biological inheritance. A hundred million dollars a year would be a small matter for this rich country. We could shave that amount from our military appropriations and only a few officers and contractors would notice it. One way to use it would be to pick out especially competent young foreigners in all lines, professional, political, commercial, industrial, scientific, literary, religious, artistic, and philanthropic, and bring them to this country. Provide each with a useful and interesting job, give him a house among congenial American neighbors. If necessary, guarantee him a salary of $10,000 per year for five years, and then of $5,000 per year for the rest of his life in addition to what he could earn in his profession. Require only that each man pledge himself to bring his family, provided he has one, learn English, and stay at least ten years.

Immediately after the World War few of the young leaders of Europe could have resisted such an offer. Even now a large percentage would jump at the chance. In each generation an expenditure of $100,000,000 per year in this way would bring to this country some 20,000 or 30,000 families, most of whom would remain permanently. Their average ability would be about like that of the 20,000 or 30,000 persons in *Who's Who*. But more important still is the fact that they would bring new germ-plasm of a high type. Their children would be far above the average in ability; a large percentage would be of *Who's Who* calibre, just as are the children of college professors and of the old-fashioned type of ministers. The effect of doubling the most competent parts of our population in a single generation would be almost incalculable. It would put this country far in the lead in almost every kind of human effort.

I do not advance this as a policy to be adopted by the United States Government, for there is grave doubt whether that would be wise. I merely advance it as a hint of what might be done under other conditions. To a certain degree just this is being done, as may be judged by studying the faculty of almost any large university and seeing how many able men are constantly being drawn from abroad. But for our present purpose this hypothetical plan for drawing the best from all over the world is merely intended as an illustration of the way in which the growing oneness of the world tends constantly to give an advantage to the regions where people are vigorous, energetic, rich, and progressive. Those are the centres of power, and by their very nature they tend to be self-perpetuating in our day far more than at any previous stage of history. Their greatest danger, it would seem, lies in the sterilization which almost invariably occurs when competent people are collected in cities. How that will influence the future is still a problem, but otherwise, provided the climate does not change, it appears as though the steady flow of able people to the great centres ought to preserve the power of those centres for many centuries.

Farther than this we cannot go in this volume. Our main argument is relatively simple. Change is the rule of history, pulsations of one kind and another are taking place all the time. The philosophy of history is merely the explanation of why the pulsations take place. Deep down among their causes lie the relief of the earth's surface, the soil, climate, and the conditions of land and water which determine the location of cities. Relief, soil, and the relation of land and water change very little from century to century, but their effect upon the distribution of man's activities and qualities changes greatly. This is partly because man's cultural progress—his inventions, discoveries, and new ideas—continually introduce new factors so that regions which at one time are of relatively little value, or even lie beyond man's powers of development, become highly valuable at a later stage. Equally important, however, and perhaps more so, is the fact that each type of geographical environment, through its influence upon occupations, health, and migration, tends to select certain types of people for its permanent inhabitants. In different stages of development different types are selected, so that the immigrants may range all the way from people like the Puritans of early Massachusetts to the bootlegging type, which now illicitly swarms across our borders in such profusion. The persons who migrate away from a region of course vary in the same way. In the black belt of Alabama, and in other southern regions of especially rich soil, for example, the earlier outward migrants were mainly white people who achieved only a mediocre degree of success, or were restless in character and dissatisfied with their life in a rich farming region. The latest outward migrants have tended to be the brighter, more ambitious type of Negroes, thus leaving a small body of unusually capable white people and a large body of relatively low colored people. Cities, likewise, receive different types of migrants according to their stage of progress. For these reasons, even though the geographical conditions remain constant, each type of region tends to pass through cycles which repeat themselves with more or less irregularity, first the pioneer stage, then high development, decay, and finally renewal by reason of fresh migrations of pioneers of some new type.

Different types of climate likewise tend to foster certain occupations and modes of life. Thus they also exercise a powerful selective influence, for one kind of person is favored and tends to survive, while another is placed at a disadvantage and tends to be eliminated. Deserts, mountains, and other regions which can scarcely be utilized except by pastoral nomads, select for preservation a far more fiery, active, dominating type than do rich agricultural regions where dangers are few, life is secure, and the best chances of survival are enjoyed by people who practise steady industry. Where famines are frequent other qualities, such as the intense economy, frugality, parsimony, and self-centredness which prevail so widely among the northern Chinese, are especially valuable as a means of preserving the agricultural population. Each climatic region, like each region where a special type of relief, soil, or relation of land and sea prevails, also seems to go through certain more or less clearly defined stages, varying from the pioneer stage when the most favorable climatic regions are seized by energetic invaders, to the stage of decay when the rural population is depleted of its best by the cities, and when the cities sterilize the able people who there concentrate.

If climatic pulsations occur, as appears to have been the rule throughout history, another potent cause of change is introduced. New opportunities and a consequent invitation to outsiders to migrate into a region may be offered by the favorable portions of a climatic cycle. On the other hand, the unfavorable part appears often to have led to over-population, poverty, political discontent, and migration to other regions. Such migrations, like practically all others, appear to be selective. In that fact, more than in any other, lies the main emphasis of this book. The general effect of geographical environment upon man's occupations, food, clothing, shelter, physical health, and mental energy is widely recognized. The idea that significant climatic pulsations have taken place during historic times seems also to be coming into general recognition. But as yet we have failed to appreciate the extent to which cycles of human development, especially when speeded up by climatic pulsations, give rise to migrations either slow or rapid, and to a drastic process of selection. Such selection, due not only to the changing impact of physical environment, but to all sorts of social, political, religious, and industrial causes, appears to be a great factor which has hitherto been largely overlooked in our attempts to interpret the world's history.

LIST OF BOOKS AND ARTICLES

BY ELLSWORTH HUNTINGTON

FROM WHICH MUCH OF THE MATERIAL OF THIS BOOK HAS BEEN DRAWN

I. BOOKS

Explorations in Turkestan. Washington, 1905.
The Pulse of Asia. Boston, 1907.
Palestine and Its Transformation. Boston, 1911.
Asia: A Geography Reader. Chicago, 1912.
The Climatic Factor. Washington, 1914.
The Red Man's Continent. New Haven, 1919.
World Power and Evolution. New Haven, 1919.
Principles of Human Geography (with S. W. Cushing). New York, 1920.
Climatic Changes (with S. S. Visher). New Haven, 1922.
Earth and Sun. New Haven, 1923.
Civilization and Climate. Third edition. New Haven, 1924.
The Character of Races. New York, 1924.
West of the Pacific. New York, 1925.
Quaternary Climates (with J. C. Jones and E. Antevs). Washington, 1925.
Modern Business Geography (with S. W. Cushing). Yonkers, 1925.
Business Geography (with F. W. Williams). Second edition. New York, 1926.
An Introduction to the Study of Sociology (with other authors). Edited by
 Jerome Davis. In press. Boston.

II. ARTICLES PUBLISHED IN BOOKS

The Fluctuating Climate of North America (in the Annual Report of the Smith-
 sonian Institution, Washington, 1912); also in list III.
Geographical Environment and Japanese Character (in Japan and Japanese-
 American Relations, Clark University Addresses; edited by G. H. Blakes-
 lee; New York, 1912); also in list III.
The Adaptability of the White Man to Tropical America (in Latin America,
 Clark University Addresses; edited by G. H. Blakeslee. New York, 1913);
 also in list III.
Solar Activity, Cyclonic Storms, and Climatic Changes (in Proceedings of The
 Second Pan-American Scientific Congress, vol. II, Washington, 1917).
Climate and the Evolution of Civilization (in The Evolution of the Earth;
 edited by R. S. Lull; New Haven, 1919).
The Factor of Health in Mexican Character (in Mexico and the Caribbean,
 Clark University Addresses; edited by G. H. Blakeslee; New York, 1920);
 also in list III.

Environment and Racial Character (in Organic Adaptation to Environment; edited by M. R. Thorpe; New Haven, 1924).

The Effect of Overpopulation on Chinese Character (in Proceedings of Sixth International Birth Control Conference, vol. II, 1926).

III. ARTICLES PUBLISHED IN MAGAZINES

This list of articles comprises only those which contain some material bearing on the subject of this book and not included in the books listed above.

The Valley of the Upper Euphrates River and Its People. Bulletin of the American Geographical Society, vol. 34, 1902, 20 pages.

The Mountains of Turkestan. The Geographical Journal, vol. 25, 1905, pp. 22–40, 139–158.

The Depression of Sistan in Eastern Persia. Bulletin of the American Geographical Society, vol. 37, 1905, 10 pages.

With a Minbashi in Turkestan. Appalachia, vol. 11, 1905, pp. 17–20.

The Mountains and Kibitkas of Tian Shan. Bulletin of the American Geographical Society, vol. 37, 1905, pp. 513–530.

The Relation of Afghanistan to Its Neighbors. The Bulletin of the Geographical Society of Philadelphia, vol. 6, 1908, pp. 111–119.

The Climate of the Historic Past. Monthly Weather Review, vol. 36, 1908, pp. 446–450.

The New Province Two Thousand Years Old. Harper's Magazine, 1908, pp. 19–30.

The Mountaineers of the Euphrates. The National Geographic Magazine, vol. 20, 1909, pp. 142–156.

Life in the Great Desert of Central Asia. The National Geographic Magazine, vol. 20, 1909, pp. 749–760.

The Afghan Borderland. The National Geographic Magazine, vol. 20, 1909, pp. 788–799 and 866–876.

The Burial of Olympia. The Geographical Journal, 1920, pp. 657–686.

Problems in Exploration: Central Asia. The Geographical Journal, 1910, pp. 395–419.

The Libyan Oasis of Kharga. The Bulletin of the American Geographical Society, vol. 42, 1910, pp. 641–661.

The Fringe of Verdure Around Asia Minor. The National Geographic Magazine, vol. 21, 1910, pp. 761–775.

The Lost Wealth of the Kings of Midas. The National Geographic Magazine, vol. 21, 1910, pp. 831–846.

Physical Environment as a Factor in the Present Condition of Turkey. The Journal of Race Development, vol. 1, 1911, pp. 460–481.

The First Americans. Harper's Magazine, vol. 122, 1911, pp. 451–462.

The Physical Environment of the Southwest in Pre-Columbian Days. Records of the Past, vol. 11, 1912, pp. 128–141.

Climatic Changes in the Nearer East: A Reply. Bulletin of the American Geographical Society, vol. 44, 1912, pp. 440–447.

Geographical Environment and Japanese Character. The Journal of Race Development, vol. 2, 1912, pp. 256–281; also in list II.

American Archæology. Harper's Magazine, vol. 124, 1912, pp. 291–301.

The Arabian Desert and Human Character. The Journal of Geography, vol. 10, 1912, pp. 169–175.

The Fluctuating Climate of North America. The Geographical Journal, 1912, pp. 264–411; also in list II.

The New Science of Geography. Yale Review, vol. 2, 1912, pp. 82–96.

The Peninsula of Yucatan. The Bulletin of the American Geographical Society, vol. 44, 1912, pp. 801–822.

Changes of Climate and History. The American Historical Review, vol. 18, 1913, pp. 214–232.

The Shifting of Climatic Zones as Illustrated in Mexico. Bulletin of the American Geographical Society, vol. 45, 1913, pp. 1–16, part I; pp. 107–116, part II.

Guatemala and the Highest Native American Civilization. Proceedings of the American Philosophical Society, vol. 52, 1913, pp. 467–487.

The Adaptability of the White Man to Tropical America. The Journal of Race Development, vol. 5, 1914, pp. 185–211; also in list II.

The Geographer and History. The Geographical Journal, 1914, pp. 19–32.

The Solar Hypothesis of Climatic Changes. The Bulletin of the Geological Society of America, vol. 25, 1914, pp. 477–590.

The Mystery of the Yucatan Ruins. Harper's Magazine, vol. 128, 1914, pp. 757–766.

A Neglected Factor in Race Development. The Journal of Race Development, vol. 6, 1915, pp. 167–184.

Our Immigrant Problem: A Discussion and Review. The Geographical Review, vol. II, 1916, pp. 458–463.

Climatic Variations and Economic Cycles. The Geographical Review, vol. 1, 1916, pp. 192–202.

The Water Barriers of New York City. The Geographical Review, vol. 2, 1916, pp. 169–183.

Prediction of Climatic Variations. The American Museum Journal, vol. 16, 1916, pp. 97–103.

Climatic Change and Agricultural Exhaustion as Elements in the Fall of Rome. The Quarterly Journal of Economics, vol. 31, 1917, pp. 173–208.

Maya Civilization and Climatic Changes. Proceedings of the Nineteenth International Congress of Americanists, 1917, pp. 150–164.

The Future of Palestine. The Geographical Review, vol. 7, 1919, pp. 24–35.

The Interpretation of the Death Rate by Climographs. Modern Medicine, vol. 1, 1919, pp. 13–22.

The Control of Pneumonia and Influenza by the Weather. Ecology, vol. 1, 1920, pp. 6–23.

Air Control and the Reduction of the Death Rate after Operations. The Modern Hospital, Part I, vol. 14, 1920, pp. 10–15; Part II, vol. 14, 1920, pp. 111–114.

The Purpose and Methods of Air Control in Hospitals. The Modern Hospital, vol. 14, 1920, pp. 271–275.

Methods of Air Control and Their Results. The Modern Hospital, vol. 14, 1920, pp. 348–353.

The Factor of Health in Mexican Character. Journal of International Relations, vol. 2, 1920, pp. 224–233; also in list II.

What the Air Does to Us. The Nation's Health, vol. 3, 1921, pp. 265–266.

Air Control as a Means of Reducing the Post-operative Death Rate. American Journal of Surgery, vol. 35, 1921, part I, pp. 82–90; part II, pp. 98–100.

Influenza and the Weather in the United States in 1919. The Scientific Monthly, vol. 17, 1923, pp. 462–471.

Geography and Natural Selection. Annals of the Association of American Geographers, vol. 14, 1924, pp. 1–16.

Climate and History as Recorded by the Big Trees, in The Big Tree and Its Story, by George H. Sherwood, Guide Leaflet No. 42; American Museum of Natural History, 1924.

The Handicap of Poor Land, Economic Geography, vol. 2, 1926, pp. 335–357.

INDEX